IPT's INDUSTRIAL HYDRAULICS TRAINING MANUAL

by

James A. Archer

Published by
IPT PUBLISHING AND TRAINING LTD.
Box 9590 Edmonton, Alberta, Canada   T6E 5X2
www.iptbooks.com
email: info@iptbooks.com
Phone (780) 962-4548   Fax (780) 962-4819
Toll Free 1-888-808-6763

Printed in Canada by
Elite Lithographers, Edmonton, Alberta

The material presented in this publication has been prepared in accordance with recognized trade working practices, codes, and procedures, and is for general in-formation only. In areas of critical importance the user should secure competent engineering advice with respect to the suitability of the material contained herein, and comply with the various codes, standards, regulations or other legal obligation. Anyone using this information assumes all responsibility and liability arising from such use.

IPT's Industrial Hydraulics Training Manual
First Printing May 2001
Second Printing January 2004
Third Printing April 2008
Fourth Printing April 2013

ISBN 13: 978 0-920855-40-9
ISBN 10: 0-920855-40-7
Copyright © 2001 by IPT Publishing and Training Ltd.

ACKNOWLEDGEMENTS

The author and publisher wish to thank the following for their assistance in developing this publication:

Illustrations: Ian Holmes – Holmes Consulting
                      Cassandra Strumecki – CAS Consulting Services
                      Ken Jurina and Cindy Joly – Top Draw

Layout and coordination of illustrations:
Sincere thanks to Cassandra Strumecki and Ian Holmes for their work organizing this book into its present format.

Proofreading: A special thank you is extended to the following for their many hours spent proofreading this book:
Robert Beaune: B.SC., Mech. Eng., M.ED., Journeyman Millwright; Instructor – Northern Alberta Institute of Technology; Technical Instructor, Mechanical – Nexen, Inc, Yemen
Bruce Basarba: B.Ed.,M.A., Journeyman Millwright; Instructor – Northern Alberta Institute of Technology; Manager of Training - Kumtor Gold Project, Kyrygzstan; and Hurricane Hydrocarbons, Kazakhstan

METRIC CONTENT

This publication is primarily designed for Canada and the United States. Canada has primarily adopted the Metric system, and it is commonly used in the United States in certain industries, however the degree of use is not consistent in either country. The application of Metric units to the wide range of hydraulic uses varies widely, as some evaluations and measuring are identified by using the Metric system only, or the in-lb-gal system only, while others may use either. Individuals performing specific evaluations and measurements will have their own preferences. Therefore both the Metric and the in-lb-gal systems are shown when practical.

ABOUT THE AUTHOR

James A. Archer: HNC Mechanical Engineering; Mining Mechanical Engineer; Journeyman Millwright; Instructor – Northern and Southern Alberta Institutes of Technology, has over thirty years experience in industrial construction and maintenance. This includes working as a journeyman millwright, construction and maintenance supervision and management, and instruction for various apprenticeship programs and seminars concerning millwright and hydraulic topics. He is co-author of IPT's Rotating Equipment Handbook.

TABLE OF CONTENTS

SECTION SIX – ACTUATORS

SECTION EIGHT
– CARTRIDGE VALVES

SECTION NINE - PROPORTIONAL
AND SERVO VALVES

SECTION
ONE
HYDRAULIC PRINCIPLES

Force

By definition, a force is anything that changes, or tends to change, the state of rest or motion in a body.

Gravity is always exerting a downward force on objects. If the object is not supported, it will accelerate downwards at a rate of 32.2 ft/sec^2 (9.8 m/s^2) at sea level. It is this continuous gravitational force that makes objects appear to have a weight. An example of a common use of a force in hydraulics occurs when a cylinder is supporting a load, as shown in illustrations #1 (in-lb-gal system) and #2 [metric SI]. The force produced by the piston has to equal the force produced by the load, otherwise the load would move.

In the in-lb-gal system, the method used to measure force is the pound-force (lbf.). The commonly used term pound (lb) will be used in the following text. Illustration #1 has a weight of 200 lb being supported by a cylinder.

The metric SI unit of force is the "newton" (N). One newton equals the force required to accelerate a 1 kg mass 1 metre per second per second (m/s^2).

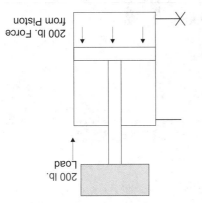

Illustration #1 — Force Opposing a Load (in-lb-gal System)

200 lb. Force from Piston

200 lb. Load

For the load to remain static, the force produced by the piston (200 lb) must be equal and opposite to that produced by the 200 lb load.

Acceleration, due to gravity, is approx. 9.8 m/s^2; therefore, a 1 kg mass exerts a force of 9.8 N at sea level.

Illustration #2 shows a cylinder supporting a mass of 100 kg.

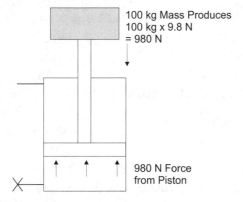

100 kg Mass Produces
100 kg x 9.8 N
= 980 N

980 N Force
from Piston

Illustration #2 — Force Opposing a Load (Metric SI)

This produces a downwards force of 100 x 9.8 = 980 N. The piston is exerting 980 N in the opposite direction.

Area

Area is the amount of surface within a specified boundary. It is specified in "square" units, regardless of its shape. Calculating the area of regular shapes is a simple mathematical process, when the correct formula is known.

For any rectangular shape:

A = L x W

Where: A = Area, L = Length
             W = Width

Calculating the areas of circular shapes is required when estimating fluid velocity in pipe or tubing, the required diameter of a cylinder to lift a load, or the torque output of a hydraulic motor.

The basic formula for the area of a circle is:

1. $A = \pi r^2$

Where: A   = Area, π = 3.142
             r   = radius of the circle

Pressure

Definition

Pressure is the measure of the intensity of a force and is determined by the amount of force that is exerted on a specified area.

The common units for measuring pressure are pounds per square inch (psi) for in-lb-gal system, and the pascal (Pa) for metric SI. One pascal is equal to a force of one newton acting on an area of one square metre.

Because the pascal is such a small unit of measurement, the kilopascal (kPa), or megapascal (MPa) is usually used in hydraulics, where one kPa is equal to 1000 pascals and one MPa is equal to 1 000 000 pascals.

In illustration #3A, a cylinder with an area of 100 square inches (11.28 inches diameter) is supporting 100 lb of force; therefore, each square inch under the piston has 1 lb of force acting on it (100 lb/100 in²), or 1 lb per square inch (1 psi).

Because cylinders, pipes, pistons etc. are usually specified by diameter, this formula is more useful when converted to:

2. $A = \pi\ d^2/4$

Where: d = diameter of the circle

Another variation of this formula that is often used is:

3. $A = 0.785\ d^2$

Where: $0.785 = \pi/4$

Example:
Find the area of a piston that has a diameter of 9.5 inches.

Using formula 2:

$A = \pi\ (9.5)^2 / 4 = 70.89$ square inches

Example: Find the area of a pipe that has a diameter of 200 mm.

Using formula 3:

$A = 0.785\ (200)^2 = 31\ 400$ square mm

$A = 0.785\ (20)^2 = 314$ square cm

$A = 0.785\ (0.2)^2 = 0.0314$ square metres

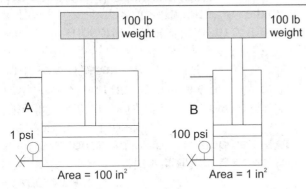

Illustration #3A, B — Pressure Supporting Load (In-lb-gal System)

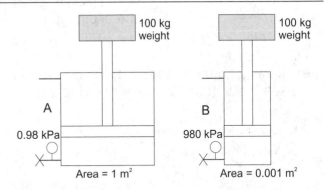

Illustration #4A, B — Pressure Supporting Load (Metric S1)

If a smaller area supports the same force, the pressure generated is much greater.

Illustration #3B shows the 100 lb load being supported by an area of 1 square inch (1.13 inches diameter). The pressure generated (100 lb/1 in^2) is 100 lb per square inch.

Illustration #4A shows a mass of 100 kilograms being supported by a cylinder with an area of 1 square metre (1128 mm diameter).

Each kilogram produces a force of approximately 9.8 N, for a total force of 980 N.

This produces a pressure of 980 N/m^2 (980 N/1 m^2) which equals 980 Pa or 0.98 kPa.

As with the in-lb-gal system example, if the same load is supported on a smaller cylinder, there will be a pressure increase. In illustration #4B, the 100 kg mass is supported on an area of 0.001 square metres (36 mm diameter). The resulting pressure is now 980 N divided by 0.001 m (force/area, see illustration #9), which equals 980 000 Pa or 980 kPa.

Because the area was reduced by a factor of 1000, the pressure was increased by the same amount. Note that these are theoretical pressures. Actual pressures to support a load will be less, due to friction in seals, etc.

Pressure in a hydraulic system transmits force. Pressure applied to a hydraulic cylinder (linear actuator) produces linear force. Pressure applied to a hydraulic motor (rotary actuator) produces torque (force applied at a radius).

Head Pressure

The pressure developed under a column of fluid is determined by the column height and the density of the fluid

The following examples are for water at 4°C (39.2°F), which has a specific gravity of 1.

In-lb-gal System:

One cubic foot of water weighs 62.4 lb. This weight is supported by the bottom of the container as shown in illustration #5A, which in this case is 144 square inches.

The force on each square inch of the bottom of the container is 62.4/144 = 0.433 lb (a column of water 1 in square and 12 in high weighs 0.433 lb)

Illustration #5A,B — Cubic Foot / Cubic Metre of Water

A. 1 Cubic Foot of Water

B. 1 Cubic Metre of Water

As the depth of water is 1 foot, the pressure generated by a 1 foot column of water is 0.433 psi.

The pressure (P) in psi at the bottom of a head of fluid is equal to:

$$P = h \times 0.433 \times sg$$

Where:

P = pressure in psi.

h = height of the column of fluid in feet.

sg = the specific gravity of the liquid (cold water has a specific gravity of 1).

The pressure (P) at the bottom of a column of water 30 ft high would be:

P = 30 x 0.433 x 1 = 12.99 psi

Metric SI Units:

The container shown in illustration #5B is a cubic metre. If filled with water, it would have a mass of 1 tonne or 1 000 kg. The force exerted on the bottom of the container, which is one metre square, would be:

1000 x 9.8 = 9 800 N.

The depth of water in the container is one metre; therefore, the pressure developed by each metre head of water is 9800 N/m^2

9 800 N/m^2 = 9 800 P = 9.8 kPa.

The pressure (P) in kPa at the bottom of a head of fluid is equal to:

P = h x 9.8 x sg

Where:

h = height of the column of fluid in metres.

P = pressure in kPa.

sg = the specific gravity of the liquid.

The pressure (P) at the bottom of a column of water 10 m high would be:

P = 10 x 9.8 x 1 = 98 kPa

Liquids Other than Water

(specific gravity not equal to 1)

When compared to cold water (specific gravity 1), a column of liquid with a specific gravity greater than 1 will have a higher pressure at the bottom of the column. A column of liquid with a specific gravity less than 1 will have a lower pressure at the bottom of the column.

For the two examples shown above, if oil with a specific gravity of 0.924 were used instead of water then:

Pressure (P) for 30 ft head of oil in psi

$P = 30 \times 0.433 \times 0.924 = 12$ psi

Pressure (P) for 10 m head of oil in kPa

$P = 10 \times 9.8 \times 0.924 = 90.55$ kPa

Gage and Absolute Pressure

When pressure is measured using a total vacuum (absolute zero pressure) as the starting or reference point it is referred to as absolute pressure (psia or kPa Abs.).

Gage pressure (psig or kPa gage) is measured using atmospheric pressure as the starting or reference point (zero). The difference between absolute zero pressure and gage zero is 14.7 psi or 101.325 kPa. To convert gage pressures to absolute pressures, add the atmospheric pressure (14.7 psi or 101.325 kPa) to the gage pressure measurement (see illustration #6).

Gage press. = abs. press. - atmos. press.

Abs. press. = gage press. + atmos. press.

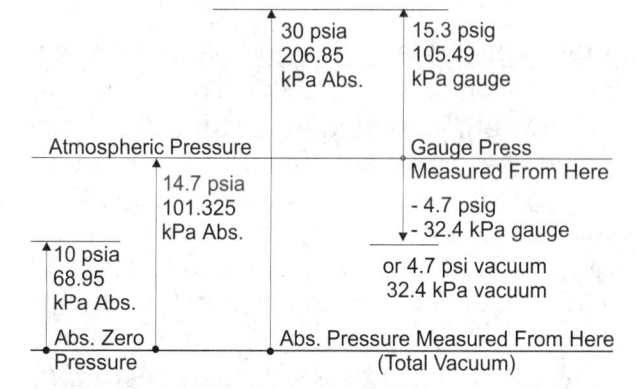

Illustration #6 — Absolute and Gage Pressure Scales

Low Pressure Measurement (Absolute)

The most common instrument used for measuring low absolute pressures is probably the mercury barometer which is shown in illustration #7. With a perfect vacuum as the reference pressure at the top of the tube, the height of the column of mercury is dependent on the pressure on the surface of the mercury.

Standard atmospheric pressure (14.7 psia or 101.325 kPa Abs.) produces a column of mercury 29.92 in or 759.97 mm high. Because the reference pressure is absolute zero, this instrument is measuring absolute pressure. The height of the mercury column will rise and fall with variations in atmospheric pressure.

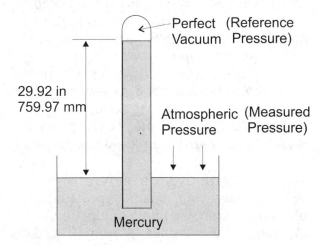

29.92 in
759.97 mm

Perfect (Reference Vacuum Pressure)

Atmospheric (Measured Pressure) Pressure

Mercury

Illustration #7 — Mercury Barometer

Low Pressure Measurement (Gage)

Low gage pressures may also be measured using mercury or water in a tube.

Illustration #8A shows a "U" tube manometer measuring gage pressures. The reference pressure in this case is atmospheric (14.7 psia or 101.325 kPa Abs.); therefore, gage pressure is being measured.

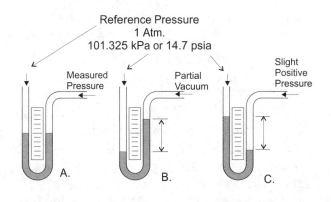

Reference Pressure
1 Atm.
101.325 kPa or 14.7 psia

Measured Pressure

Partial Vacuum

Slight Positive Pressure

A. B. C.

Illustration #8A, B, C — Gage Pressure Measurement Using "U" Tube Manometer

Illustration #8B is measuring a pressure lower than atmospheric (vacuum or negative pressure) and illustration #8C is measuring a pressure above atmospheric (positive pressure).

Note: When gage pressure is used, pressure less than atmospheric is referred to as either "negative pressure" or "vacuum". Negative gage pressure can only go down to minus 14.7 psig [minus 101.325 kPa] (see illustration #6). Vacuums are normally referred to in inches (or mm) of mercury (Hg). Where 0 inches [0 mm] Hg vacuum is equal to atmospheric pressure and 29.92 inches [759.97 mm] Hg vacuum is equal to a total vacuum.

When absolute pressure is being used, only positive numbers are possible. Any absolute pressure below 14.7 psia or 101.325 kPa Abs. is a vacuum.

The distance between the two levels of liquid for a given pressure will depend on what type of liquid is in the "U" tube. For very slight changes in pressure, water may be used. For larger changes in pressure, mercury is often used.

For water:

1 in = 0.433/12 = 0.0361 psi

1 mm = 9.8/1000 = 0.0098 kPa = 9.8 Pa

For mercury:

1 standard atmosphere is equal to 29.92 inches or 759.97 mm.

Therefore: 1 in = 14.7/29.92 = 0.491 psi

1 mm = 101.325/759.97
= 0.133 kPa = 133 Pa

Gage Pressure Calculation

The minimum pressure specified for a pump suction is 7 inches [178 mm] Hg vacuum. If this pump were fitted with a pressure gage on the suction, what would be the minimum pressure in psig [kPa gage] to equal 7 inches [178 mm] Hg. vacuum?

Note: Hg is the symbol for mercury.

7 inches Hg x 0.491 psi per inch Hg = 3.4 psi vacuum or minus 3.4 psig.

[178 mm Hg x 0.133 kPa per mm Hg = 23.7 kPa vacuum or minus 23.7 kPa gage]

Absolute Pressure Calculation

The minimum pressure allowed on a pump suction is 11.5 psia [79 kPa Abs]. If this were measured using a "U" tube mercury manometer, how many inches (mm) of mercury would this be?

Because the "U" tube manometer measures gage pressure, convert the absolute pressure to gage pressure.

Gage press. = abs. press. - atmos. press.

Gage pressure = 11.5 psia - 14.7 = -3.2 psig

[Gage pressure = 79 kPa -101 = - 22 kPa gage]

-3.2 psig/0.491 psi per inch Hg
        = 6.5 inches Hg vacuum

[-22 kPa gage/0.133 kPa per mm Hg
        = 165 mm Hg vacuum]

Pressure Units

- Pounds per square inch is the in-lb-gal system of pressure measurement and is equal to a force of one pound exerted on an area of one square inch.
- Pascal, kilopascal, and megapascal are the metric SI units of pressure. The pascal is such a small unit that kilopascal and megapascal are used for most hydraulic applications. One pascal is equal to a force of 1 newton exerted on an area of one metre.
- Bar and millibar are metric terms that are not used in SI. One bar (1000 millibars) is equal to 100 kPa. The bar is sometimes used to specify hydraulic pressures. Atmospheric pressure is often reported in millibars.
- Torr is a metric term, but not used in SI. One torr is equal to 1 mm Hg. The torr is primarily used for low pressure measurements of less than 25 mm Hg absolute.

Force-Area-Pressure Relationships

The mathematical relationship can easily be remembered by using the Force - Area - Pressure triangle shown in illustration #9.

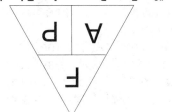

Illustration #9 — Force-Pressure-Area Triangle

Where: F = Force
        A = Area
        P = Pressure

$$(F = A \times P) \text{ or } (A = F / P) \text{ or } (P = F / A)$$

When using these formulae, the units must be compatible. Table #1 shows some of the more common units used for pressure and the matching units to be used for the calculations.

- Inches [or mm] of water (H_2O) are used to measure low pressures and pressure differentials. One inch of H_2O equals 0.0361 psi [one mm H_2O = 0.0098 kPa.].

- Inches [or mm] of mercury (Hg) are used to measure low pressures and pressure differentials. One inch of mercury equals 0.491 psi [one mm Hg = 0.133 kPa.].

- Head of liquid is used in many pumping applications and measures pressure or potential energy with respect to the height of a column of fluid. Cold water (specific gravity = 1) is usually the standard liquid. For liquids other than cold water, the specific gravity has to be taken into account when converting to psi or kPa.
One foot head H_2O equals 0.433 psi
One metre head H_2O = 9.8 kPa

Force (F)	Area (A)	Pressure (P)
lb	in^2	psi
N	m^2	Pa
N	mm^2	MPa

Table #1 — Matching Units for Force/Area/Pressure Calculations

Note: A 1 kilogram mass exerts a force of 9.8 N.

When two of the variables are known, the third can be calculated.

Pascal's Law

When pressure is applied to a confined fluid, the pressure is transmitted equally throughout that fluid, and is exerted perpendicular to every surface in the container. The piston in illustration #10 is creating pressure due to the force exerted by the weight on the piston. This pressure is applied to every surface within the system.

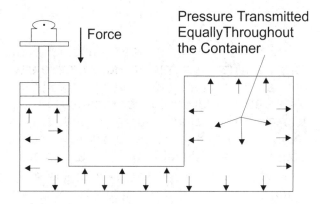

Illustration #10 — Pascal's Law

Force Multiplication

Pascal's Law permits the use of pressure developed in one place to be used elsewhere; and allows forces to be multiplied through the use of various piston areas (surface).

Illustration #11 shows pressure being developed by a force acting on a small diameter piston.

This pressure is transmitted throughout the system and is acting on the area of the large diameter piston, which produces a force that is five times greater than that applied to the small diameter piston.

Although the increase in force is five times as great, there is a corresponding loss in distance and velocity.

The small piston has to move five times as far as the large diameter piston. The speed of the small diameter piston will be five times greater than that of the large diameter piston.

This is similar to the mechanical advantage of many mechanical systems, such as gear, pulley, and lever mechanisms, where distance or speed is sacrificed for an increase in force or torque. Friction has been ignored in this example, but would be a significant factor in an actual system.

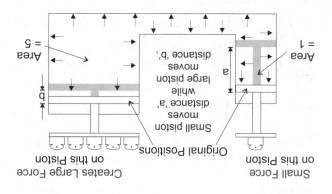

Illustration #11 — Force Multiplication

Pressure Intensification

Some circuits may require pressures in excess of those produced by the system pump. A pressure intensifier (illustration #12) may be used where low volumes of high pressure fluid is required.

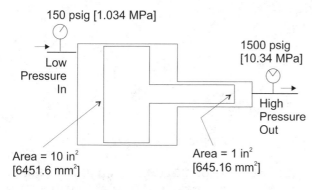

Illustration #12 — Pressure Intensifier

In illustration #12, 150 psi [1.034 MPa] is applied to the low pressure side of the intensifier.

The low pressure piston, which has an area of 10 in² [6451.6 mm²] will produce a force of:
(F = A x P) (from illustration #9)
Using lb, in² and psi [N, mm², and MPa] (see Table #1)
F = 10 x 150 = 1,500 lb
[F = 6451.6 x 1.034 = 6671 N].

At the discharge, a force of 1,500 lb [6671 N] on the high pressure (small diameter) piston which has an area of 1 in² [645.16 mm²] will produce a pressure of:
(P = F/A) (from illustration #9)
P = 1,500/1 = 1,500 psi
[P = 6671/645.16 = 10.34 MPa].

A ratio of 10 to 1 on the piston areas, produces a pressure increase of 10 to 1.

Note: This is the ratio of piston areas, or the square of their diameters.

Pressure intensification will also occur when the outlet from the rod end of a cylinder is restricted or blocked.

Referring to illustration #13. The cylinder will act in the same manner as the intensifier shown in illustration #12. The cap end of the cylinder is the low pressure side and the rod end, which has a reduced working area due to the area of the piston rod, is the high pressure side.

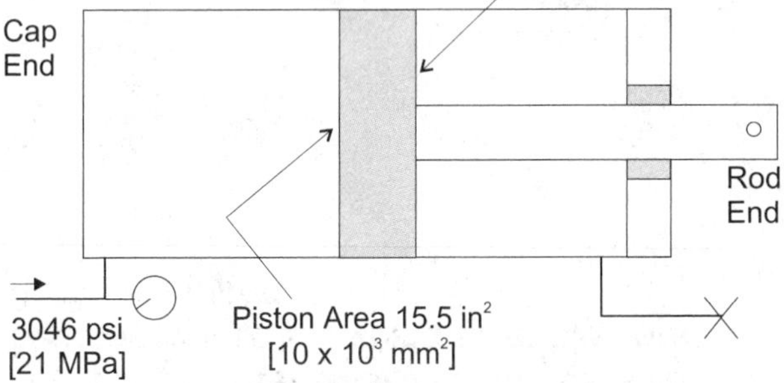

Illustration #13 — Pressure Intensification - Rod End

3046 psi [21 MPa]

Piston Area 15.5 in² [10 x 10³ mm²]

Rod End

Cap End

Effective Piston Area 7.75 in² [5 x 10³ mm²]

In this example, 3,046 psi [21 MPa] is applied to the cap end of the cylinder. The force produced on the piston is:

(F = A x P) (see illustration #9)

Using lb, in² and psi [N, mm², and MPa] (see Table #1)

F = 15.5 x 3,046 = 47,213 lb

[F = 10 x 10³ x 21 = 210 x 10³ N]

The resulting pressure in the rod end of the cylinder will be:

(P = F/A) (from illustration #9)

P = 47,213/7.75 = 6,092 psi

[P = (210 x 10³)/(5 x 10³) = 42 MPa]

A piston area ratio of 2 to 1 increased the pressure by two.

Again, it should be noted that these are theoretical pressures and forces. Actual values will differ, depending on the amount of friction involved.

How Pressure is Created

In hydraulic systems, pressure is created whenever there is a resistance to fluid flow. The resistance to flow will occur when:

1. A load is placed on linear and rotary actuators (cylinders and motors).
2. An orifice is placed in a line to control flow.
3. Fluid moves through pipes, hoses and valves (the resistance to flow in this case is caused by friction).

Without resistance to flow there will be no pressure buildup. The load on an actuator can be measured by the pressure it takes to operate that actuator.

The hydraulic pump shown in illustration #14A discharges 5 gpm [18.9 litres/min.] into an open line. If the line is short and the diameter of the pipe is large enough to ensure that the frictional resistance is negligible, the pressure on the pressure gage will be 0 psig.

When the valve in the discharge line is partially closed as shown in illustration #14B, the restriction forces the pressure to rise as the 5 gpm [18.9 litres/min.] is forced through the smaller opening. As the valve is closed further, the pressure will continue to rise until something breaks, or the drive to the pump stalls.

With a positive displacement hydraulic pump there is no theoretical limit to the pressure rise as the restriction or load is increased.

It is for this reason that hydraulic systems must have some type of pressure relief built into the system.

Illustration #14C shows a typical load on a pump that produces pressure in the discharge line. The discharge pressure will be dependent on the amount of weight on the cylinder (load) and the area of the cylinder. The load is creating a resistance to flow.

If the load on the cylinder is increased, the pressure developed between the pump and the cylinder will increase by a corresponding amount. The purpose of the hydraulic pump is to produce fluid flow. The resistance to the flow creates the pressure.

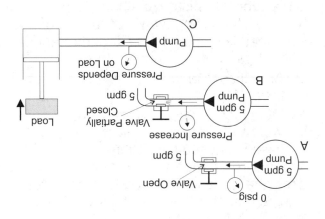

Illustration #14 — Creation of Pressure.

Pressure Required to Move a Load

The examples shown in illustrations #3 and #4 considered the theoretical pressures required to support a load on a cylinder. If it is required to actually move the load, the pressure would be higher due to:

1. The amount of friction that has to be overcome.
2. The back pressure in the return line.
3. The energy required to accelerate the load up to speed.

This is the same for both linear (cylinders) and rotary (hydraulic motors) actuators. Regarding the amount of friction that has to be overcome for rotary actuators, most manufacturers will specify the efficiency of the actuator as a percentage. For cylinders, manufacturers may indicate the force required to overcome the friction as a percentage of the theoretical force available.

The back pressure in the return line can be checked with a pressure gage.

The theoretical pressure required for acceleration can be calculated using the following formula:

F = ma

Where:

	Metric Units	In-lb-gal System
F = Force	N	lb
m = mass	kg	w/g*
a = acceleration	m/s^2	ft/sec^2

*w = weight in pounds
*g = acceleration due to gravity = 32.2 ft/sec^2

On an operating system with a known load, observing the pressures at the inlet to the actuator when the actuator is traveling at a constant speed will indicate the pressures required to overcome the sum of:

- The load
- Actuator friction
- Discharge line pressure

Subtracting the theoretical load pressure and the discharge line pressure will give the pressure required to overcome friction.

Note: The discharge line pressure will have to be corrected on a differential cylinder due to the piston area difference.

When the load is started from standstill, the inlet pressure will rise much higher than the constant speed pressure because of the extra force required to overcome static friction and accelerate the load up to speed.

The rise in inlet pressure will also depend on the characteristics of the directional control valve and will often reach the pressure the setting of the system relief valve.

Flow of Liquids

Flow Through Pipe

It is pressure that causes flow. For flow to occur in a constant diameter pipe, the pressure will always be lower on the downstream side of any particular point. In illustration #15, the pressure at point "A" is higher than point "B". The higher pressure at point "A" is required to overcome the friction that occurs between point "A" and point "B". The magnitude of the pressure drop will depend on the velocity and viscosity of the fluid being pumped. High velocities and high viscosities produce more friction and hence higher pressure drops.

Illustration #15 shows how the pressure in a length of tubing will vary along the length of the tubing, as fluid is pumped through it. If the output of the pump is increased, the pressure at "A" will increase from 'x' to 'y'. There will also be a corresponding increase in the pressure at locations "B, and C". The pressure at "D" will remain the same, which is atmospheric. A similar increase in pressures would occur if a smaller diameter pipe were used, instead of an increase in pump volumetric output.

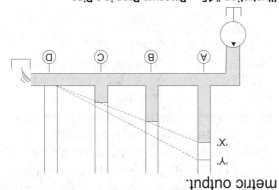

Illustration # 15 — Pressure Drop in a Pipe

In hydraulic systems, it is important to correctly size the piping to ensure that there is not an excessive pressure drop over the length of pipe or tubing. A large diameter pipe will have lower velocities and hence lower friction losses than a smaller diameter pipe, when pumping the same volume.

Flow Through an Orifice

The orifice shown in illustration #16A will have zero flow due to the equal pressures on both sides of the orifice. The orifice in illustration #16B will have some flow through it due to the 100 psi [689 kPa] pressure difference.

Assuming the orifices are the same sizes, the amount of flow will be higher in illustration #16C, because of the greater pressure difference across the orifice. In illustrations #16B and #16C, the amount of flow in gallons or litres per minute will depend on the size of the orifice and the viscosity of the liquid.

Both fixed and adjustable orifices are used to control the flow of liquids.

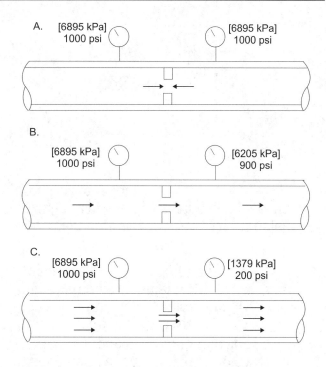

Illustration #16 — Flow Through an Orifice

The required clearances on many moving parts of valves, pumps and actuators act as orifices when there is a pressure difference across the clearance. By making the clearance small, manufacturers keep leakage to a minimum. As parts become worn, the original clearances become larger causing internal leakage to increase. Higher leakage rates cause heat to be added to the system (see "Heat Generation.").

Flow Measurement - Flow Rate

Flow rate is measured using the volume of flow, divided by time. Flow rate is most commonly measured as gallons or litres per minute.

Note: In this section, cubic inches or US gallons are used for the in-lb-gal system of volume. The conversion from US gallons to British (Canadian) imperial gallons is:

1 US gallon = 0.83267 Canadian gallons
1 US gallon = 231 cubic inches
1 US gallon = 3.785 litres

1 Canadian gallon = 1.20095 US gallons
1 Canadian gallon = 277.42 cubic inches
1 Canadian gallon = 4.546 090 litres
1 cubic metre = 1000 litres.
1 litre = 1000 cubic centimeters
1 litre = 1 cubic decimeter
1 decimeter = 10 centimetres

Volume Measurement

The volume of any regular shaped object is calculated by multiplying the cross sectional area by the length.

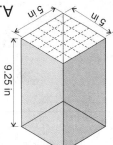

A.
5 in
5 in
9.25 in

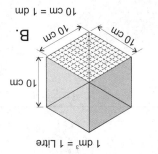

B.
10 cm
10 cm
10 cm
10 cm = 1 dm
1 dm³ = 1 Litre

Illustration #17 — Volume Measurement

The volume of the container shown as illustration #17A, is 5 inches x 5 inches x 9.25 inches = 231.25 cubic inches (in^3), which also equals approximately one US gallon.

The one litre container in illustration #17B is equal to 10 cm x 10 cm x 10 cm = 1000 cubic centimetres (cm^3). A cubic metre would contain 1000 of these one-litre containers.

To calculate the volume of a cylinder multiply the area of the cylinder by the length.

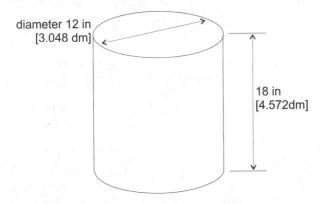

diameter 12 in
[3.048 dm]

18 in
[4.572dm]

Illustration #18 — Volume of a Cylinder

Using the formula A = $\pi d^2/4$, the volume of the cylinder in illustration #18 is:

In-lb-gal System Calculation:

Volume = $(\pi(12)^2/4)$ x (18) = 2,036 in^3

If this is divided by 231 (cubic inches per gallon)

Volume = 2,036/231 = 8.814 US gallons.

Metric Calculation:

Note: The metric length unit of decimetres (10 cm or 100 mm) is used when the volume is required in litres.

Volume = $(\pi(3.048)^2/4)$ x (4.572)
        = 33.36 litres.

Velocity

Speed is measured as distance divided by time; for example, inches, feet, or metres, per minute or second.

Velocity = distance divided by time

For Example:
km per hour
feet per minute
inches per second
metres per second

Actuator Speed (Cylinders)

There are three variables related to cylinder piston speed:

1. Flow rate into the cylinder (Fl)
2. Area of the piston (A)
3. Velocity of the piston (V)

The mathematical relationship is shown with a flow-area-velocity triangle in illustration #19.

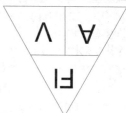

Illustration #19 — Flow-Area-Velocity Triangle

Where:

$$(Fl = A \times V) \text{ or } (A = Fl/V) \text{ or } (V = Fl/A)$$

When using these formulae, the units must be compatible. Table #2 shows some of the more common units used for flow rate and the matching units to be used for calculations.

Table #2 — Matching Units for Flow Rate/Velocity/Area Calculations

Flow Rate (Fl)	Velocity (V)	Area (A)
in³/min.(s)	in/min.(s)	in²
feet³/min.(s)	feet/min.(s)	ft²
litres/min.	dm/min.(s)	dm²
m³/min.(s)	m/min.(s)	m²
cm³/min.(s)	cm/min.(s)	cm²

If two of the three variables are known, the third can be calculated.

Note: The above units and formulae are also applicable for calculations of areas, velocities and flow rates in pipe and tubing.

In-lb-gal System Calculation:

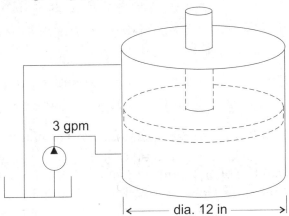

Illustration #20 — Piston Velocity (In-lb-gal System)

Referring to illustration #20, a 12 inch diameter piston is extended using a 3 gpm pump. Find the velocity when extending.

Information provided is:
Pump output (Fl) is 3 gpm.
Diameter of the piston is 12 inches
(from this (A) can be calculated).

From table #2, when using in³/min. for the flow rate (Fl) and in² for the area (A) the velocity (V) will be in in/min.

Convert gpm to in³/min. (1 gallon = 231 in³)
3 gpm = 3 x 231 = 693 in³ / minute
Piston area = $\pi(12)^2/4 = 113.1$ in²
From illustration #19, V = Fl/A
V = 693/113.1 = 6.13 in/minute

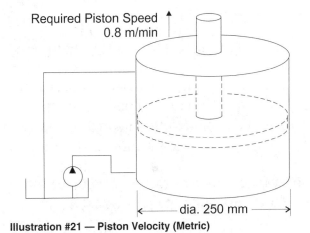

Illustration #21 — Piston Velocity (Metric)

Flow of Liquids

Actuator Speed (Hydraulic Motors)

There are three variables related to hydraulic motor speed. They are:

1. Flow rate into the motor (Fl)
2. Motor displacement per revolution (Disp)
3. Rotational speed of the motor (Vr)

The mathematical relationship is shown in illustration #22, where:

(Fl = Disp x Vr) or (Disp = Fl / Vr)
or (Vr = Fl / Disp)

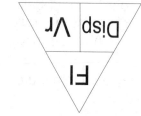

Illustration #22 — Flow-Displacement-RPM Triangle

Metric Calculation:

Referring to illustration #21, a 250 mm diameter piston is to be extended at 0.8 m/min. Find the required pump output in litres per minute.

Information provided is:
Piston velocity (V) is 0.8 m/min.
Diameter of the piston is 250 mm (from this (A) can be calculated).

From table #2, when the flow rate (Fl) is litres per minute, velocity (V) should be in dm/min. and area (A) should be dm².

Change the required velocity (V) to dm/min.
(1 m = 10 dm)
V = 0.8 m/min. x 10 = 8 dm/min.

Change the diameter to decimeters
(1 dm = 100 mm)
Diameter = 250 mm/100 = 2.5 dm

Piston area (A) = $\pi(2.50)^2/4 = 4.908$ dm²
From illustration #18, Fl = A x V
Fl = 4.908 x 8 = 39.28 litres/min.

As before, when using these formulae, the units must be compatible. Table #3 shows some of the more common units used for flow rate and the matching units used for calculations.

Flow Rate (Fl)	Rotational Speed (Vr)	Displacement (Disp)
in^3/min.(s)	rpm(s)	in^3/revolution
ft^3/min.(s)	rpm(s)	ft^3/revolution
cm^3/min.(s)	rpm(s)	cm^3/revolution
dm^3/min.(s) litres/min.(s)	rpm(s)	dm^3/revolution litres/revolution
m^3/min.(s)	rpm(s)	m^3/revolution

Table #3 — Matching Units for Flow Rate/rpm/Displacement Calculations

If two of the three variables are known, the third can be calculated.

In-lb-gal System Calculation:

Referring to illustration #23, a hydraulic motor with a displacement of 10 in^3 per revolution has a speed of 1000 rpm.

Find the required pump output assuming zero internal leakage.

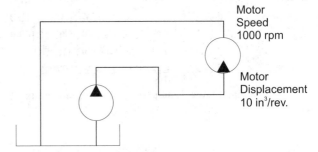

Illustration #23 — RPM of a Hydraulic Motor (In-lb-gal System)

The information provided is:
Motor speed (Vr) is 1000 rpm.
Motor displacement (Disp) is 10 in^3/revolution.

When using rpm (Vr) and in^3/revolution (Disp) the flow rate (Vr) will be in^3/min. (see table #3).

From illustration #20, Fl = Disp x Vr

Vr = 1000 rpm

Disp = 10 in^3/revolution

Pump output (F1) will be:

Fl = 1000 x 10 = 10,000 in^3 per minute

If the pump output is required in US gallons per minute:

Fl (gal/min.) = Fl (in^3/min.)/231

Fl = 10,000/231 = 43.29 gal/min.

Metric Calculation:

Referring to illustration #24, a pump (output 40 litres per min.) is supplying oil to a hydraulic motor with a displacement of 100 cm^3/revolution. What will be the motor rpm (assuming zero internal leakage)?

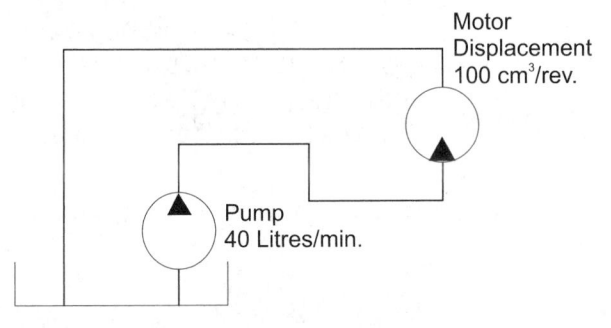

Illustration #24—RPM of a Hydraulic Motor (Metric)

The information provided is:

Pump output (Fl) is 40 litres/min.

Motor displacement (Disp) is 100 cm^3/revolution.

When using litres/min. (Fl) and litres/rev (Disp) the velocity (Vr) will be rpm (see table #3).

Convert motor displacement (cm^3/revolution) to litres/revolution

1 litre = 1000 cm^3.

Disp = 100/1000 = 0.1 litres/revolution

From illustration #22, Vr = Fl/Disp

Vr = 40/0.1 = 400 rpm

Note: For both cylinders and hydraulic motors, flow rate and the cylinder or motor size have determined the speed. Pressure has not entered into the equation. Pressure has no bearing on the theoretical speed of the actuator; however higher pressures will often cause higher internal leakage rates, especially on hydraulic motors. This will cause a decrease in speed. The speed loss is due to a reduction in the flow available to drive the motor (caused by the internal leakage), not a lack of pressure.

Flow Measurement - Velocity

Flow velocity is measured using feet or metres per second. The velocity through a pipe will be directly related to the flow rate (gpm, litres/min., in^3/min., m^3/min., etc.) and the diameter of the pipe.

There are three variables related to cylinder piston speed:

1. Flow rate through the pipe or tubing (Fl)
2. Area of the pipe or tubing (A)
3. Velocity of the fluid (V)

The mathematical relationship is shown in the illustration #19 Flow – Area – Velocity triangle.

Where:

(Fl = V x A) or (V = Fl/A) or (A = Fl/V)

See table #2 for matching units for calculations.

In-lb-gal System Calculation:

A pump inlet line is to have a maximum fluid velocity of 3 feet/second. The maximum pump output is 50 gpm. What size inlet line should be installed?

The information provided is:

Maximum velocity (V) is 3 feet/second

Maximum pump output (Fl) is 50 gpm

(The pipe inside diameter is specified in inches, therefore area (A) should be in in^2)

When fluid velocity (V) is in/min. and fluid flow rate (Fl) is in^3/min. the area of the pipe (A) will be in^2 (see table #2).

Convert pump output (gpm) to in^3/min.

(1 US gallon = 231 in^3)

$$Pump\ output\ (Fl) = 50 \times 231$$
$$= 11,550\ in^3/min.$$

Convert fluid velocity, (V) from ft/s to in/min.

$$Fluid\ velocity\ (V) = 3 \times 12 \times 60$$
$$= 2160\ in/min.$$

From illustration #19, A = Fl/V

A = 11550/2160 = 5.35 in^2

Where A = minimum area of the inlet line:

Calculate the diameter using area of 5.35 in^2

$A = \pi d^2/4$, therefore $d = \sqrt{A \times 4 /\pi}$

Diameter (d) = $\sqrt{(5.35 \times 4)/\pi}$ = 2.61 in

This would be the minimum inside diameter of the inlet line to the pump.

A 3 inch schedule 40 pipe would be the size to use as the ID is 3.068 in (see Section Three and the Appendix for pipe dimensions).

Metric Calculation:

The working (pressure) lines of a hydraulic circuit is to have maximum velocity of 5 m/s. The maximum flow rate is 200 litres/min. What size of pipe should be used?

Information provided is:

Maximum fluid velocity (V) is 5 m/s

Maximum flow rate (Fl) is 200 litres/min.

When fluid velocity (V) is cm/s and fluid flow rate (Fl) is cm^3/s, the area of the pipe (A) will be cm^2 (see table #2).

Convert flow rate from litres/min.) to cm^3/s (1 litre = 1000 cm^3)

Fl = 200 x 1000/60 = 3333 cm^3/s

Convert fluid velocity (V) m/s to cm/s (1 m = 100 cm)

V = 5 x 100 = 500 cm/s

From illustration #19, A = Fl/V

A = 3333/500 = 6.67 cm^2

Where A = minimum area of the working line:

Calculate the diameter (d) using area of 6.67 cm^2

A = πd^2/4, therefore:

Diameter $= \sqrt{6.67 \times 4 / \pi}$
$= 2.91$ cm = 29.1 mm

This would be the minimum inside diameter of the pipe. As this is a working line the maximum pressure would have to be specified before a suitable size of pipe could be chosen.

See Section Three and the Appendix for pipe dimensions, schedule numbers, and working pressures.

Effect of Changing Pipe Size

Illustration #25 shows 49 gpm [185.5 litres/min.] fluid flowing through a 2 inch [50.8 mm] inside diameter pipe. The velocity is 5 ft/s [1.5 m/s]. When this pipe is swaged down as shown, to 1 inch [25.4 mm] diameter, the velocity will quadruple to 20 ft/s [6.1 m/s] as it passes into the smaller diameter. This is because the area of the 1 inch [25.4 mm] diameter pipe is only one quarter of the area of the 2 inch [50.8 mm] diameter pipe. The friction losses will also quadruple in the smaller diameter section as long as the flow stays laminar.

If the flow becomes turbulent, friction losses in the small diameter section may become sixteen times that in the large diameter section.

Illustration #25 shows the major change in fluid velocity when a change in pipe diameter is made. It is important that when making piping changes to a system, not to change any pipe diameters without first checking what the effect will be on fluid velocity.

To illustrate the effect of making a slight change in pipe size, consider a system that has a small 3.8 gpm [14.4 litres/min.] pump, which is fitted with a half inch, schedule 40 suction line. A half inch schedule 40 pipe has an inside diameter of 0.622 inch [15.8 mm].

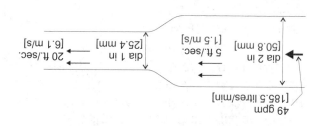

Illustration #25 — Velocity and Pipe Diameter Reduction

49 gpm [185.5 litres/min]

dia 2 in [50.8 mm] 5 ft./sec. [1.5 m/s]

dia 1 in [25.4 mm] 20 ft./sec. [6.1 m/s]

The velocity in the suction would be:

$V = Fl/A$ (illustration #19)

$V = (3.8 \times 231/60)/(\pi \times 0.622^2/4)$

$[V = (14.4 \times 0.001/60)/(\pi \times 0.0158^2/4)]$

$V = 48.1$ inches/second = 4 feet/second

$[V = 1.22$ m/s$]$

This is the maximum velocity for suction lines (table #4).

If for some reason schedule 80 pipe is used instead of schedule 40 pipe, the inside diameter would then be 0.546 inch [13.9 mm]. The velocity in the suction would now be:

$V = (3.8 \times 231/60)/(\pi \times 0.546^2/4)$

$[V = (14.4 \times 0.001/60)/(\pi \times 0.0139^2/4)]$

$V = 62.5$ inches/second = 5.2 feet/second

$[V = 1.58$ m/s$]$

This velocity is more than 25% higher than the maximum recommended velocity for suction lines (see table #4). Depending on a number of factors, which include oil temperature, suction lift, length of suction line, number of fittings in the suction line, etc., this higher velocity could cause cavitation.

Recommended Maximum Fluid Velocities

Because high velocities can cause cavitation, excessive energy loss, and a consequent heat build up, there are recommended maximum fluid velocities for various parts of the system. These are shown in table #4

Suction lines	2 to 4 feet/second
	[0.6 to 1.2 m/s]
Return lines	10 to 15 feet/second
	[3.1 to 4.6 m/s]
Working lines	
(500 - 3000 psi)	15 - 20 feet/second
	[4.6 to 6.1 m/s]
(3000 - 5000 psi)	15 to 30 feet/second
	[4.6 to 9.1 m/s]

Table #4 – Recommended Maximum Fluid Velocities

Note: Fluid velocity is controlled by sizing the line diameter in relation to the maximum flow.

Laminar and Turbulent Flow

As fluid flows through a pipe, it can be thought of as particles flowing in hundreds of small streams. When the flow is laminar as shown in illustration #26A, the streams are parallel to one another, but are moving at different velocities.

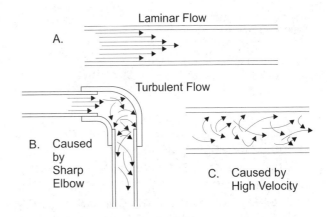

Illustration #26A, B, C — Laminar and Turbulent Flow

The streams closest to the pipe walls are moving slowly, while the fluid in the center is moving more rapidly. When the flow is laminar, there is minimum energy loss due to friction.

Turbulent flow, in illustration #26B occurs when the streams of oil are no longer following parallel flow paths. This will first occur where there are abrupt changes in direction, or cross section, or other obstructions. Turbulence will also occur in straight runs of pipe when fluid velocities become excessive, as shown in illustration #26C.

To reduce the possibility of turbulence, lines should be sized to keep fluid velocity within the guidelines shown in table #4. The pipe runs should be as straight as possible, and the number of fittings kept to a minimum. The use of tubing, instead of pipe, is recommended where possible.

Flow Intensification (Differential Cylinders)

When sizing lines and specifying filters, it is important to realize that the return flow from a differential cylinder varies, depending on whether the cylinder is being retracted or extended.

Illustration #27 — Cylinder Being Extended

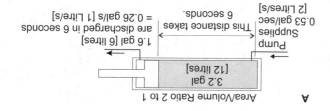

A Area/Volume Ratio 2 to 1

3.2 gal [12 litres]

Pump Supplies 0.53 gal/sec [2 Litres/s]

This distance takes 6 seconds.

1.6 gal [6 litres] are discharged in 6 seconds = 0.26 gal/s [1 Litre/s]

Illustration #27 shows a cylinder with a 2 to 1 volume ratio (3.2 gal [12 litres] to fill on extension, 1.6 gal [6 litres] to fill on retraction) being extended. When 0.53 gal/s [2 litres/s] is entering the cap end of the cylinder, only 0.26 gal/s [1 litre/s] is flowing out the rod end.

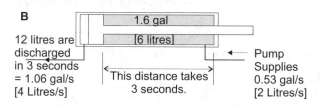

Illustration #28 — Cylinder Being Retracted

Illustration #28 shows the same cylinder being retracted. When 0.53 gal/s [2 litres/s] is entering the rod end of the cylinder, 1.06 gal/s [4 litres/s] is being exhausted from the cap end. This is double the amount being supplied by the pump.

A return line filter may have been rated for the maximum flow from the pump, but as illustration #28 indicates, a filter in the return line would have to handle double the pump output.

Parallel Flow Paths

Whenever fluid flow enters a tee, the fluid will take the line of least resistance. Illustration #29 shows the output from a pump being joined by a tee to two hydraulic cylinders.

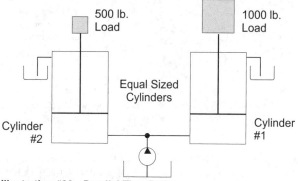

Illustration #29—Parallel Flow Paths

With equal cylinder diameters, the pressure required to raise cylinder #1, will be twice the pressure required to raise cylinder #2. Cylinder #2 will move first, and cylinder #1 will not move until cylinder #2 has completed its stroke and the pressure has built up high enough to overcome the load on cylinder #1.

When trouble shooting a problem circuit, with a lack of pressure in the system, it is all too easy to fault the pump. It is often found that there is a bypass such as a valve being open, and the flow is taking the easiest flow path, thus not allowing the pressure to build up.

Series Flow Path

As mentioned earlier in this section, pressure is the result of a resistance to flow. When there is a single flow path, pressure at the upstream end (towards the pump) has to be high enough to overcome all resistance along that flow path.

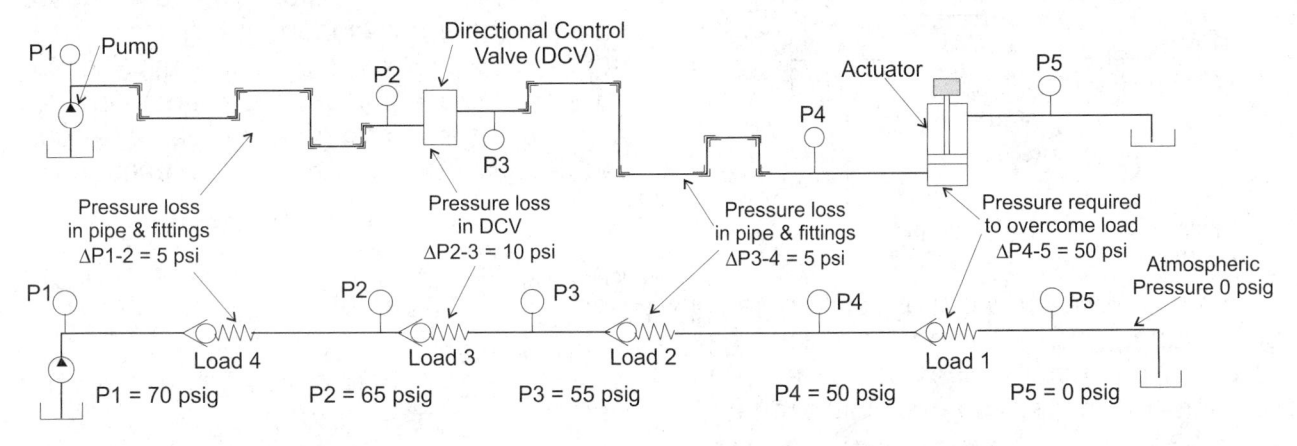

Illustration #30 — Series Flow Path

Referring to illustration #30, it may be assumed that as long as there is 50 psi [345 kPa] at the pump to overcome the highest resistance (load #1), the fluid will flow.

This is not so.

Pressure at P4 will be 50 psig [345 kPa] to overcome load #1, which is represented by a 50 psi [345 kPa] spring loaded check valve. For pressure to overcome load #2, which is also represented by a spring loaded check valve, it will require 5 psi [34 kPa] to overcome the spring and an additional 50 psi [345 kPa] to overcome the pressure at P4. P3 will therefore read 55 psig [379 kPa].

This happens all the way down the line and P1 will read 70 psig [483 kPa]. The pressure resulting from more than one resistance, in a series flow path, is the sum of all resistance.

Bernoulli's Equation

Bernoulli's equation concerns the relationship between fluid velocity, pressure, and elevation. Flow and pressure are the basis of power hydraulic principles, elevation is not considered a factor.

The total energy contained by a constant flow of pressured fluid is the sum of the kinetic energy (KE) (from velocity) and potential energy (PE) (from pressure). Based on the fact that energy cannot be created or destroyed, the total energy at points 1, 2, and 3 in illustration #31 will be the same value for a specific flow rate.

Total Energy$_1$ = Total Energy$_2$ = Total Energy$_3$

$(KE_1 + PE_1) = (KE_2 + PE_2) = (KE_3 + PE_3)$

The initial conditions at point 1 are:

Velocity = V1. Pressure = P1.

As the fluid moves into the reduced area of pipe (point 2) the velocity (V2) must increase due to the smaller cross section, which increases the amount of kinetic energy (KE). For the equation: $(KE_1 + PE_1) = (KE_2 + PE_2)$ to remain true, PE_2 must decrease as KE_2 increases and consequently the pressure P2 must decrease.

As the fluid moves to point 3, conditions become the same as at point 1. The velocity V3

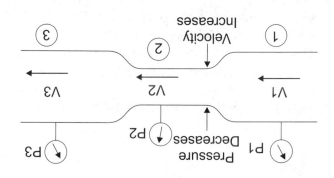

Illustration #31 — Bernoulli's Principle

drops to the same value as V1 and the pressure P3 increases to become the same value as P1.

The above is true if there is no energy losses due to friction, however friction is a fact of life and there will be a slight energy loss through-out, causing the pressure P3 to be slightly less than P1.

Note: Bernoulli's principle is an important factor in the design of some hydraulic components. For example, when oil is flowing through spool valves, the changes in velocity and the consequent pressure changes are taken into account in the design of the valve. If maximum flow rates are exceeded, the pressure changes may be large enough to unbalance the axial forces on the spool, which could cause problems with actuation.

Energy, Torque and Power

Energy

Work is done whenever a force is applied through a distance. Force and displacement are two essential elements of work. If a force is applied to an object with no movement, then there has been no work done. When work is done, energy is expended. Energy comes in a variety of forms, such as mechanical energy, thermal or heat energy, chemical energy, and nuclear energy.

The in-lb-gal system of measurement for work or energy is, foot pounds (ft/lbs) for mechanical energy, and British thermal units (Btu) for heat energy.

Illustration #32A shows a 1,000 lb load being raised 3 feet. The amount of work done by the cylinder = 1,000 x 3 = 3,000 ft lbs

The Btu is the amount of heat required to raise 1 lb of water 1°F.

To convert mechanical energy to heat energy, one Btu = 778 ft lbs

If the energy used to raise the load in illustration #32A were converted to heat, it would equal 3,000/778 = 3.86 Btu.

The metric SI system uses Joules for all forms of energy (1J = 1 N•m).

Illustration #32B shows a mass of 510 kg being raised one metre. The 510 kg mass exerts a force of 5000 N on the cylinder rod.

Energy = force x distance

The energy provided by the cylinder to move this load a distance of one metre is 5000 x 1 = 5000 N•m = 5000 J = 5 kJ.

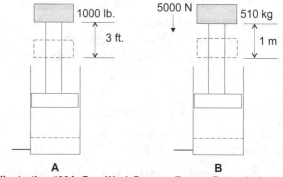

Illustration #32A, B — Work Done or Energy Expended

Note: The metric terms, calorie (international) and Calorie (dietetic) are not used in SI. For heat measurement, One calorie raises 1 gram of water 1°C (one calorie = 4.186 J). One kilocalorie (international) will raise 1 kg of water 1°C (one kilocalorie = 4.186 kJ).

The Calorie used by nutritionists is equivalent to the international kilocalorie (differentiated by the use of the upper case C for the nutrition Calorie). One Calorie (nutrition) equals 1 kcal (international).

Torque

When a force is applied at a radius to cause an object to rotate about an axis, the product of the force and the radius is referred to as torque. Torque is the turning or twisting effect of a force.

$$Torque = Force \times Radius$$
$$Work\ done\ by\ torque = torque \times 2\pi$$

The in-lb-gal system of torque is usually either pound feet (lb ft) or pound inches (lb in).

The SI unit of torque is the newton metre (N•m).

The pressure required to move a hydraulic cylinder is determined by the load on the cylinder and its diameter (size). Hydraulic motors are similar in that the pressure required to rotate the motor is dependent on the torque load on the motor shaft and the displacement (size) per revolution.

Power

If the time taken to do work or use energy is considered, then power is being measured. Power is the amount of energy used per unit of time. Common units for measuring power are the horsepower (HP) and the watt (W).

in-lb-gal System Power Measurement

1 HP = 550 ft lb of work done per second

1 HP = 33,000 ft lb of work done per minute

In illustration #33, the 550 pound weight is raised one foot in one second. Therefore the rate of work being done is 550 ft lb/second, which equals one horsepower.

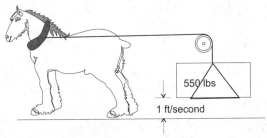

Illustration #33 — One Horsepower

If this was carried on for one minute, the 550 pound load would be raised 60 feet. The rate of work being done in this case would be 60 x 550, which equals 33,000 ft lb/minute, which also equals one horsepower.

1 HP = 550 ft lb/second
1 HP = 33,000 ft lb/minute
In relation to heat energy:
1 HP = 42.4 Btu/minute

Metric Power Measurement

The metric system of power is the watt (W) where:

One watt = 1 Joule/second (J/s)

The watt is a relatively small unit, therefore kilowatt (kW) and megawatt (MW) are commonly used.

1 kW= 1000 W
1 MW= 1 000 000 W

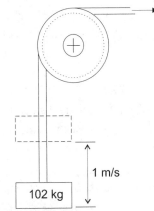

Illustration #34 — One kilowatt.

In illustration #34, the energy used to raise the 102 kg load a distance of one metre is:

Energy = force x distance

Where:

Force= Mass x Acceleration (due to gravity)

Force = 102 kg x 9.8 m/s²

Distance = 1 m

Energy = 102 x 9.8 x1 = 1000 Joule or 1 kJ

If the time taken to expend this amount of energy is one second, the power used would be 1000 J (1 kJ) per second, which equals 1000 watts or one kilowatt:

Watts (W) = Joules (J)/second

kW = kJ/s

Power Conversion

To convert power from in-lb-gal system to Metric SI.

746 W = 1 horsepower = 0.746 kW

1 kW = 1.34 horsepower

Hydraulic Power (in-lb-gal system)

When there is flow and pressure in hydraulic systems the hydraulic horsepower can be calculated.

Hydraulic HP = (gpm x psi)/1714

This is strictly the HP from the pressurized moving fluid.

Power to Drive a Pump

To calculate the HP required to drive the pump, the efficiency (eff) of the pump is required. The HP to drive the pump will be:

HP = ((gpm x psi)/1714) x (100/eff (%))

Power and Torque from an Actuator

If one knows the efficiency of a hydraulic actuator, the pressure and flow to that actuator, the power output of the actuator can be calculated.

The power output of a hydraulic actuator will be:

HP (from actuator) = ((gpm x psi)/1714) x (efficiency (%)/100)

If the rpm of the hydraulic motor is known, it is possible to calculate the torque output.

The general formula for HP for any rotating equipment is:

HP = 2π x rpm x torque (ft lbs)/33,000

From this:

Torque (ft lbs) = (33,000/2π) x (HP/rpm)

Torque (ft lbs) = 5252 x HP/rpm

Torque (in lbs) = 5252 x 12 x HP/rpm

Torque (in lbs) = 63025 x HP/rpm

By substituting the motor displacement per revolution and pressure for HP, the theoretical torque from a hydraulic motor can be expressed as:

Torque (in lbs) = psi x displ/2π

Where: displ = motor displacement per revolution (in^3)

psi = pressure at inlet to motor.

If the efficiency is known, the actual torque can be calculated.

Torque (in lbs) = (psi x displ/2π) x (eff/100)

Note: The motor torque output at a specific pressure is determined by the displacement per revolution.

Hydraulic Power (Metric)

Using flow and pressure through a pipe, the hydraulic power is calculated as follows:

Hydraulic power (Watts) = Pressure (Pa) x Flow (m^3/s)

As kilowatts (kW), kilopascals (kPa) and litres are more common units of measurement, this basic equation can be converted to:

kW = (kPa) x ℓ/s/1000

This is strictly the power from the pressurized moving fluid.

Power to Drive a Pump

To calculate the power required to drive a pump, the efficiency of the pump is required.

The power to drive a pump will be:

$$kW = (kPa \times \ell/s/1000) \times (100/efficiency)$$

Power and Torque from an Actuator

Similarly, if one knows the efficiency of a hydraulic actuator, and the pressure, and flow to that actuator, the power output of the actuator can be calculated.

The power output of a hydraulic actuator will be:

$$kW = (kPa \times \ell/s/1000) \times (efficiency (\%)/100)$$

If the rpm of the hydraulic motor is known, it is possible to calculate the torque output.

The general formula for power for any rotating equipment is:

$$Watts = torque (N \bullet m) \times rpm \times 2\pi/60$$

From this:

$$Torque (N \bullet m) = (Watts \times 60)/(rpm \times 2\pi)$$
$$Torque (N \bullet m) = 9.55 \times Watts/rpm$$
$$Torque (N \bullet m) = 9550 \times kW/rpm$$

By substituting the motor displacement and pressure for kW, the theoretical torque from a hydraulic motor can be expressed as:

$$Torque (N \bullet m) = kPa \times displ/2\pi$$

Where:

Displ = motor displacement per revolution (litres)

kPa = pressure at inlet to the motor

If the efficiency is known, the actual torque can be calculated.

$$Torque (N \bullet m) = kPa \times Displ/2\pi \times (eff/100)$$

Note: The motor torque output at a specific pressure is determined by the displacement per revolution.

Heat Generation

Mechanical machines generate heat due to the friction of parts sliding and rolling against each other. These friction losses waste power and make a machine inefficient.

A gearbox that has 100 HP [75 kW] input and is 85% efficient will only produce 85 HP [63 kW] at the output shaft. The lost 15 HP [11 kW] is converted to heat. As mentioned earlier, 1 HP = 42.4 Btu/minute [1 kW = 1 kJ/s]; therefore, the amount of energy heating up the gearbox equals 42.4 x 15 = 636 Btu/minute [11 kJ/s]. This quantity of heat increases the temperature of the gearbox until the heat dissipation from the gearbox equals the heat input (636 Btu/minute) or [11 kJ/s].

If the machine temperature becomes too high due to ambient conditions or extremely high friction losses, some external method of cooling may be employed, such as oil coolers or forced air fans.

Similar energy losses are realized in hydraulic systems. Power in the system that is not used to produce useful work is converted to heat. Whenever there is flow with a corresponding pressure drop that does no useful work, there is power loss. Flow multiplied by pressure represents power.

The following example will illustrate how heat is generated in a hydraulic circuit by wasted power. Consider the simplified circuit shown in illustration #35.

The 50 gpm [3.15 litres per second (ℓ/s)] fixed displacement pump supplies oil to a 2:1 ratio cylinder that has a flow control valve set at 20 gpm [1.262 ℓ/s] controlling the speed when extending. The relief valve is set at 3,000 psi [20 684 kPa].

The cylinder is retracted at full speed (no flow (speed) control).

The amount of wasted power is equal to the total hydraulic power generated at the pump discharge minus the useful power being used by the system.

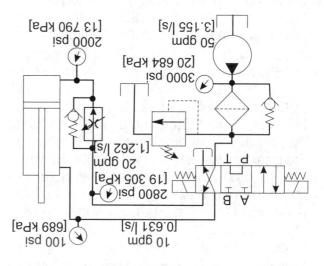

Illustration #35 — Circuit - Cylinder Extending

Consider the extending operation:

Assume that pressures are constant at the values shown in illustration #35.

The 50 gpm [3.15 (ℓ/s)] pump operates at 3,000 psi [20 684 kPa]. The hydraulic power generated at the pump discharge equals:

(HP = psi x gpm/1714)
3,000 x 50/1714 = 87.51 HP
[kW = kPa x ℓ/s/1000]
[20 684 x 3.155/1000 = 65.258 kW].

At the cylinder, useful power is equal to the power available from the fluid at the inlet minus the power available from the fluid at the discharge.

Power from the fluid at the cylinder inlet (cap end):

HP= 2,000 x 20/1714 = 23.34 HP
[Kilowatts = 13 790 x 1.262/1000 = 17.403 kW]

Power from the fluid at the cylinder discharge (the flow from the discharge is half that at the inlet due to the cylinder having a 2:1 area ratio):

HP = 100 x 10/1714 = 0.58 HP

[Kilowatts = 689 x 0.631/1000 = 0.435 kW]

Useful power produced by the cylinder
= 23.34 − 0.58 = 22.76 HP

[Useful power produced by the cylinder
= 17.403 − 0.435 = 16.968 kW]

The amount of wasted power is equal to the hydraulic power at the pump discharge minus the useful power, which equals:

87.51 - 22.76 = 64.75 HP

[65.258 -16.968 = 48.290 kW]

The majority of the wasted power is the result of the pressure drops at the relief valve and the flow control valve, the remainder is losses in the piping and directional control valve.

A list of the wasted power for the circuit shown in illustration #35 (cylinder being extended) is:

Relief valve

30 gpm @ 3,000 psi	= 52.51 HP
[1.893 ℓ/s @ 20,685 kPa	= 39.155 kW]

Pipes & DCV

20 gpm @ 200 psi	= 2.33 HP
[1.262 ℓ/s @ 1,378 kPa	= 1.739 kW]

Flow control

20 gpm @ 800 psi	= 9.33 HP
[1.262 ℓ/s @ 5516 kPa	= 6.961 kW]

Return piping

10 gpm @ 100 psi	= 0.58 HP
[0.631 ℓ/s @ 689 kPa	= 0.435 kW]

Total lost power

in-lb-gal systems	= 64.75 HP
[Metric units	= 48.290 kW]

The heat being added to the system when the cylinder is being extended is:

Btu/minute = 64.75 HP x 42.3

Btu/minute = 2,739

[48.290 kJ/s]

Consider the retracting operation:

The pressures are as shown in illustration #36. There is no useful work being done. All the energy is being used to force the oil through the pipes and valves and overcome the friction of lowering the cylinder.

The 50 gpm [3.155 ℓ/s] pump operates at 800 psi [5516 kPa].

The hydraulic power generated at the pump discharge equals:

(HP = psi x gpm/1714)

800 x 50/1714 = 23.34 HP

[kW = kPa x ℓ/s/1000]

[5 516 x 3.155/1000 = 17.403 kW]

The heat being added to the system when the cylinder is being retracted is:

Btu/minute = 23.34 x 42.3

Btu/minute = 987 Btu/minute

[17.403 kJ/s]

Consider the complete operation:

Consider one hour of operation where 30 minutes is spent extending, 15 minutes is spent during retraction, and for 15 minutes the cylinder is stationary.

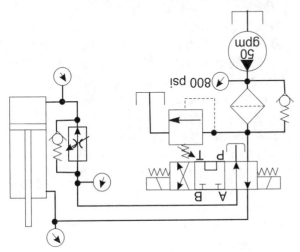

Illustration #36 — Circuit Cylinder Retracting

When the cylinder is stationary it is assumed that the heat into the system is negligible as all the pump output is directed back to tank through the directional control valve. Heat input into the system is as follows:

Extension

30 minutes/hr x 2764 Btu/minute
= 82,920 Btu/hr
[30 minutes/hr x 48.290 x 60 kJ/min.
= 86 922 kJ/hr]

Retraction

15 minutes/hr x 987 Btu/minute
= 14,805 Btu/hr
[15 minutes/hr x 17.403 x 60 kJ/min.
= 15 663 kJ/hr]

System Total

Total heat into the system equals:
82,920 + 14,805 = 97,725 Btu/hr
[86 922 + 15 663 = 102 585 kJ/hr]

Heat Dissipation

Heat is lost throughout the system, due to the differences in temperature between the components, piping, reservoir, etc., and the ambient temperature. When this temperature difference is small, such as at start up, there is very little heat lost to the surroundings.

The temperature of the system will rise until the temperature difference is high enough to produce a heat loss that equals the heat input into the system. When this occurs, the temperature will stabilize and that will be the operating temperature for that particular operating condition.

Various operating procedures will produce different amounts of heat that is added to the system.

One of the functions of the oil reservoir is to act as a heat exchanger by passing the heat from the oil, through the walls, to the surrounding atmosphere.

The location and size of the reservoir will have a direct influence on its heat dissipating abilities. A large reservoir in a cool, well venti-lated area will dissipate much more heat than a smaller reservoir in an enclosed hot location.

On the occasion where the reservoir does not have a large enough surface area to dis-sipate the heat, or the system is operating in a high temperature environment, or the sys-tem is very inefficient, additional cooling may be required.

This may be accomplished by relocation of the reservoir, the use of an oil cooler, cooling fins on the reservoir, a cooling fan, or any combination of the above.

The amount of heat that is radiated from a steel surface with only natural convection can be calculated using the following formula:

Heat loss per hour = k x A x ΔT

Where:

Heat loss per hour = The heat radiated from the surface per hour (Btu) [kJ]

k = The heat loss constant for a steel surface, which is:
(a) 2.54 when using ft² and degrees F
(b) 51.9 when using m² and degrees C.

A = The area of the radiating surface (ft²) [m²]. For oil reservoirs it is recommended to use only the area of the sides of the reservoir and not include the top and the bottom (the top does not contact the oil, and the bottom due to its location does not easily radiate heat).

ΔT = The temperature difference between the ambient air and the radiating surface in degrees Fahrenheit (°F) [degrees Celsius (°C)].

Considering the previous example used to explain heat generation:

The 50 gpm [3.11 l/s] pump in illustration #35 would require a reservoir of approx. 150 gallons [568 litres]. The actual size of the reservoir, allowing for air space, could be 3 ft x 3 ft x 3 ft [0.914 m x 0.914 m x 0.914 m] (see Section Four for recommended size of reservoirs).

Using only the sides of the reservoir to calculate the radiating area:

Radiating area = 3^2 x 4 sides = 36 ft^2
[0.914^2 x 4 = 3.34 m^2]

Assuming that the ambient air temperature is 70°F [21 °C] and the sides of the reservoir are at the maximum recommended oil temperature of 140°F [60°C], the temperature difference is then 140 - 70 = 70°F
[60 - 21 = 39°C]

The heat radiated from the reservoir
Btu/hr = 2.54 x 36 x 70 = 6400 Btu/hr
[kJ/hr = 51.9 x 3.34 x 39 = 6770 kJ/hr]

In the previous example, when the oil is at the maximum recommended temperature for petroleum oils (140°F) [60°C], the amount of heat being radiated from the reservoir (6400 Btu/hr) [6770 kJ] is very small compared to the amount of heat being added to the system (97,725 Btu/hr) [102 585 kJ/hr]. For this system to run on a continuous basis, it would have to have some other form of heat removal, such as an oil cooler.

This system was deliberately made inefficient to illustrate how easily overheating can occur. For simplicity other losses such as the friction losses in the hydraulic pump and cylinder were ignored.

Graphical Symbols

At present there are two standards that cover fluid power graphical symbols: ISO and ANSI. There is a world wide agreement to use the ISO symbols, but during the transition, either standard may be encountered depending on the origin of the drawing. ISO symbols will be used where possible in this publication.

Illustration #37 shows how the graphical symbols are combined to form a schematic diagram of a simple hydraulic circuit. The major components in the circuit shown are a double acting cylinder and a pump. Fluid direction, flow and pressure are controlled by a separate valve for each of these functions.

The directional control valve allows the cylinder to be operated in both directions. The extending speed is controlled by the flow control valve. The retracting speed is not adjustable. The directional control valve is solenoid actuated, springs return the valve to the center position when the solenoids are not energized. When in this center position, both lines to the cylinder are closed off and the pump output is directed back to the reservoir.

Table #5 shows some of the more common graphical (ISO) symbols that may be used to construct a simple hydraulic circuit.

For a more complete list of symbols, see the Appendix.

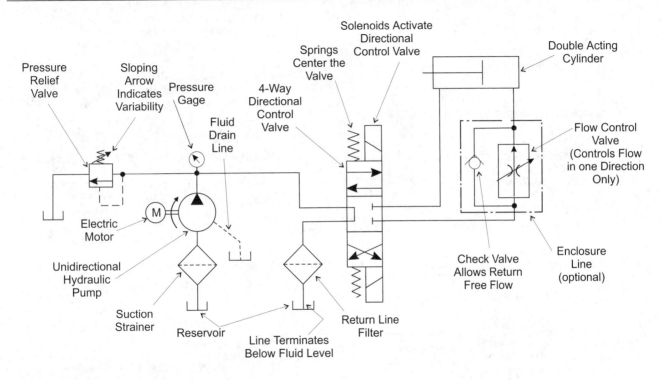

Illustration #37 — Typical Schematic Diagram

Table #5 — ISO Graphical Symbols (see Appendix for more complete list)

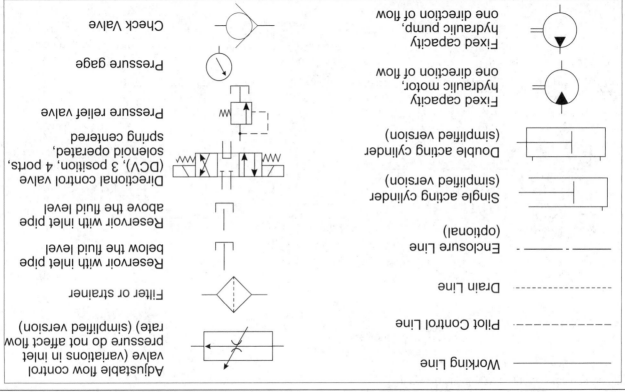

Working Line	
Pilot Control Line	
Drain Line	
Enclosure Line (optional)	
Single acting cylinder (simplified version)	
Double acting cylinder (simplified version)	
Fixed capacity hydraulic motor, one direction of flow	
Fixed capacity hydraulic pump, one direction of flow	

Adjustable flow control valve (variations in inlet pressure do not affect flow rate) (simplified version)	
Filter or strainer	
Reservoir with inlet pipe below the fluid level	
Reservoir with inlet pipe above the fluid level	
Directional control valve (DCV), 3 position, 4 ports, solenoid operated, spring centered	
Pressure relief valve	
Pressure gage	
Check Valve	

SECTION ONE QUESTIONS

Hydraulic Principles

1. The metric SI unit of force is the newton.
   - ❏ true
   - ❏ false

2. At sea level a 140 kg mass exerts a force of:
   - ❏ 140 kg
   - ❏ 1372 newtons
   - ❏ 290 lb
   - ❏ 140 newtons

3. Using the formula $A = \pi d^2/4$, what the area of a circle that is 52 mm diameter?
   - ❏ 1122.1 mm^2
   - ❏ 1218.3 mm^2
   - ❏ 2123.7 mm^2
   - ❏ 4247.4 mm^2

4. One MPa is equal to 10 kPa.
   - ❏ true
   - ❏ false

5. The hydraulic pressure required to support a 100 pound load on a hydraulic cylinder with a piston area of 25 square inches would be:
   - ❏ 4 psi
   - ❏ 8 psi
   - ❏ 10 psi
   - ❏ 25 psi

6. The hydraulic pressure required to support a 350 kg load on a hydraulic cylinder with an area of 0.25 m^2 would be:
   - ❏ 8.61 kPa
   - ❏ 13.72 kPa
   - ❏ 15.91 kPa
   - ❏ 18.32 kPa

7. A one foot column of water generates 0.433 psi of head pressure.
   - ❏ true
   - ❏ false

8. A one metre column of water generates 100 P of head pressure.
   - ❏ true
   - ❏ false

9. The pressure generated by a 10 foot head of oil with a
    specific gravity of 0.96 would be:
    ❏ 4.16 psi
    ❏ 5.24 psi
    ❏ 6.31 psi
    ❏ 7.40 psi

10. The pressure generated by a 6 metre head of oil with a
    specific gravity of 0.96 would be:
    ❏ 44.31 kPa
    ❏ 48.19 kPa
    ❏ 52.86 kPa
    ❏ 56.45 kPa

11. The mercury barometer measures:
    ❏ gage pressure
    ❏ absolute pressure

12. The "U" tube manometer measures:
    ❏ gage pressure
    ❏ absolute pressure

13. A pressure of 6 inches of water is equal to:
    ❏ 0.02166 psi
    ❏ 0.2166 psi
    ❏ 2.166 psi
    ❏ 21.66 psi

14. A pressure of 200 mm of water is equal to:
    ❏ 1960 Pa
    ❏ 2240 Pa
    ❏ 1960 kPa
    ❏ 2240 kPa

15. A pressure of 3 inches of Hg is equal to:
    ❏ 0.01473 psi
    ❏ 0.1473 psi
    ❏ 1.473 psi
    ❏ 14.73 psi

16. A pressure of 30 mm of Hg is equal to:
    ❏ 4 kPa
    ❏ 5 kPa
    ❏ 6 kPa
    ❏ 7 kPa

17. If the minimum pressure specified for a pump suction is 9
    inches Hg vacuum, what would this pressure be in psig?
    ❏ - 2.553 psig
    ❏ - 4.419 psig
    ❏ + 2.553 psig
    ❏ + 4.419 psig

18. If the minimum pressure specified for a pump suction is 200 mm Hg vacuum, what would this pressure be in kPa gage?
    - ❑ - 43.8 kPa gage
    - ❑ + 43.8 kPa gage
    - ❑ - 26.6 kPa gage
    - ❑ + 26.6 kPa gage

19. Convert 9 psia to psig (atmospheric pressure equals 14.7 psia):
    - ❑ - 5.7 psig
    - ❑ + 23.7 psig
    - ❑ - 23.7 psig
    - ❑ + 5.7 psig

20. Convert 60 kPa abs to kPa gage (atmospheric pressure equals 101 kPa Abs.):
    - ❑ + 161 kPa gage
    - ❑ - 161 kPa gage
    - ❑ + 41 kPa gage
    - ❑ - 41 kPa gage

21. The pascal is the metric SI unit of pressure.
    - ❑ true   ❑ false

22. The bar is a metric SI unit of pressure.
    - ❑ true   ❑ false

23. Inches or feet of water would be used to measure high pressures.
    - ❑ true   ❑ false

24. Pascal's law concerns the flow of liquid in a hydraulic system.
    - ❑ true   ❑ false

25. The force output from a cylinder is dependent on the pressure, not on the cylinder diameter.
    - ❑ true   ❑ false

26. If the input pressure to a pressure intensifier is 600 psi and the area ratio is 5:1, the output pressure will be:
    - ❑ 120 psi
    - ❑ 300 psi
    - ❑ 1200 psi
    - ❑ 3000 psi

27. If the system relief valve is set at 1200 psi it is possible that rod end of a 2:1 ratio cylinder will be exposed to 2400 psi.
    - ❑ true   ❑ false

28. The pressure generated by a pump as it extends a cylinder is independent of the load on the cylinder.
    - ❑ true   ❑ false

29. A hydraulic pump with the discharge line open to the reservoir will not produce any pressure.
   ❏ true   ❏ false

30. If the discharge line from a positive displacement hydraulic pump were blocked, serious damage to the pump or drive may occur.
   ❏ true   ❏ false

31. List 4 factors that contribute to the pressure that is required to move a load from a standstill:

   Answer: _____

   _____

32. The efficiency of an actuator will be determined by the amount of internal friction present.
   ❏ true   ❏ false

33. When there is a constant flow through a pipe there will be constant pressure from one end of the pipe to the other.
   ❏ true   ❏ false

34. An increase in the flow rate through a pipe will increase the pressure difference from one end of the pipe to the other.
   ❏ true   ❏ false

35. With regards to the flow through an orifice, an increase in the pressure difference across the orifice will:
   ❏ have no effect if it is a sharp edged orifice
   ❏ only effect the flow rate if the viscosity changes
   ❏ Increase the flow rate
   ❏ reduce the flow rate

36. The volume of an 8 inch diameter cylinder, 14 inches long is:
   ❏ 1.055 US gallons
   ❏ 2.349 US gallons
   ❏ 3.046 US gallons
   ❏ 4.981 US gallons

37. The volume of an 160 mm diameter cylinder, 400 mm long is:
   ❏ 8.04 litres
   ❏ 9.18 litres
   ❏ 9.50 litres
   ❏ 10.12 litres

38. A 5 gpm pump is used to extend an 18-inch diameter piston. What will be the speed of the extending piston in inches per minute?
   ❏ 2.47 in/min
   ❏ 4.54 in/min
   ❏ 6.31 in/min
   ❏ 9.08 in/min

39. A cylinder piston is extended at 1.2 m/min. Find the required pump output in litres per minute if the cylinder diameter is 110 mm.
   - ❏ 0.0114 litres/min
   - ❏ 0.114 litres/min
   - ❏ 1.14 litres/min
   - ❏ 11.4 litres/min

40. A hydraulic motor with a displacement of $1.75 \, in^3$/revolution is required to run at 1200 rpm. What is the required flow rate to the motor in gallons/minute?
   - ❏ 4.21 gal/min
   - ❏ 9.09 gal/min
   - ❏ 12.61 gal/min
   - ❏ 15.89 gal/min

41. A hydraulic motor with a displacement of 0.25 litres/revolution is supplied with fluid flow rate of 0.5 litres/second. What will be the speed of the motor?
   - ❏ 60 rpm
   - ❏ 80 rpm
   - ❏ 120 rpm
   - ❏ 240 rpm

42. The maximum velocity through a suction line is 4 feet/sec. If the maximum pump output is 35 gal/min, what would be the minimum area of the suction line?
   - ❏ $1.985 \, in^2$
   - ❏ $2.807 \, in^2$
   - ❏ $4.982 \, in^2$
   - ❏ $6.813 \, in^2$

43. From question 42, what would be the minimum inside diameter of pipe?
   - ❏ 1.89 inches
   - ❏ 2.58 inches
   - ❏ 3.89 inches
   - ❏ 4.32 inches

44. A pipeline will have a maximum flow rate of 15 litres/sec. If the maximum velocity is to be 5 m/sec, what is the required minimum area of the inside of the pipe?
   - ❏ $0.2 \, dm^2$
   - ❏ $0.3 \, dm^2$
   - ❏ $0.4 \, dm^2$
   - ❏ $0.5 \, dm^2$

45. From the previous question, what would be the minimum inside diameter of the pipe?
 - ❏ 0.143 dm
 - ❏ 0.618 dm
 - ❏ 1.115 dm
 - ❏ 1.893 dm

46. If the velocity of fluid flowing through a 6 inch diameter line is 4 feet/sec, what would be the fluid velocity if the line was swaged down to 3 inches diameter?
 - ❏ 8 feet/sec
 - ❏ 12 feet/sec
 - ❏ 16 feet/sec
 - ❏ 20 feet/sec

47. Laminar flow will always occur in straight pipe or tubing, regardless of the velocity.
 - ❏ true　　　　　　　　❏ false

48. Bends and fittings increase the possibility of:
 - ❏ laminar flow
 - ❏ reduced pressure drop
 - ❏ turbulent flow
 - ❏ lower flow rates

49. If a differential cylinder is to have the same speed in both directions, there must be a higher flow rate to or from the:
 - ❏ rod end
 - ❏ cap end

50. When fluid flows through a tee with unequal size branches, the major flow will always be in the largest diameter.
 - ❏ true　　　　　　　　❏ false

51. A 6 inch diameter cylinder with a load of 11,000 pounds and a 9 inch diameter cylinder with a 7,000 pound load are connected to the same fluid supply. Which cylinder will raise first?
 - ❏ 6 inch diameter
 - ❏ 9 inch diameter
 - ❏ both at the same time

52. Referring to question 51, what will be the required pressure to raise the cylinder that moves first?
 - ❏ 100 psi
 - ❏ 110 psi
 - ❏ 120 psi
 - ❏ 160 psi

53. Referring to question 51, what will be the required pressure to raise the cylinder that moves second?
   - ❏ 160 psi
   - ❏ 241 psi
   - ❏ 311 psi
   - ❏ 389 psi

54. The pressure required to enable fluid to flow through a line having various resistances in series is the sum of all the resistances.
   - ❏ true   ❏ false

55. As fluid flows through a line, the pressure will increase at the point where the fluid velocity is increased due to a reduction in line diameter.
   - ❏ true   ❏ false

56. The amount of energy required to raise a 400 pound load 12.5 feet is:
   - ❏ 5000 ft lbs
   - ❏ 4200 ft lbs
   - ❏ 6400 ft lbs
   - ❏ 4000 ft lbs

57. The amount of energy required to raise a 600 pound load 4 feet is:
   - ❏ 2.031 Btu
   - ❏ 3.085 Btu
   - ❏ 3.597 Btu
   - ❏ 4.873 Btu

58. The amount of energy required to raise a 600 kg load 5 metres is:
   - ❏ 29.4 kJ
   - ❏ 30.2 kJ
   - ❏ 32.8 kJ
   - ❏ 36.9 kJ

59. If a 3000 pound load is raised 6 inches in 3 seconds, the power expended is:
   - ❏ 0.250 HP
   - ❏ 0.350 HP
   - ❏ 0.909 HP
   - ❏ 1.263 HP

60. A 3000 kg load is raised at a rate of 0.5 m/s. How much power is being used?
   - ❏ 14.7 kW
   - ❏ 15.8 kW
   - ❏ 17.2 kW
   - ❏ 19.4 kW

61. *40 HP converted to kW is equal to:*
   - ❑ 0.029 kW
   - ❑ 0.298 kW
   - ❑ 2.984 kW
   - ❑ 29.84 kW

62. *60 kW converted to HP is equal to:*
   - ❑ 32.91 HP
   - ❑ 43.87 HP
   - ❑ 62.91 HP
   - ❑ 80.43 HP

63. *What hydraulic horsepower is developed when a pump discharges 20 gpm at 1500 psi?*
   - ❑ 11.3
   - ❑ 14.8
   - ❑ 17.5
   - ❑ 21.3

64. *The horsepower required to drive a pump that is 92% efficient and discharging 30 gpm at 2000 psi is:*
   - ❑ 12.4
   - ❑ 16.8
   - ❑ 23.9
   - ❑ 38.05

65. *What would be the power output from a hydraulic motor that is 88% efficient and receives 20 gpm of fluid at 2000 psi?*
   - ❑ 15.8
   - ❑ 20.54
   - ❑ 22.7
   - ❑ 23.8

66. *A hydraulic motor has a displacement of 6 in^3 per revolution and is 90% efficient. If the operating pressure is 3000 psi, what torque is being developed by the motor?*
   - ❑ 1489 in lb
   - ❑ 1698 in lb
   - ❑ 2145 in lb
   - ❑ 2578 in lb

67. *A pump discharging 50 litres/min at 15 MPa is developing how many kW?*
   - ❑ 12.5 kW
   - ❑ 13.8 kW
   - ❑ 14.6 kW
   - ❑ 16.9 kW

68. The power required to drive a pump that is 92% efficient and discharging 120 litres/min at 14 MPa is:
    - ❏ 30.43 kW
    - ❏ 31.73 kW
    - ❏ 32.89 kW
    - ❏ 35.97 kW

69. A hydraulic motor has a displacement of 1.5 litres per revolution and is 90% efficient. If the operating pressure is 20 MPa, what torque is the motor developing?
    - ❏ 4297 N·m
    - ❏ 4398 N·m
    - ❏ 4499 N·m
    - ❏ 4539 N·m

70. How much heat is being added to the system when the total output from a 20 gpm pump is being relieved over the relief valve at 2000 psi?
    - ❏ 879.4 Btu/min
    - ❏ 987.2 Btu/min
    - ❏ 1041 Btu/min
    - ❏ 1428 Btu/min

71. How much heat is being added to the system when the total pump output of 80 litres/min is being relieved over the relief valve at 15 MPa?
    - ❏ 12 kJ/s
    - ❏ 14 kJ/s
    - ❏ 17 kJ/s
    - ❏ 20 kJ/s

72. The dimensions of a reservoir are 2 foot wide by 4 foot long and the sides are 3 foot high. If the temperature of the fluid is 130 degrees F and the ambient temperature is 65 degrees F, what is the approximate heat loss from the reservoir per hour?
    - ❏ 4598.4 Btu/hour
    - ❏ 4937.1 Btu/hour
    - ❏ 5578.9 Btu/hour
    - ❏ 5943.6 Btu/hour

73. The dimensions of a reservoir are 0.8 m wide by 1.5 m long and the sides are 0.9 m high. If the temperature of the fluid is 55 degrees C and the ambient temperature is 18 degrees C, what is the approximate heat loss from the reservoir per hour?
    - ❏ 7950 kJ/hour
    - ❏ 8190 kJ/hour
    - ❏ 8730 kJ/hour
    - ❏ 8850 kJ/hour

SECTION TWO
HYDRAULIC FLUIDS

Fluid Functions

Hydraulic fluids have four main functions, and depending on how well a fluid can carry out these functions, will determine its suitability as a hydraulic fluid.

These four functions are:

a. Power Transmission
b. Lubrication
c. Sealing
d. Cooling

Power Transmission

Power transmission is the primary function of the hydraulic fluid. It must be able to flow easily through transmission lines with a minimum of energy loss due to friction. The amount of energy loss will be directly affected by the viscosity of the fluid. The compressibility of the fluid will also affect the power transmission efficiency. This is referred to as the "Bulk Modulus." (which is the reciprocal of compressibility).

Fluid with a high bulk modulus (compress very little) will transmit power instantaneously to various parts of the system. This is desirable for such machines as CNC (computer numerical control) machine tools used in manufacturing, where smooth operation, exact positioning, and constant speeds are required. Fluid with a high bulk modulus will transmit shock waves throughout the system more readily than fluid with a low bulk modulus, which may be detrimental to some systems.

Bulk modulus of an oil is relative to the temperature. As the temperature increases, the bulk modulus becomes less. A mineral oil may have a bulk modulus that ranges from 300,000 psi [2068 MPa] to 150,000 psi [1034 MPa] as the temperature ranges from 70°F [21°C] to 200°F [93°C]. The compressibility of petroleum based oils is approximately 0.5% per 1000 psi [6895 kPa], this relates to a bulk modulus of 200,000 psi [1379 MPa].

Lubrication

The ability of the fluid to prevent metal to metal contact of sliding and rotating hydraulic parts is extremely important to the life of hydraulic components. To accomplish this, the fluid must be able to maintain a fluid film between the parts at the temperatures and pressures encountered (see illustration #38).

Typical *sliding spool* moves back and forth on a *thin film of oil*. The *fluid film* seals between *high and low pressure areas.*

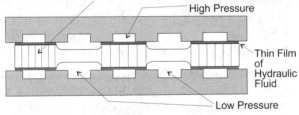

Illustration #38 — Fluid Lubrication and Sealing

Sealing

Many hydraulic components rely on a very small allowance between mating parts to control leakage. A prime example is the spool of a directional control valve. If the oil viscosity is too low, excess leakage may take place (see illustration #38).

Cooling

If the heat generated due to friction were not removed quickly, the resulting temperature increase would soon damage components. Some liquids have a high specific heat value and are more suitable than others at absorbing and carrying away heat. Depending on the hydraulic system, the heat carried by the fluid is either dissipated by the reservoir or removed by a heat exchanger.

Fluid Properties

Viscosity

Viscosity is probably the most important property when considering an oil for a specific purpose. Viscosity is a measure of a fluid's resistance to flow. A thick fluid that pours and flows slowly has a high viscosity. A fluid that is thin and flows easily is said to have a low viscosity.

Factors that change the viscosity of a fluid:

a. Viscosity will change as the temperature changes (viscosity decreases as the temperature rises); therefore, it is important to specify the temperature when specifying the viscosity of an oil.

b. Large pressure changes also affect viscosity. The viscosity increases as the pressure increases. This affect is not easily measured and all viscosity specifications will be at atmospheric pressure.

This pressure/viscosity relationship is especially important in bearing and gear lubrication where film pressures may be 175,000 to 200,000 psi.

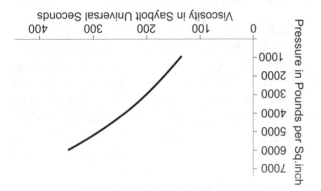

Illustration #39 — Viscosity increase with increase in Pressure

Note: This viscosity/pressure relationship will vary depending on the type of oil tested. The example shown in illustration #39 is for a typical petroleum based oil at constant temperature.

The change in viscosity with pressure may not be significant in any but ultra-high pressure systems where the increase in viscosity may cause appreciable pressure drop.

c. The viscosity of non-Newtonian fluids will decrease as the rate of shear is increased.

A Newtonian fluid is one in which the shear stress is directly proportional to the rate of shear (see illustration #40) and whose viscosity is constant at a given temperature and pressure. Most petroleum oils are Newtonian when the temperature is above the cloud point, (see "Pour Point/Cloud Point").

A non-Newtonian fluid is one where, at a constant temperature, the viscosity changes as the shear rate changes. Grease is a common non-Newtonian fluid, and will have an "apparent" viscosity.

Some oils have high viscosity indexes because of polymeric thickeners added to the oil. When these oils are subject to increasing shear rates, the viscosity will decrease (are non-Newtonian).

If the amount of shear causes the breakdown of the polymers, then a permanent viscosity reduction will be realized.

Other substances in the oil, such as wax crystals (which may form at low temperatures) and other insoluble particles, will also cause an oil to have non-Newtonian characteristics.

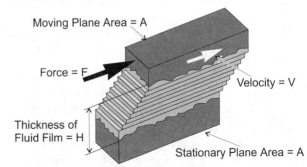

Illustration #40 — Measuring Shear Stress & Rate

This type of oil will have an apparent viscosity, the value of which, will depend on the shear rate. The type of rotating viscometer used for testing will determine the shear rate (refer Absolute Viscosity, page 61).

It is important to realize that viscosity has to be matched to the application. Equipment that operates outside where the winter temperatures are sub zero will require an oil that will allow cold weather start ups, yet stay sufficiently viscous (thick enough) to ensure adequate lubrication and sealing at operating temperatures.

If the viscosity of the hydraulic fluid is too high:

- Power will be lost overcoming the extra friction.
- The system will operate at a higher temperature due to internal friction.
- There will be increased pressure drops throughout the system.

If the viscosity of the hydraulic fluid is too low:

- Cylinders may creep due to valve leakage.
- The pump output may be reduced due to internal leakage.
- Actuators may slow down due to seal leakage (this may be compounded by a reduced pump output).
- The temperature may increase when pressurized fluid leaks back to a low pressure area with no work being done (see Section One, "Heat Generation").
- There may be increased wear and friction due to metal to metal contact of sliding parts.
- Systems may operate more slowly, if resistance to flow in the pressure line causes the relief valve to open.
- Pumps may cavitate due to low suction pressures.

Measuring Viscosity

There are two methods used for measuring viscosity, they are:

1. Absolute (Dynamic) Viscosity
2. Kinematic (Relative Viscosity

1. Absolute (Dynamic) Viscosity

Absolute viscosity is a measure of the resistance encountered when shearing one parallel plane of fluid over another. This is shown in illustration #40.

The absolute viscosity is equal to:
Shear Stress/Shear Rate = (F/A)/(V/H)
See illustration #40 for F, A, V and H.
Absolute Viscosity = $[N/m^2]/[(m/s)/m]$
= $N/m^2 \cdot s$ = Pa•s (Pascal second)

Note: the SI unit of absolute viscosity is the pascal second (Pa•s) or the millipascal second (mPa•s).
Where 1000 mPa•s = 1 Pa•s

The most common units used by the petroleum industry for absolute viscosity are the **poise (P)**, and the **centipoise (cP)**, which is used in the cgs (centimeter-gram-second) system of units (100 cP = 1 P).

There is a direct relationship between to the SI unit of Pa•s and the cgs unit of poise, it is:

1 poise (P) = 0.1 Pa•s = 100 mPa•s.
1 centipoise (cP) = 0.001 Pa•s = 1 mPa•s.

A number of rotating viscometers may be used to physically measure the absolute viscosity, depending on the type of fluid being tested, and the conditions to be simulated.

The Cold Cranking Simulator (CCS) (ASTM D2602) uses a high shear rate to simulate the cranking of a cold engine.

The Brookfield Rotary Viscometer (ASTM D2983) measures the cold fluidity characteristics of oils under low shear conditions.

The Mini-Rotary Viscometer (MRV) (ASTM D3829 and D4684) is also a low shear test for measuring cold fluidity characteristics and borderline pumping temperatures.

When measuring the viscosity of oils at low temperatures, (0°C and lower) the absolute viscosity (poise or centipoise) is usually used.

Table #6 displays the typical properties of two similar oils, examples A and B. These oils are designated as "All Purpose" hydraulic fluids, designed for use in farm, construction and off highway equipment. Used in this type of service, they are often exposed to extremely low temperatures.

Referring to table #6, *Example A*, which has a Brookfield viscosity of -33°C (-27.4°F) @ 50 Poise is more suitable for lower temperatures than *Example B*, which has a Brookfield viscosity of -21°C (-5.8°F) @ 50 Poise. Assuming 50 Poise was the maximum viscosity allowed by a particular hydraulic system for cold start ups, *Example B* would reach this value when the temperature reached -21°C, which is much sooner than *Example A*, which can go to -33°C before this viscosity is reached.

Hydraulic Properties		
Typical Properties	Example A	Example B
Kinematic Viscosity		
cSt @ 40°C	32	55
cSt @ 100°C	7.2	9.3
Brookfield Viscosity, °C		
@200 Poise	-42	-30
@100 Poise	-38	-26
@50 Poise	-33	-21
Pour Point, °C	-48	-39
Flash Point (COC), °C	170	220
Color, (ASTM)	2.5	2.0
Aniline Point, °C	93	99
Operating Temperature Range, °C	-35 to 70	-25 to 80
Rust Test (ASTM D665B)	Pass	Pass
Timken OK Load, kg	6	7

Table #6 — Properties of Two Typical Hydraulic Oils

2. Kinematic (Relative) Viscosity

Kinematic viscosity is usually used when measuring and comparing viscosities at higher temperatures. Two standard temperatures for measuring kinematic viscosity are 40°C and 100°C (104°F and 212°F).

Measuring Kinematic Viscosity: Illustration #41 shows the kinematic viscosity of an oil sample being tested. It is determined by timing a fixed volume of oil through a capillary tube and then applying a formula for that particular viscometer.

The SI unit of measuring Kinematic viscosity is m^2/s or mm^2/s.

Where 1 m^2/s = 1 000 000 mm^2/s

The most common unit used by the petroleum industry is the **centistoke (cSt),** which is numerically equivalent to **mm^2/s**.

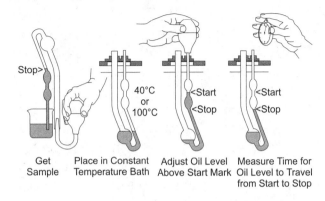

Get Sample | Place in Constant Temperature Bath | Adjust Oil Level Above Start Mark | Measure Time for Oil Level to Travel from Start to Stop

Illustration #41 — Viscometer Measures Kinematic Viscosity

Calculating Kinematic Viscosity: Kinematic viscosity is the ratio of the absolute viscosity of a liquid to its density. When the absolute viscosity and the density of a fluid at the same temperature is known, the kinematic viscosity can be calculated as follows.

Kinematic Visc.(cSt)
= Absolute Visc.(cP)/Density[kg/dm^3]

When using the above formula to calculate kinematic viscosity, the data used for absolute viscosity and density must be at the same temperature. Densities of oils are usually given at 15°C (59°F), however densities at other temperatures can be approximated for most oils by subtracting 0.00065 kg/dm³ for each 1°C increase in temperature.

$$(kg/dm^3 = kg/m^3 \times 10^{-3})$$

Other units of relative viscosity are sometimes used. Some of these are: Saybolt Universal Seconds (SUS), which has been common in North America, Redwood Seconds, which was a common British measurement, and Engler degrees, used in other European countries.

Conversion tables for the various viscosities are available. Table #7 shows the ISO viscosity grade system for industrial oils with the corresponding kinematic viscosities in centistokes and Saybolt viscosities in Saybolt Universal Seconds.

Viscosity Designations				
Viscosity System Grade	ISO Standard 3448 ASTM D-2422 Mid-point viscosity cSt	All Viscosities at 40°C. Use ASTM D-341 to convert to other temperatures		
		Kinematic Viscosity Limits Min.	Max.	Approx. SUS Units
ISO VG 2	2.2	1.98	2.42	32
ISO VG 3	3.2	2.88	3.52	36
ISO VG 5	4.6	4.14	5.06	40
ISO VG 7	6.8	6.12	7.48	50
ISO VG 10	10	9.00	11.0	60
ISO VG 15	15	13.5	16.5	75
ISO VG 32	32	28.8	35.2	150
ISO VG 68	68	61.2	74.8	315
ISO VG 150	150	135	165	700
ISO VG 320	320	288	352	1500
ISO VG 680	680	612	748	3150
ISO VG 1000	1000	900	1100	4650
ISO VG 1500	1500	1350	1650	7000

Table #7 — Industrial Fluid Lubricant Viscosity Designations

Table #8 shows the approximate viscosity equivalents at the same temperature for Kinematic, Saybolt, Engler Degrees and Redwood Seconds. As can be seen from table #7, the ISO grade corresponds to the viscosity in centistokes at 40°C (104°F). Some oil companies list their products using this same system. For example, the kinematic viscosity of one type of oil, *Nuto H 32* oil (hydraulic oil for general industrial machinery) at 40°C is 32 cSt. *Nuto H 46 is 46 cSt at 40°C.* Other industrial and hydraulic oils are often similarly designated.

It is important to remember that viscosity varies inversely with the temperature; therefore, viscosity is always specified at a certain temperature. Kinematic viscosity is specified at 40°C and 100°C (104°F and 212°F).

Viscosity Equivalents			
Kinematic cSt	Saybolt SUS	Engler Degrees	Redwood Seconds
2	33	1.11	32
4	39	1.31	38
6	46	1.49	44
7	49	1.58	47
10	59	1.84	56
12	66	2.03	63
14	74	2.23	69
16	81	2.44	76
18	89	2.66	83
20	98	2.88	90
25	119	3.47	108
30	142	4.08	127
35	164	4.71	146
40	187	5.35	166
45	210	5.99	186
50	233	6.63	206
60	279	7.93	247
70	325	9.24	287
80	371	10.5	328
90	417	11.9	369

Table #8 — Approximate Viscosity Equivalents

Viscosity Index (VI)

As the temperature increases, fluid viscosity decreases. The change in viscosity as the temperature changes is not the same for all fluids.

Two different oils may have the same viscosity at 40°C (104°F) but will have different viscosity at 100°C (212°F). The Viscosity Index (VI) is a measure of the rate of change of viscosity as the temperature changes and is specified as a number. VI is determined from a formula, using viscosities at 40°C and 100°C (ASTM D - 2270). The viscosity of a fluid with a high VI will change less as the temperature changes, than that of a fluid with a low VI.

Table #8 (cont'd) — Approximate Viscosity Equivalents

Viscosity Equivalents			
Kinematic cSt	Saybolt SUS	Engler Degrees	Redwood Seconds
100	463	13.2	410
120	556	15.8	492
140	649	18.4	574
160	741	21.1	656
180	834	23.7	738
200	927	26.3	820
250	1158	32.9	1025
300	1390	39.5	1230
350	1621	46.1	1434
400	1853	53.0	1639
450	2085	59.0	1844
500	2316	66.0	2049
600	2779	79.0	2459
700	3243	92.0	2869
800	3706	105.0	3279
900	4169	118.0	3689
1000	4632	132.0	4098
1200	5559	158.0	4918
1400	6485	184.0	5738
1600	7412	211.0	6557
1800	8338	237.0	7377
2000	9265	263.0	8197

Fluid used in hydraulic systems subject to extremely cold temperatures on start up, will have a higher VI requirement than the fluid used in systems that operate only in moderate temperature environments. Illustration #42 is a graphical comparison of three hydraulic oils that have differing viscosity indexes.

Although only the viscosities at 40°C and 100°C (104°F and 212°F) were known, it is now quite easy to find the approximate viscosities of these oils at any temperature. For example, the viscosity of Nuto H 46 at 50°C (122°F) is 30 cSt (see bold line in illustration #42).

Although illustration #42 shows a straight line for viscosity versus temperature, the line would show a curve if all actual values were plotted, with the curve becoming more pronounced as the viscosity becomes greater than 1000 cSt.

Fluid	@40°C	@ 100°C	VI
Univis N 32	32 cSt	6.5 cSt	160
Nuto H 32	32 cSt	5.3 cSt	92
Nuto H 46	46 cSt	6.5 cSt	92

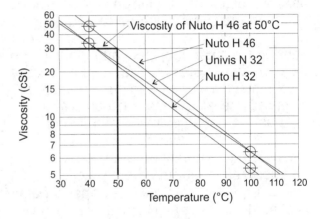

Illustration #42 — Comparison of Viscosity Indexes

The curve is not significant at viscosities lower than this. If the viscosity/temperature relationship is required for extremely low temperatures (viscosities are above 1000 cSt), a chart similar to illustration #43 will be required (contact your oil supplier or the manufacturer).

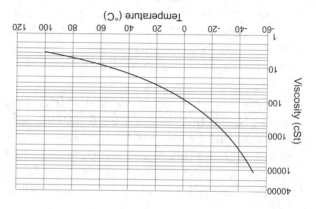

Illustration #43 — Detailed Viscosity/Temp. Graph

Choosing Correct Viscosity

The grade of oil recommended by the equipment manufacturer may not take into account any changing or unusual conditions that may take place where the equipment is being used. Temperatures may be much higher or lower than average, or new components with different requirements may have been added to the system.

To choose a fluid that will have the correct viscosity when the system is at operating temperature, and also to determine the lowest temperature at which the system can be put on moderate load, four items of information are required.

1. The maximum and minimum operating viscosities for the equipment in the system, usually set by the system pump and obtained from the equipment manufacturer. This example will assume the use of a Racine radial piston pump. From table #9, the maximum and minimum operating viscosities are 65 cSt and 10 cSt respectively.

Pump/Motor Viscosity Guidelines -- (FOR EXAMPLE PURPOSES ONLY)				
Equipment	Operating		Start Up Under Load	Optimum (cSt)
	Min. (cSt)	Max. (cSt)		
Hagglunds Denison - Bulletin 2002-1				
Piston pumps	10	162	1618	30
Vane Pumps	10	108	862	30
Racine - Form No. S-106				
FA; RA; K Vane pumps	15	216	864	26-54
Radial piston pumps	10	65	162	21-54
Axial piston pumps	14	450	647	32-65
Vickers - data sheet 1-286				
Inline piston pumps & motors	13	54	220	-
Angle piston, vane & gear pumps & motors	13	54	860	-
MHT vane motors	13	54	110	-
Mannesmann Rexroth				
Axial piston pumps	16	100	1000	16-36
V3, V4 vane pumps	25	200	800	25-160
R4 radial pumps	10	200	-	-

Table #9 — Hydraulic Pump/Motor Viscosity Guidelines -- (FOR EXAMPLE PURPOSES ONLY)

2. The upper and lower operating temperatures. This is not the ambient temperature, or the minimum temperature at start up, but the temperature range of the fluid when it is operating. This will be an estimate to start with, and then can be accurately checked when the equipment is running.

   For this example, the upper and lower temperatures have been estimated as 70°C and 30°C (158°F and 86°F).

3. The maximum start up viscosity for the system hydraulic pump (under load). For a Racine radial piston pump it is 162 cSt. See table #9 for viscosity guidelines.

4. The viscosity of the oil being considered. In this case the viscosities of three oils being considered are as follows:

Fluid	@40°C	@100°C
Nuto H 32	32 cSt	5.3 cSt
Nuto H 46	46 cSt	6.5 cSt
Nuto H 100	100 cSt	11.0 cSt

This information is plotted on a viscosity/temperature chart, shown in illustrations #44 to #48. The viscosity/temperature charts are available from various oil companies.

The steps for plotting the information on the viscosity/temperature chart and checking to see if a particular oil will be suitable with regards to viscosity are as follows:

1. Draw two horizontal lines that represent the maximum and minimum operating viscosities (65 cSt and 10 cSt) (see illustration #44).

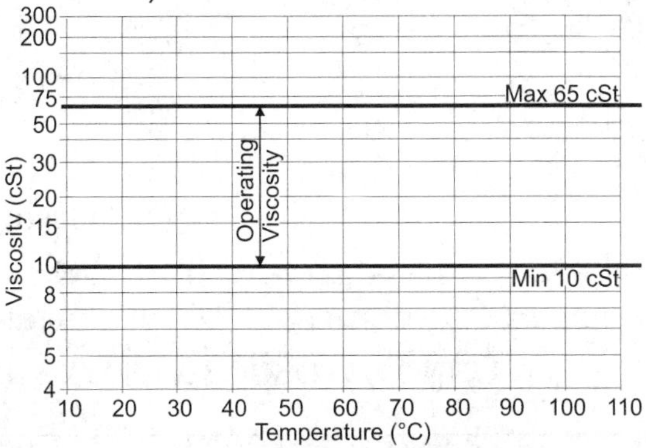

Illustration #44 — Maximum and Minimum Viscosities

2. Draw two vertical lines to represent the estimated high and low operating temperatures (70°C and 30°C). The four lines now form a rectangle (see illustration #45).

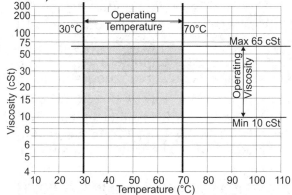

Illustration #45 — High and Low Operating Temperatures

3. From the viscosity information given by the oil manufacturer, plot the viscosity points at 40°C and 100°C (104°F and 212°F) for the oils being checked. Connecting these two points will produce a diagonal viscosity/temperature line for each of the oils (see illustration #46).

4. Check to see if the diagonal viscosity/temperature line representing the oil in question intersects the vertical high and low operating temperature lines between the two horizontal maximum and minimum operating viscosity lines (see illustration #46).

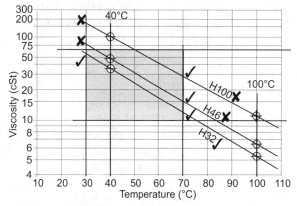

Illustration #46 — Viscosity Temperature Lines

For the three oils shown, the lower diagonal line (Nuto H 32) is the only suitable oil for this application.

The upper diagonal lines (Nuto H 46 and Nuto H 100) are unsuitable for this particular application because they intersect the 30°C (86°F) temperature line above 65 cSt, indicating that the viscosity will be too high at 30°C (at 30°C the viscosity of Nuto H 100 and Nuto H 46 are 165 cSt and 80 cSt respectively).

5. To check for the minimum temperature that a moderate load could be applied when using Nuto H 32 in this example (see illustration #47):

a) draw a horizontal viscosity line representing the maximum start up viscosity under load (162 cSt)

b) extend the diagonal line that represents Nuto H 32 through this line

c) draw a line down vertically from the intersection of these two lines. This will indicate the lowest start up temperature under load (10° C (50°F)).

6. The maximum and minimum operating temperature limits for the selected oil can also be determined from this chart. Vertical lines are drawn from where the diagonal viscosity/temperature line intersects the maximum and minimum operating viscosity lines (see illustration #48). In this case the temperature limits for this oil in this application is 74°C and 26°C (165°F and 79°F).

Illustration #47 — Lowest Start Up Temperature

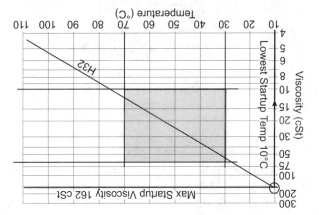

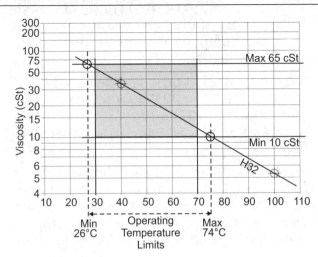

Illustration #48 — Temperature Limits

Note: For maximum oil life, the upper temperature should be maintained below 55°C (131°F).

Note: Table #9 is for example purposes only. Viscosity requirements for components should be obtained from the manufacturer.

Pour Point/Cloud Point

Pour point is defined as the lowest temperature at which oil will flow. As the temperature of the fluid drops, the oil becomes increasingly resistant to flow. This is due to the thickening of the oil that accompanies a reduction in temperature, and may also be exacerbated by the formation of wax crystals. Eventually a temperature is reached when the fluid will no longer flow, which is the pour point (ASTM D97-66). The pour point of a hydraulic fluid is an important consideration if the system is exposed to very low temperatures. The oil should have a pour point that is at least 10° C (50° F) lower than the lowest expected temperature. In some oils when the temperature becomes low enough, wax crystals form, and the oil becomes cloudy in appearance. The temperature at which this becomes noticeable is known as the cloud point. The wax crystals may temporarily plug filters if oils are in service below their cloud point.

Flash Point/Fire Point

The flash point of oil is a measure of its flammability. If the temperature of the oil is increased, a point will eventually be reached when the fluid produces enough vapors that will burn if ignited. At flash point, the combustion will be momentary. If the temperature is increased, the production of vapor will become high enough to support continuous combustion when ignited. Then the fire point has been reached. For most petroleum oils the fire point is usually about 30°C (86°F) above the flash point. Specification tables for most oils only list the flash point.

The flash point of hydraulic fluids will vary depending on the type of fluid being considered. Typical petroleum based hydraulic fluid will range from just over 100°C (212°F) to over 200°C (392°F).

Fire resistant fluids such as Phosphate Ester and Polyol Ester will range from 235°C (455°F) to 280°C (536°F).

Oxidation Resistance

Oxidation is the chemical reaction between a substance (in this case oil) and oxygen. Most hydraulic fluids and all petroleum based oils are subject to oxidation, which reduces the useful life of the oil. Oil refiners use additives to increase the basic oxidation resistance of oil.

There are a number of conditions that increase the oxidation rate of a hydraulic oil they are:

- High temperatures (above 60°C (140°F) the oxidation rate increases dramatically)
- High pressures
- Agitation
- Catalysts such as iron and copper
- Contaminants (both solid and liquid)

The products of oxidation may show up as insoluble products such as resins, varnish and sludge, which may cause sticking, blockages and wear in hydraulic parts, or as soluble products which increase the acidic level and may cause corrosion throughout the system.

Corrosion Prevention

Corrosion is the term usually used when there is a chemical reaction between metal and another substance. Two common forms of corrosion are, when rusting occurs (oxygen and iron combine to become ferric oxide), or when acidic substances damage metal parts. Tests are carried out (ASTM D 665) to determine how effective an oil may be in protecting iron or steel from rust and corrosion. Corrosion causes surface damage to the affected part. In conjunction with this, rust particles are abrasive, and will eventually cause damage to other hydraulic components.

Demulsibility

This is defined as the ability of an oil to separate from water.

If there is a possibility of the hydraulic fluid being contaminated with water, it is important to know how quickly the oil and water will separate.

With the water separated from the oil, the water can be dealt with. If the water and oil remain as an emulsion, system components may be damaged due to corrosion or accelerated wear. Tests are carried out to determine the demulsibility (ASTM D-1401 and ASTM D-2711). A solution of 40 ml of oil and 40 ml of water is agitated and allowed to settle. At specific times, the degree of separation is measured.

An oil with a high degree of demulsibility will not require as much time in the reservoir to separate from the water.

Demulsibility specifications are usually shown as follows:

Demulsibility, ASTM D-1401 after 30 min. Water/Oil/Emulsion (ml)	40-40-0

This indicates that after 30 minutes the water/oil solution has completely settled out to again become 40 ml water and 40 ml oil.

Fluid Types

Petroleum Based Fluids

Petroleum based oils (often referred to as mineral oils) are the most common fluids for hydraulic purposes, due to their relatively low cost, availability and natural suitability for this application. Petroleum oil naturally protects against rust, has excellent lubricating, sealing and heat absorption qualities. The effectiveness of these qualities may be increased, and other qualities may be added by various refining methods and the use of additives.

Fire Resistant Fluids

Hydraulic systems, designed for a particular fire resistant fluid will have no more problems than systems designed for conventional hydraulic fluids. There are more potential problems when existing systems are converted from using regular petroleum fluids to a fire resistant fluid.

Because of the varying properties of fire resistant fluids, the manufacturer of both the hydraulic components, and the fire resistant fluid should be consulted before going ahead with a conversion. Special attention should be paid to the following:

- Filter and strainer selection
- Compatibility of seals and gaskets
- Compatibility of paints and plastics
- Compatibility of instrumentation equipment
- Pump rating and maximum RPM
- Required pump inlet conditions (pipe size and absolute pressure)
- Various metal alloys or coatings that may be present such as zinc, cadmium, aluminum, copper, etc. or metal combinations that may cause galvanic action
- Maximum and minimum temperature limits
- Fluid checks that may require laboratory facilities

There are four general types of fire resistant fluids. Three types have varying amounts of water present, while the fourth type includes the synthetic fluids.

Fluids with water present usually require that the upper operating temperature be kept below 50°C (122°F) to prevent excessive vaporization of water and additives. Depending on the type and water concentration, the temperature must be kept above a minimum value to prevent freezing and separation. Generally, conventional seal materials are compatible except possibly for cork and leather which absorb water. Monitoring of the fluid must be carried out to maintain the correct percentage of water as vaporization takes place.

1. High Water Base Fluids (ISO HFA): Most common are solutions of 95% water and 5% soluble oil (oil in water emulsion). Used primarily for low pressure, low temperature systems, where high anti-wear properties are not essential.

Maximum operating temperatures should be kept below 50°C (122°F). Because of the higher specific gravity, pump suctions require a greater absolute pressure on the pump inlet than when using regular petroleum based oils.

2. Invert Emulsions (ISO HFB): This is a water in oil emulsion where the water droplets are dispersed in a continuous phase of petroleum oil. The water content is maintained between 35% to 45% to provide fire resistant qualities.

The invert emulsions come much closer than the 95/5 emulsions to approximating the performance of good mineral oils, due in part to the higher oil content and the addition of additives to reduce wear and corrosion.

3. Water and Glycol Fluids (ISO HFC): Consists of 35% to 50% water content, with the remainder being glycol. Additives are also used to control viscosity, alkalinity, foaming, corrosion, and lubricity.

Water and glycol fluids perform well at low temperatures, although high speeds and loads are not recommended. Certain paints, metals such as magnesium and aluminum, or any other metals containing or coated with zinc or cadmium, should not be used. If used there may be a possible reaction causing gummy residues.

4. Synthetic Fire Resistant Fluids (ISO HFD): This type of fluid, which does not contain water, is suitable for high pressure. It is designed for high temperature use. It is suitable for hydraulic systems in close proximity to high temperature sources. This may occur in various steel manufacturing processes, steam turbine auxiliaries, and plastic injection molding. It is also recommended where the cause or propagation of a fire due to leaks or spills would be especially disastrous.

Generally these fluids approximate the performance of petroleum based oils with regard to lubricating ability, resistance to corrosion, oxidation, and foam resistance. Two common synthetic fluids are, phosphate ester and polyol ester.

Phosphate Ester: has a high specific gravity which may require special attention be paid to pump suction conditions. The viscosity index is usually low, which may prevent it being used on systems with low start up temperature (unless heaters are used). Generally, conventional seals, hoses, and packings are not compatible and have to be replaced with materials such as, viton, butyl rubber, EP (ethylene-propylene) rubber, silicon, teflon and nylon.

Polyol Ester: has a specific gravity similar to mineral oil and does not require any special pump inlet considerations. It has a high viscosity index and is therefore suitable for varying temperature conditions.

It is compatible with seals and hoses used for petroleum oil based systems. It is also compatible with standard petroleum based hydraulic fluids, as well as Phosphate Ester type, and oil-synthetic blends. It is NOT compatible with any water based fluids.

Biodegradable Fluids

Up until the late 1800's, all lubricants were based on vegetable or animal fats, or water. Then refined petroleum oil produced a cheap and suitable substitute. Recently however, concern over the environment has produced an interest in using lubricating and hydraulic fluids that are less damaging to the environment.

Generally, fluids that contain carbon are biodegradable when supplied with the correct conditions (bacteria, oxygen and a suitable temperature); therefore, all mineral and synthetic oils will eventually be converted to CO_2 and water.

The problem is that this is a lengthy process. For an oil to be environmentally friendly, it has to breakdown relatively quickly (be readily biodegradable) and also should be somewhat non-toxic.

There are a number of manufacturers of biodegradable oils, including several of the large multinational oil corporations.

Most biodegradable hydraulic oils are vegetable oil based.

There are three main classes of environmentally friendly oils. These are natural and synthetic esters, and polyglycols. Canola is the most common oil used to provide natural esters for the production of industrial oils. Synthetic esters and polyglycols are manufactured from alcohol and fatty acids.

Hydraulic oil is usually based on natural esters blended with synthetic esters and an additive package.

Canola-based oils have an upper temperature limit of 80°C (176°F), whereas synthetic ester has an upper limit of 120°C (248°F). However cost usually limits the use of an entirely synthetic hydraulic oil. It is especially important with vegetable based oils to prevent water contamination.

Synthetic and natural esters are compatible with mineral and synthetic hydrocarbon fluids (one exception is high detergent diesel oils). They also cause some swelling of seals made from nitrile or neoprene rubber.

Biodegradable oils are used in situations where any inadvertent release will cause damage to animal and plant life. Industries such as forestry, hydro-electric and thermal power generation, railroads, food processing and shipping are the most likely customers for this type of fluid.

Fluid Contamination

Fluid is contaminated when it contains any substance or material that is either unwanted or adversely effects the fluid power system and/or components.

Hydraulic fluid contamination may be in the form of gases, liquids, or solids.

The amount and type of contamination that a fluid contains can only be determined by specific tests. Most tests require the use of a laboratory.

Detailed studies have shown that 70% of the loss of usefulness of equipment was due to surface degradation. It can be seen from illustration #49 that 50% of the surface degradation is caused by mechanical wear and 20% by corrosion.

Solid contaminant particles are one of the major causes of abrasive wear, sticking problems, and blockages of hydraulic components.

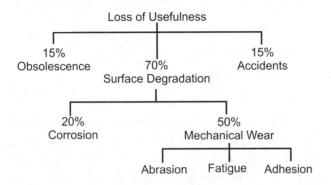

Illustration #49 — Loss of Equipment Usefulness

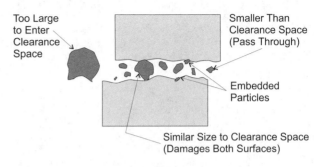

Illustration #50 — Abrasive Wear

The size of particles compared to the amount of the clearance between moving parts is an important consideration (refer to illustration #50).

Particles that are too large to enter the clearance space may not initially cause damage, but eventually they may either cause components to jam or will be broken down small enough to enter the clearance space.

Particles that are the same size or slightly smaller than the clearance space cause the most damage when they enter the clearance space.

Particles that are the same size as the clearance space may remove metal from both surfaces as they pass through.

Particles smaller than the clearance space may become embedded in one surface and then act as a cutting tool to remove metal from the opposite surface. Very fine particles may pass straight through without causing abrasive damage, although a thickness build-up of these fine particles may cause stickiness and erratic operation.

Contamination Sources

There are four sources of system contamination. These are:

1. Maintenance
2. Built in
3. Ingressed
4. Internally generated

Illustration #51 is a pictorial diagram of a simple circuit showing these sources of contamination.

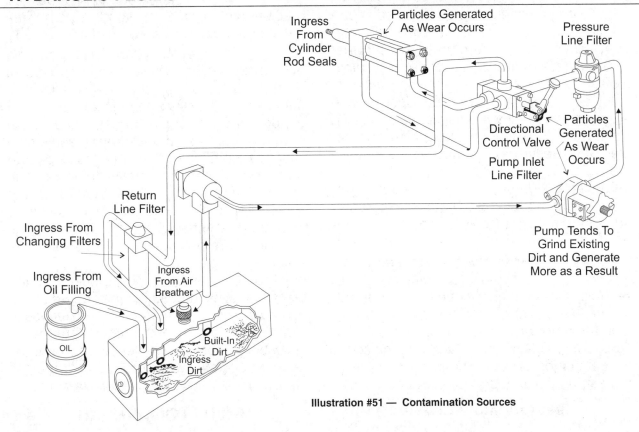

Illustration #51 — Contamination Sources

1. Maintenance: Whenever a hydraulic system is opened up and worked on by maintenance personnel, it is almost impossible not to add contaminants to the system. It is essential that every effort be made to reduce this to an absolute minimum. Washing down before dismantling, plugging or covering opened lines with plastic or tape, and ensuring that parts being installed are spotlessly clean are some of the precautions that must be taken. Only lint free rags should be used during maintenance. Accessing strainers and changing filters requires proper work procedures to ensure contamination doesn't take place. When adding new oil, either to fill the system or to top up, the fluid being added may be contaminated to a level higher than that recommended for the system, or careless procedures may cause contaminants to be introduced into the system.

The cleanliness of new hydraulic fluid will vary widely, but typically will be somewhere between 16/14 and 21/19.

See "Specifying the Contamination Level". This level of contamination is higher than the maximum suggested particle level for many systems. Thus there may be a requirement that any oil being added to the system be pumped in through a high efficiency filter (refer to "Location of Filters").

2. Built in Contamination: When a system is assembled, extreme care must be taken to ensure that contamination is kept to a minimum. Sometimes new components will contain contaminants. Flushing with clean hydraulic fluid will reduce the amount of contaminants. Systems, after assembly or extensive maintenance, should be thoroughly flushed before being put into service with a low viscosity fluid. The fluid, which may be a special flushing fluid or the actual system fluid at a higher temperature than normal, should be circulated at velocities high enough to produce turbulence that will remove as much contamination as possible.

It is important that the fluid is filtered as the flushing takes place. The filters should be able to bring the contamination level down to two ISO contamination codes below the required level for that system (see "Specifying the Contamination Level"). After flushing, a period of off-load running should ensure that all possible contamination has been removed before full load operation takes place.

3. Ingressed Contamination: During operation, contamination can enter the system from the immediate surroundings. Likely entry points are; piston rod seals, motor and pump shaft seals, reservoir vents, and pipe and tubing connections to the reservoir. Systems that are operating in extremely dirty conditions will possibly have more ingressed contamination than a system in a clean environment. Particular attention should be paid to piston rod and shaft wiper seals.

In some cases rubber boots may be fitted on piston rods.

The vent on the reservoir may require a high grade filter rather than the usual mesh strainer. Another source of ingressed contamination is water entering the reservoir in the form of vapor. Some systems may have a large reservoir capacity to accommodate a number of cylinders. When the cylinders are extended, the level in the reservoir falls. If the air entering through the vent has high humidity and the system is shut down and allowed to cool, moisture will condense in the reservoir. In some cases it may be necessary to ensure that the exchange air does not contact the oil in the reservoir. This may be accomplished by using a mechanical barrier, such as a rubber membrane between the oil and air in the reservoir.

4. Generated Contamination: As a system is operating, particles are generated due to the gradual wear of components.

These particles are particularly damaging, as they are often extremely hard due to work hardening.

Wear will be kept to a minimum if the system is initially clean and adequate filtration maintains this condition. Wear is generated in the following manner:

Abrasive Wear - Hard particles becoming trapped between two moving surfaces. Material may be removed from one or both surfaces. Refer to illustration #50.

Adhesive Wear - Minimal fluid film between moving surfaces allow metal to metal contact. The high points momentarily weld together and are then torn apart as movement continues.

Fatigue Wear - Refer to illustration #52. Very small or fine cracks develop on, or just under, the surface of components due to elastic deformation. As more of these develop, they eventually join and particles of metal are released from the surface.

Elastic deformation may come from large particles being trapped between two surfaces as shown in illustration #52. Or it may be due to load pressure between two surfaces such as when an anti-friction bearing rolling element is loaded and runs continually in a raceway. The loaded surfaces flatten out slightly, and then return to their original shape (elastic deformation).

Illustration #52 — Fatigue Wear

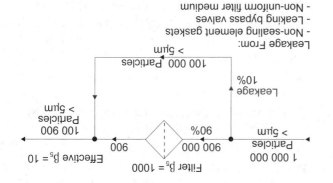

Filter $\beta_s = 1000$

Effective $\beta_s = 10$

1 000 000 Particles >5μm

900 000

90%

900 000

100 000 Particles >5μm

Leakage 10%

900

100 900 Particles >5μm

Leakage From:
- Non-sealing element gaskets
- Leaking bypass valves
- Non-uniform filter medium

The number of times that this has to occur (fatigue cycles) before fatigue cracks appear will depend on a number of variables, which are primarily, the types of material involved, and the amount of deformation.

Cavitation Wear - Fluid in low pressure (below the vapor pressure of the fluid at that temperature) areas, may contain pockets or bubbles of vapor. When low pressure vapor containing fluid becomes highly pressurized, the vapor pockets implode (violently collapsing inward) on the metal surface. Over time this causes the metal to break away.

Erosive Wear - Refer to illustration #53. High velocity fluid impacting continually on a surface will eventually "eat" away the metal.

Contamination particles in the oil will increase the rate of erosion. Metering devices and throttling orifices are often most affected.

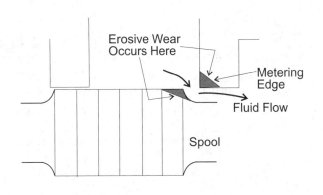

Illustration #53 — Erosive Wear

Corrosive Wear - A chemical reaction between the metal and the fluid, or substances in the fluid, which degrades the surface and produces another product. For example oxygen combines with iron to form iron oxide (rust).

Measuring Solid Contamination

The micrometre (μm) or micron is the common unit of measurement for particle and filter pore sizes.

$$1μm = 1metre/1\ 000\ 000$$
$$= 1mm/1000 = 0.001mm$$
$$1μm = 1\ inch/25,400 = 0.000,039\ in$$
$$25μm = 0.001\ inches\ (approximation)$$

Illustration #54 compares the significant particle sizes with familiar objects. Solid contaminant particles come in all sizes. The most harmful particle size is less than 40 micrometers. The unaided eye can only detect objects greater than 40 micrometers, which means that visual inspection cannot be used to determine whether or not contamination is present.

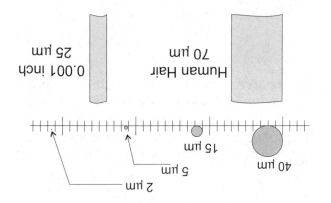

2 μm
5 μm
15 μm
40 μm

Human Hair
70 μm

0.001 inch
25 μm

Illustration #54 — Size Comparison

Particles smaller than 5 micrometers are referred to as silt. A number of methods used to measure the amount of solid contaminants present in a particular sample of fluid are shown in table #10.

Measuring Solid Contaminants			
Method	**Units**	**Benefits**	**Limitations**
Optical particle count	Number per ml	Provides accurate size and quantity distribution	Sample preparation time
Automatic particle count	Number per ml	Fast, repeatable	Sensitive to concentration and non-particulate contaminants eg. H_2O, air, additives
Gravimetric	mg/l	Indicates total amount of contaminants	Cannot distinguish particle size
Spectrometry	ppm	Identifies and quantifies contaminant material	Cannot size contaminants. Some methods insensitive above $8\mu m$
Patch test	Black vs. white	Rapid assessment of contaminant in field. Allows microscopic view of contaminants.	Not quantitative

Table #10 — Measuring Solid Contaminant Levels

Methods that provide the number and size of particles in a sample must be used when the contamination rating is based on particle counts, such as with the ISO 4406 code. Thus, optical or automatic particle counting methods are normally used.

Specifying the Contamination Level

The ISO 4406 Solid Contaminant Code specifies the level of cleanliness of a fluid with regard to solid particles. Other types of contaminants, such as other liquids or gases, are not considered in this code.

A particle count is carried out on a sample of oil to determine the number of particles larger than 5 micrometers and 15 micrometers. The number of particles in these two ranges is then referenced to a standard chart (see table #11) giving a simple two number system.

An example is an oil sample, rated at ISO 19/14.

The '19' refers to the number of particles that are greater than 5 micrometers in size. The '14' refers to the number of particles that are greater than 15 micrometers in size. In this particular example, (ISO 19/14) the particle count per millilitre may have been as follows:

3,200 particles over 5 micrometers, 112 of these were over 15 micrometers

From table #11, the 3,200 particles over 5 micrometers is between 2,500 and 5,000 (2.5k and 5k), which gives a range number 19. The 112 particles over 15 micrometers is between 80 and 160, which gives a range number 14. Therefore, the ISO code for this amount of contamination would be 19/14.

Note: The reason that the number of particles per millilitre can be less than one (see table #11) is that particle counts may be run on samples up to 100 millilitres and then extrapolated back to 1 millilitre.

As can be seen from table #11, higher numbers in the ISO contamination code (range number) indicate higher levels of contamination.

Table #11 — ISO 4406 Code and Contamination Levels

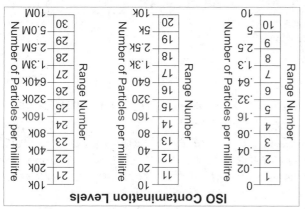

ISO Contamination Levels

Range Number	Number of Particles per millilitre
1	.01
2	.02
3	.04
4	.08
5	.16
6	.32
7	.64
8	1.3
9	2.5
10	5
	10

Range Number	Number of Particles per millilitre
11	10
12	20
13	40
14	80
15	160
16	320
17	640
18	1.3k
19	2.5k
20	5k
	10k

Range Number	Number of Particles per millilitre
21	10k
22	20k
23	40k
24	80k
25	160k
26	320k
27	640k
28	1.3M
29	2.5M
30	5.0M
	10M

One weakness of this system is that a build up of silt particles that are smaller than 5 micrometers would not be picked up. To address this problem, at least one organization has adopted a three number system that accounts for three particle sizes, which are 2, 5 and 15 micrometers. In the example shown for the 19/14 fluid, the particle count per millilitre from the sample may now appear as follows:

23,100 particles over 2 micrometers

3,200 particles over 5 micrometers

112 over 15 micrometers

From table #11, the 23,100 particles over 2 micrometers would be in the 22 range, the number of particles over 5 and 15 micrometer are the same, therefore the three number code would be 22/**19/14**. The 19/14 shown in **bold** is to indicate the ISO 4406 code.

Allowable Contamination Levels

Establishing the correct maximum allowable level of contamination for a particular system is essential if the expected component life is to be realized for a minimum maintenance cost. If the allowable contamination level is too high, operational problems will eventually show up and the result will be costly down time and expensive component replacement or repair. On the other hand, time, money and resources will be wasted if the allowable contamination level is set too low.

Manufacturers of hydraulic system components specify the cleanliness level required for various components based on the type of component and the maximum operating pressure.

The system cleanliness requirement will be determined by the component that requires the cleanest fluid (lowest ISO Solid Contamination (SC) code).

Some typical cleanliness requirements for components operating up to 3000 psi and using 100% petroleum oil are shown in table #12.

For example, if a basic system using petroleum fluid with a maximum system pressure of 2500 psi consisted of the following components:

- Variable piston pump (15/13)
- Direction control valve (18/15)
- Flow control valve (17/14)
- Pressure control valve (17/14)
- Axial piston motor (16/13)

The variable piston pump would set the maximum allowable contamination level at ISO SC Code 15/13.

Most manufacturers specify the required maximum contamination level assuming that the system will be using petroleum based fluids and operating in moderate conditions.

Cleanliness Requirements

Table #12 — Typical Cleanliness Requirements (up to 3000 psi)

Component	ISO SC Code
Fixed vane pump	17/14
Fixed piston pump	16/14
Variable piston pump	15/13
Directional Control Valve (solenoid)	18/15
Pressure control valve	17/14
Flow control valve	17/14
Servo valve	14/11
Cartridge valve	16/13
Cylinder	18/15
Vane motor	17/14
Axial piston motor	16/13
Gear motor	18/15
Radial piston motor	17/13

If any of the following conditions are expected, the manufacturer should be consulted as the cleanliness level will probably have to be set lower:

- Hydraulic fluid that is not 100% petroleum oil.
- High vibration and shock loads are expected.
- Fluid temperatures may occasionally go above 70°C (158°F).
- System may be subject to start-ups at temperatures below -18°C (0°F).
- There is a critical dependence on the system with regards to a process or safety to personnel.

The use of non petroleum fluids such as water based or synthetic fire resistant fluids may also require that special attention be paid to filter elements and housings.

Filters

Filtration Efficiency

The terms "filter" and "strainer" are often used interchangeably. A strainer is basically a coarse filter that uses wire mesh to trap particles. Table #13 gives the opening size of the standard US sieve number.

Sieve Numbers		
US Sieve No.	Opening (inches)	Opening (micrometers)
50	0.0117	297
60	0.009	238
70	0.0083	210
100	0.0059	149
140	0.0049	105
200	0.0029	74
270	0.0021	53
325	0.0017	44
Paper	0.00039	10

Table #13 — Opening Size for US Sieve Numbers

Filters usually have smaller pore sizes than strainers, and retain contaminants as the fluid takes a tortuous path passing through the porous medium.

Filters are usually rated in at least one and sometimes two of the following ways, "absolute and nominal ratings," and "beta ratio".

Absolute Rating - is an indication of the largest pore opening in the filter element and theoretically, particles of this size or larger will be trapped. Mesh strainers, which are sized by the US Sieve No. or mesh number (see table #13), may be given an absolute rating. The largest pore size for 200 mesh would be 74 μm or 0.0029 in (one micrometre [μm] or micron equals one thousandth of a millimeter). This does not mean that all particles larger than this will be trapped. Some particles will be long and thin, and if suitably oriented, will pass through. Also, depending on the pressure difference across the filter, a larger particle may deform the square opening and get through.

Nominal Rating - is an arbitrary value given by the manufacturer. A filter with an absolute rating of 25 μm would probably have a nominal rating of around 10 μm. This should indicate that the filter would take out all particles of 25 μm or larger, but would probably take out most particles larger than 10μm. This is not specific and for this reason most filters are now being rated as follows.

Beta Ratio (βx) - is the ISO standard for rating the efficiency of hydraulic and lubrication filters (ISO 4572). The ratio is determined for a specified particle size (x) and is the ratio of the number of particles greater than x (>x) upstream of the filter, divided by the number of particles >x, downstream of the filter.

The Beta ratio for a filter is determined using a multi-pass filter test system, (see illustration #55), that is designed to be representative of typical hydraulic and lubricating circuits.

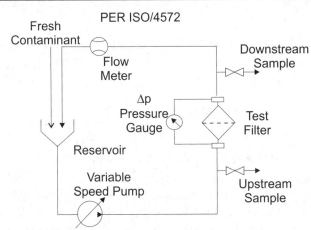

Illustration #55 — Multipass Test for Beta Ratio

Filter Beta Ratio			
Filter	**Particles > 5μm**		β_5
	In	**Out**	
A	10,000	5,000	2
B	10,000	100	100
C	10,000	50	200

Table #14 — Beta Ratio

Contaminated fluid from the reservoir is pumped through the test filter. The upstream and downstream fluid samples are run through a particle counter to determine their respective particle counts.

Table #14 shows the effectiveness of three different filters with regards to particulate removal and their resulting Beta ratio.

In table #14, the Beta ratio (β_x) of the filter under test is calculated by dividing the number of particles in the upstream flow, by the number of particles in the downstream flow, based on a specified particle size (x). In this case, the specified particle size is 5 µm and larger; therefore, (x) is 5.

Filter "A" had 10,000 particles going in, and 5,000 coming out that were 5 mm and larger.

The Beta ratio β_5 for the three filters are:
Filter "A" β_5 = 10,000/5000 = 2
Filter "B" β_5 = 10,000/100 = 100
Filter "C" β_5 = 10,000/50 = 200

The removal efficiency of the filter equals the number of particles removed, divided by the number of particles entering:

For filter "A" ($\beta_5 = 2$)
removal efficiency = 5000/10 000 = 50%

For filter "B" ($\beta_5 = 100$)
removal efficiency = 9900/10 000 = 99%

For filter "C" ($\beta_5 = 200$)
removal efficiency = 9950/10 000 = 99.5%

The removal efficiency can also be calculated from the Beta ratio.

Removal Efficiency:
= (Beta ratio - 1) x 100/Beta ratio:

For $\beta_5 = 2$,
Removal Eff. = (2-1) x 100/2 = 50%

For $\beta_5 = 100$,
Removal Eff. = (100-1) x 100/100 = 99%

For $\beta_5 = 200$,
Removal Eff. = (200-1) x 100/200 = 99.5%

A particular filter can have many different Beta ratios ($\beta_{(x)}$), that will vary, depending on the particle size used as reference (x).

Table #15 — Beta Values and Removal Efficiency

Beta Values

β value at x μm (βx)	Removal Efficiency % of particles > x μm	Downstream Count when filter is challenged upstream with 10^6 particles > x μm
1.0	0	1,000,000
1.5	33	670,000
2.0	50	500,000
20	95	50,000
50	98.0	20,000
75	98.7	13,000
100	99.0	10,000
200	99.5	5,000
750	99.87	1,333
1000	99.90	1,000
10,000	99.99	100

Table #15 shows the significance of Beta values in the actual removal efficiency.

To be effective and maintain the designed Beta ratio, a filter must be designed to eliminate any chance of bypass or internal leakage around the filter element. The effect of leakage is shown in illustration #56.

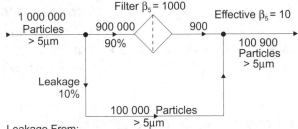

Leakage From:
- Non-sealing element gaskets
- Leaking bypass valves
- Non-uniform filter medium

Illustration #56 — Affects of Leakage on Beta Ratio

The filter in illustration #56 has a $\beta_5 = 1000$. When there is 10% leakage past the filter, the affective Beta ratio becomes 10^6 divided by 100,900 = 9.91. The filtration efficiency changed from 99.9% when there is no bypass, to 90% when there is 10% of the fluid bypassing.

Note: It should be noted that the above tests are carried out in controlled laboratory conditions. In an actual hydraulic system, filters are subject to more rigorous conditions. Vibration, variations in temperature, and pulsating flow rates will quickly reduce the actual Beta ratio on lower quality filters.

Location of Filters

The position of filters in any system will depend on the intended function of the filter. Regardless of the location in the system, the filter housing location should be such that filter elements are easily accessible for servicing.

This is often a neglected feature with suction strainers, and servicing often requires that the reservoir be drained to access the strainer. Generally, filters are placed to accomplish one of the three following functions:

a. Prevent contamination from entering the system.

b. Maintain or improve the cleanliness of the system.

c. Ensure that specific components receive clean fluid.

a: Prevent contamination from entering the system: There are two main sources of ingression controlled by filters. They include, air entering reservoirs as the fluid level drops, and fluid addition when topping up or refilling. Filtering the air entering a reservoir is relatively simple as long as the reservoir is properly sealed and all the air enters and leaves at a specific location.

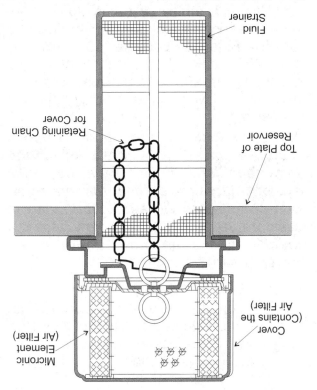

Retaining Chain for Cover

Top Plate of Reservoir

Fluid Strainer

Micronic Element (Air Filter)

Cover (Contains the Air Filter)

Illustration #57 — Filler/Breather

Illustration #57 shows a combination fluid strainer and air filter.

Fluid being poured in is strained, and air passing through is filtered. The rating of the air filter element will depend on the type of hydraulic system. Air filters rated for removing 3μm particles and larger should be used on sensitive and high pressure systems.

The filler strainer would be used to strain the fluid as it is poured into the reservoir. It should be noted that filler strainers will prevent only the largest of particles from entering (see table #13 for US sieve sizes). When adding fluid to the system in this manner, it is virtually impossible not to add contaminants to the reservoir. The fluid from the supplier may not be at the required cleanliness level.

In addition, the fluid has often been transferred from one or more containers before being poured into the reservoir, adding to the chance of contaminants being introduced. In this situation, every precaution should be made to ensure that as little contamination as possible is added to the system.

On more critical systems it is preferable to ensure that the fluid entering the system is filtered through a high efficiency low micron filter.

Two methods can be used to accomplish this. Use a separate filter transfer system, shown in illustration #58, or use the return line filter by pumping hydraulic fluid directly into the return line upstream of the filter. Refer the schematic shown in illustration #61, which has provision for connecting a filling pump, just upstream of the return line filter.

b: Maintain or improve the cleanliness of the system: Filters located to improve the cleanliness of the system are placed either in the pressure line, the return line, or in an off line situation. Various combinations of these locations may also be used.

A bypass type pressure line filter can be located immediately after the pump and before the pressure relief. A schematic diagram is shown in illustration #60A.

The bypass valve prevents excessive pressure differential across the filter element. If the filter starts bypassing, unfiltered oil will pass through to the system components. It is therefore important that this type of filter have a pressure differential, or bypass indicator which is either visual, electrical, or both.

If a non bypass type filter is used, as shown in illustration #59, it should be placed after the relief valve. This is shown in illustration #60B.

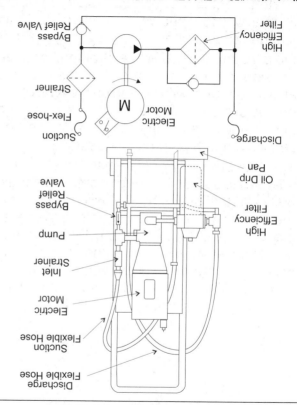

Illustration #58 — Fluid Transfer System

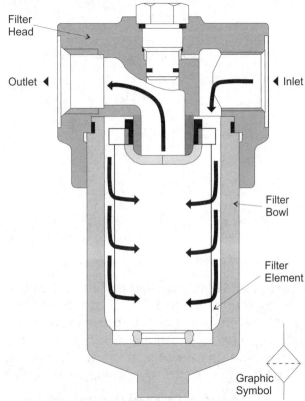

Illustration #59 — Pressure Filter - Non Bypass

Non bypass filter elements should be able to withstand high pressure differentials without collapsing. If the filter doesn't have a high collapse pressure rating, there is the chance that the element may rupture if it becomes plugged by contaminants, resulting in the release of large amounts of contaminants into the flow of oil going to the components. High pressure differentials may be realized on cold starts, where the viscosity is abnormally high, or when the filter becomes saturated with contaminants.

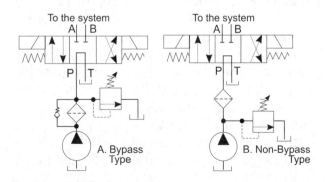

Illustration #60A,B — Pressure Line Filtration

Return line filters will improve the cleanliness, as long as a high percentage of the pump volume per minute will pass through the filter. Illustration #61 shows a partial schematic that has all of the pump output passing through a bypass type return filter.

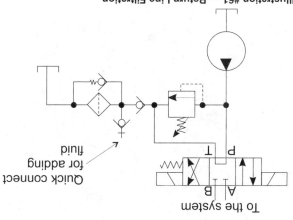

To the system

Quick connect for adding fluid

Illustration #61 — Return Line Filtration

When sizing a return line filter in either gallons or litres per minute, it is important to realize that if cylinders with a high differential ratio are used, then the flow in the return may be more than double the pump output (for more information on flow intensification, see Section One "Flow Intensification (Differential Cylinders)". Illustration #62 shows a cutaway of a typical return line filter.

Off line filtration is often used when a system operates for periods of time with the pump in compensation, or when systems are subject to pulsating or varying flow rates. Off-line filtration may be either designed into the circuit (permanent) as the schematic shows in illustration #63, or be a portable system as shown in illustration #58. Off-line filtration may also be used for adding fluid to the system.

c: Ensure that specific components receive clean fluid: A filter or strainer may be placed immediately upstream of a component in a number of situations.

These are:

- Where components are particularly sensitive to solid contamination, such as servo and proportioning valves.
- Where the consequence of a component failure is unacceptable due to the resulting cost in equipment or downtime.
- Where a component failure would result in injury to people, or safety would be jeopardized.

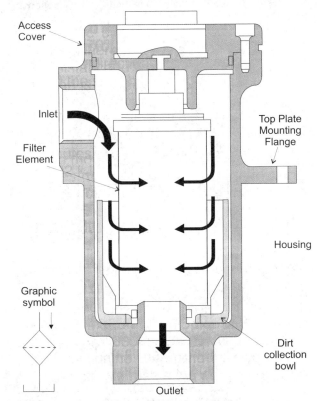

Access Cover

Inlet

Filter Element

Top Plate Mounting Flange

Housing

Graphic symbol

Dirt collection bowl

Outlet

Illustration #62 — Return Line Filter - Non Bypass

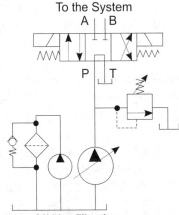

To the System

A   B

P   T

Illustration #63 — Off Line Filtration

- If the reservoir has a pour in type fill system, the pump may be equipped with a
suction strainer or filter, in case any large
particles are inadvertently added to the
reservoir. This is usually a large mesh
(around 100 mesh) pleated strainer, with
a bypass valve feature, to ensure that the
pump will not cavitate, should the strainer
become blocked.

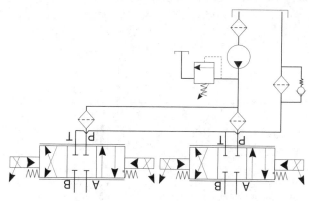

Illustration #64 — Component Isolation Filtration

Illustration #64 shows a schematic with isolation filters for the pump and proportional
directional valves, as well as return line filtration for systemic contamination control.

Illustration #65 shows an isolation filter directly below a servo valve.

The Filtering Media

Filtration is achieved by forcing the liquid
through a porous material which has very
small openings. Theoretically, any contaminant particles that are larger than the openings will be prevented from passing through.
The size of particle that actually passes
though the filter, will also be influenced by the
pressure difference across the filter and the
ease with which the filter media deforms.

Component isolation filters should not be
finer than the system filters, or they will perform as the general system clean up filters,
and have a shortened life. Servo and proportioning valves often require isolation filtration
due to their sensitivity to contamination.

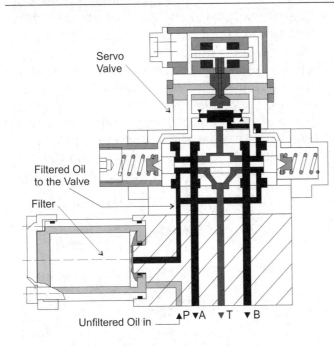

Illustration #65 — Component Isolation Filtration

When a particle, slightly larger than the pore size, becomes trapped at the entrance to an opening, the pressure may be high enough to force the particle through by deforming the media material, regardless of the fact that the particle is larger than the original opening. The shape of the contaminant particle, its orientation to the opening, and the type of media, will also have a bearing on the size of particles that get through.

Long thin particles may pass through a surface type filter, but would have less chance to pass through a depth type filter where the flow path is tortuous.

There are two basic types of filtering media used in hydraulic systems. These are the surface type and the depth type.

Surface Type Media: The flow path through a surface type filter is a straight line. The contaminant particles accumulate on the surface of the material. Refer to illustration #66.

This feature makes them reusable by washing the contaminants off in a solvent bath. The most common surface type of filter is the mesh strainer. This consists of woven strands of stainless steel wire or nylon filament. The diameter of the woven strands and the number of strands per inch in both length and width, will determine the opening size. The number of strands per inch (length and width) are given a "US Sieve Number", which is shown in table #13.

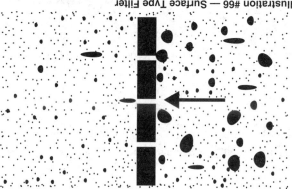

Illustration #66 — Surface Type Filter

A 100 mesh strainer will have 100 strands per inch in both directions. This means each square inch of material will have approximately 10,000 pores. The size of these pores or openings will be 0.0059 in (149 μm) square (see table #13).

The surface type filter, as shown in illustration #67, is typically used as a suction strainer. The mesh screen is usually pleated to provide a greater filtering area.

The inside of the screen is supported (perforated metal tube or weldmesh) to prevent the screen from collapsing as the fluid flows to the inside.

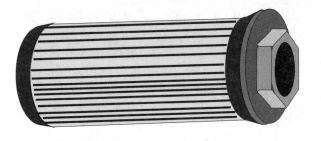

Illustration #67 — Typical Inlet Strainer

Depth Type Media: When low micron filtration is required, depth media is usually used. From illustration #68 it can be seen that the fluid will have to make a tortuous route to travel through the depth type media. Although the term "depth media" implies thickness, the material used appears quite thin.

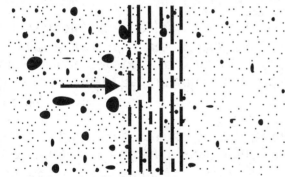

Illustration #68 — Depth Type Filtering Media

Usually it is a mat of cellulose paper or inorganic fibers, laid down in a random pattern and bonded to each other.

The thickness of the fibers will have a great effect on the performance of the filter. Illustration #69 shows the importance of fiber diameter with regards to the flow path area. The larger diameter cellulose fibers take up most of the area for one 3 µm opening. In contrast, the much finer inorganic fibers allow for many 3 µm opening in the same area.

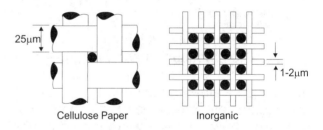

25µm

1-2µm

Cellulose Paper   Inorganic

Illustration #69 — Importance of Fiber Size

The greater number of pores ensures that the material will have a larger dirt holding capacity and a lower pressure difference (ΔP) across the filter.

The inorganic material is usually of glass fiber which produces a mat of relatively even pore size. This is inert to most chemicals and unlike cellulose will not tend to swell when in contact with oil or water.

Due in part to the fact that most of the contaminant particles contained by the filtering media are inside the media, depth filters are not usually reusable.

The media usually has support on both sides and is pleated to provide a larger surface area for a given diameter of filter element. See Illustration #70.

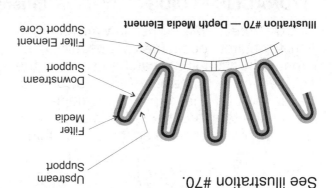

Illustration #70 — Depth Media Element

- Support Core
- Filter Element
- Downstream Support
- Filter Media
- Upstream Support

Selection of Filters

When selecting filters, the required cleanliness of the system and the location of the filters are major considerations.

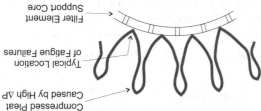

Illustration #71 — Deformation of Element

- Filter Element Support Core
- Typical Location of Fatigue Failures
- Compressed Pleat Caused by High ΔP

Typically, the upstream and downstream support is wire mesh and the element support core is a perforated steel tube.

A cheaply made filter element may not have adequate upstream and downstream support. Pulsating flows and/or high pressure differences (ΔP) across the filter media will deform poorly supported media as shown in illustration #71. This will eventually cause failure of the element. Unfiltered oil will then pass through the filter to the system.

When a system is in service, a regular sampling and analysis program will determine if the required cleanliness has been reached and is being maintained. If the required cleanliness is not being maintained, a check should first be made to ensure that an excess of contamination is not coming from external sources. If this is not the case, filter placement, element Beta ratios, and element size should be re-evaluated. Filter manufacturers and suppliers are the best source of information regarding the expected performance of various filter housings and elements.

The life of a filter will depend on a number of variables. The initial cleanliness of the system will directly affect filter life on start up. Once the system is at or below the required cleanliness, every effort must be made to keep it at this level. Any increase in the amount of contamination will cause increased internal wear. This in turn will increase the amount of generated contamination.

The amount of ingressed contamination must be kept to a minimum. Careful attention to reservoir vents, maintenance practices, and design features such as piston rod boots or covers can achieve this.

Some manufacturers may list the "dirt capacity", which is the amount of contamination that can be added to the filter test system before the terminal ΔP is reached. It is impossible to relate this to filter life in an actual operating system. One important feature that effects service life is the size or area of the element.

Experience has shown that filter service life increases at a greater rate than the increase in filter area. If the filter area is doubled, the service life will be somewhat greater than double. This is probably due to the reduced flow rate per area through the filter, allowing the filter to operate more efficiently for a longer period of time.

Filter manufacturers will specify the maximum flow rate for a particular filter and often provide a graph of flow versus pressure drop for both the filter housing and the filter element. Illustrations #72 and #73 shows a typical pressure drop through a filter housing and a filter element respectively for various flow rates. The total pressure drop would be equal to the ΔP of the housing, plus ΔP of the element for a specific flow rate.

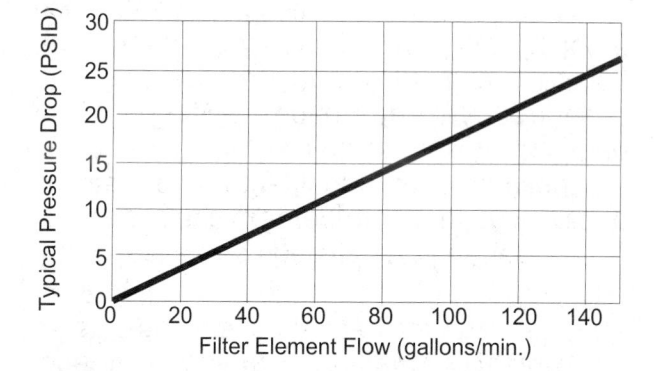

Illustration #73 — Filter Pressure Drop with Flow Rate

Note: The pressure drops specified by filter manufacturers are for new filter elements. As soon as they are in service and start to load up with contaminants, the pressure drop (ΔP) for a particular flow rate will begin to increase, see illustration #74. Pressure drop is also related to viscosity, and an increase in viscosity (e.g. on cold start ups) will make ΔP higher

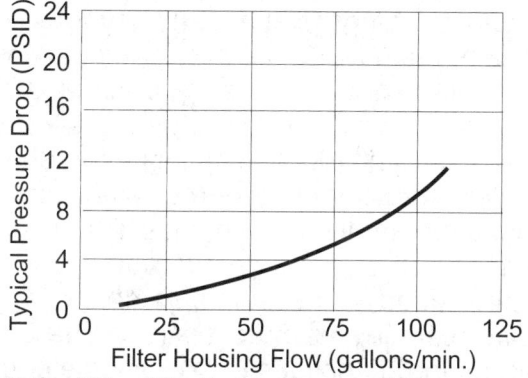

Illustration #72 — Filter Housing Pressure Drop with Flow Rate

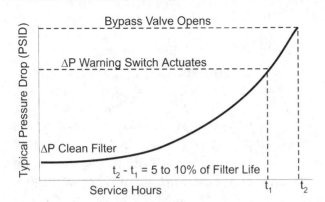

Illustration #74 — ΔP Increase With Dirt Loading

It is preferable that filters are fitted with pressure differential (ΔP) indicators, that will give an easy to read indication when a filter element requires changing.

Illustration #74 also shows how a warning switch could be set so that only a slight percentage of service life of the filter is lost, if the filter is changed immediately.

Suction Strainers: Suction strainers should be fitted with a bypass valve that has the flow characteristics to ensure that the pump will not cavitate when full pump flow is going through the valve. If the system is operated outdoors, where the temperature on start up may be very low (viscosity high), it may be advisable not to have a suction strainer.

The filter should also be large enough, so that when partially blocked by contaminants, the pressure drop will not be sufficient to cavitate the pump or open the bypass valve. A typical suction strainer is shown in illustration #67.

Pressure Line Filters: Any filter located in a line that may receive full system pressure is a pressure line filter. The filter housing and seals must be rated for this pressure.

Pressure line filter elements that have no by-pass may also be required to withstand high ΔP, abrupt flow and pressure changes, and possible pump pulsations.

It is therefore important that these filter elements are chosen with these factors in mind. A ruptured element will release a large amount of contaminants into the system. Pressure filters are more expensive than return line filters and are usually used on systems with components that have a low dirt tolerance. A typical pressure line filter is shown in illustration #59.

Return Line Filters: Due to lower pressures, lower maximum ΔP, and low flow velocities (in a well designed system), return line filters offer an economic method of achieving high filtration efficiencies.

If only return line filtration is used, contamination from the reservoir, ingressed contamination, and contamination being generated by components, will pass completely through the system before being filtered.

Another factor to note is that the drain line from equipment such as a hydraulic motor should return directly to the reservoir, thereby bypassing any filtration, to avoid the back pressure from the return filter. This unfiltered oil will then be pumped through the system without being filtered.

When sizing return line filters, consider the fact that the filter may have to handle more than the maximum volumetric pump output if high ratio differential cylinders are in use. A typical return line filter is shown in illustration #62.

Handling of Fluids

It is important that all hydraulic and lubricating fluids be stored and handled in such a manner that contamination products are not added to the fluid. In some cases, as the fluid is being pumped into the system, it will require filtering so that it is cleaner than when it came from the supplier.

It is recommended that:

- Oil drums are stored on their sides in a covered area.
- The top of the drum should be thoroughly cleaned before opening the bung.
- All containers, hoses, etc. are checked for cleanliness before being used.
- After use, hoses should be drained and plugged, containers should be drained and covered with plastic sheet.
- If a pump is used to transfer and filter the oil into the system, the filter should be at least equal to the finest filter in the system with regards to Beta ratio.
- Portable filtration systems equipped with fine filters may be required on sensitive high pressure systems.

Fluid Sampling and Testing

Laboratory analysis of lubricating and hydraulic oil is an essential part of a complete planned preventive maintenance scheme. Regular testing of hydraulic oil will alert the maintenance team to any problems regarding filter effectiveness, wear of components, contaminant ingression and the general fluid quality. The filters in the system are designed to achieve and maintain the required fluid cleanliness. The only way to confirm this is to have the oil tested at a laboratory. If the fluid is not at the target cleanliness level, the following points may have to be considered:

Any new or extra points of ingression.

- Maintenance practices, especially with regards to filling or top up.
- Beta ratio of filters.

- Placement of filters.
- Size or number of filters.
- Filter housing problems, such as bypass valve leaking.

The information that is obtained from the laboratory report will depend on what tests were ordered. Most laboratories will provide sample bottles and an oil sample pump. The following are some of the tests that may be ordered:

- Particle size distribution.
- Oil properties, such as viscosity, viscosity index, pour point, flash point, etc.
- Contamination from other fluids such as glycol and water.
- Acidic levels.
- Additive depletion.
- Composition of metallic particles.

Note: *If a filter analysis is performed in conjunction with the oil analysis, abnormal conditions may be spotted sooner than when only using an oil analysis.*

Taking a representative sample is extremely important. Some systems will have a sampling point designed into the system. This is often located in the return line, ahead of the filter. If this is not the case, then samples may have to be taken from the reservoir using a pump. It is important that the system be operating, or just recently shut down, so that the sample is truly representative of the fluid.

Note: *Extreme care must be taken not to pollute the sample as it is being taken. Flush system oil through the sampling lines and containers, before taking the actual sample. Seal and identify the containers immediately.*

SECTION TWO QUESTIONS

Hydraulic Fluids

1. List the four functions of hydraulic fluid

   Answer: _____

   _____

2. The bulk modulus of an oil is independent of the temperature.

   ❏ true   ❏ false

3. The compressibility of petroleum based oils is approximately 0.5% per 1000 psi.

   ❏ true   ❏ false

4. High viscosity oil may cause excess internal leakage in components.

   ❏ true   ❏ false

5. A thick fluid that pours and flows slowly is said to have a low viscosity.

   ❏ true   ❏ false

6. The viscosity of hydraulic fluid decreases as the temperature rises.

   ❏ true   ❏ false

7. The viscosity of oil is independent of any pressure changes.

   ❏ true   ❏ false

8. The viscosity of grease will change as the shear rate changes.

   ❏ true   ❏ false

9. List four possible outcomes of having the viscosity of hydraulic fluid too high:

   Answer: _____

   _____

10. List four possible outcomes of having the viscosity of hydraulic fluid too low:

    Answer: _____

    _____

11. List the two methods used to measure viscosity:

    Answer: _____

    _____

12. What is the SI unit of absolute viscosity?

    ❏ Pascal second
    ❏ Saybolt universal second
    ❏ Redwood second
    ❏ mm^2/second

13. What is the SI unit of Kinematic viscosity?
   ❏ Pascal second
   ❏ Saybolt universal second
   ❏ Redwood second
   ❏ mm^2/second

14. An oil is designated as ISO VG 68. What would be the approximate viscosity in centistokes (cSt) at 400°C (see table #7)?
   ❏ 40
   ❏ 52
   ❏ 68
   ❏ 72

15. The viscosity index (VI) of an oil will change as the temperature changes.
   ❏ true   ❏ false

16. Equipment that is subject to low temperature starts will require fluid that has a high viscosity index.
   ❏ true   ❏ false

17. The result of plotting a viscosity versus temperature graph is a straight line.
   ❏ true   ❏ false

18. The maximum start up viscosity for the system is usually set by the:
   ❏ actuator
   ❏ directional control valve
   ❏ relief valve
   ❏ pump

19. The temperature at which wax crystals begin to form and change the appearance of the oil is know as the:
   ❏ pour point
   ❏ cloud point
   ❏ flash point
   ❏ fire point

20. An oil that is at its flash point temperature will spontaneously ignite.
   ❏ true   ❏ false

21. The fire point temperature of an oil is higher than the flash point.
   ❏ true   ❏ false

22. List four factors that will increase the oxidation rate of an oil:
   Answer: _____

   _____

23. An oil with a high degree of demulsibility will:
   - ❏ require a long time to separate from water
   - ❏ require a short time to separate from water
   - ❏ will not separate from water
   - ❏ will never become an emulsion

24. A hydraulic system designed to operate on petroleum based fluid can not be converted to operate on fire resistant fluid.
   - ❏ true   ❏ false

25. All fire resistant fluids must not be allowed to come into contact with water.
   - ❏ true   ❏ false

26. All biodegradable oils are synthetically manufactured.
   - ❏ true   ❏ false

27. Some biodegradable oils are suitable for hydraulic systems.
   - ❏ true   ❏ false

28. Which of the following contaminants is the major cause of wear and sticking problems?
   - ❏ liquid
   - ❏ fluid
   - ❏ air
   - ❏ solid

29. Solid contaminant particles that are too large to enter the clearance space between moving parts will:
   - ❏ not be a problem
   - ❏ eventually cause problems
   - ❏ not be picked up by the pump
   - ❏ cause immediate problems

30. List four sources of contamination:

   Answer: _____

   _____

31. New hydraulic fluid is always completely free of contamination.
   - ❏ true   ❏ false

32. After assembling a new system what procedure should be followed to reduce the amount of built in contamination?

   Answer: _____

   _____

33. List four likely entry points for ingressed contamination:

   Answer: _____

   _____

34. To prevent the contaminants present in air from contaminating the hydraulic fluid a rubber or plastic membrane may be used in the reservoir.
   - ❏ true   ❏ false

35. *Contamination particles that are the result of component wear are not usually a problem because they are generally very soft.*
    - ❏ true   ❏ false

36. *The rate of erosive wear will be increased if the fluid contains solid contaminants.*
    - ❏ true   ❏ false

37. *Below a certain size, solid particles are usually referred to as silt. What is this size?*
    - ❏ 5 micrometers
    - ❏ 10 micrometers
    - ❏ 15 micrometers
    - ❏ 40 micrometers

38. *The ISO 4406 Solid Contaminant Code uses two particle sizes when specifying the amount of contamination, they are:*
    - ❏ 5 and 10 micrometers
    - ❏ 5 and 15 micrometers
    - ❏ 10 and 15 micrometers
    - ❏ 10 and 40 micrometers

39. *The ISO contamination code of 19/14 is cleaner than 17/11.*
    - ❏ true   ❏ false

40. *The maximum operating pressure and the system components has a direct bearing on the required cleanliness level for a hydraulic system.*
    - ❏ true   ❏ false

41. *The pump is always the component that sets the cleanliness requirements for a hydraulic system.*
    - ❏ true   ❏ false

42. *A mesh strainer with a US Sieve number of 270 (53 micrometre opening) would have an absolute rating of:*
    - ❏ less than 53 micrometres
    - ❏ 53 micrometers
    - ❏ more than 53 micrometres

43. *A mesh strainer with a US Sieve number of 270 (53 micrometre opening) would have a nominal rating of:*
    - ❏ less than 53 micrometres
    - ❏ 53 micrometres
    - ❏ more than 53 micrometres

44. *The ISO standard for rating hydraulic filters is:*
    - ❏ nominal rating
    - ❏ absolute rating
    - ❏ beta ratio
    - ❏ both nominal and absolute rating

45. During a filter test for beta ratio using particles 5 micrometres and larger, a filter had 10,000 particles on the upstream side and 80 particles on the downstream side of the filter. The filter would be rated at:

❏ $\beta_5 = 100$
❏ $\beta_5 = 125$
❏ $\beta_5 = 150$
❏ $\beta_5 = 200$

46. For a filter rated at $\beta_5 = 150$, the removal efficiency would be:

❏ 99.66%
❏ 97.25%
❏ 98.50%
❏ 99.33%

47. Name two sources of contaminant ingression that can be controlled by filters:

Answer: _____

_____

48. The relief valve must always be between the pump and a bypass type filter.

❏ true   ❏ false

49. The relief valve must always be between the pump and a non bypass type filter.

❏ true   ❏ false

50. Return line filters may have to deal with flow rates greater than the maximum pump output.

❏ true   ❏ false

51. Component isolation filter should have the highest removal efficiency of all the system filters.

❏ true   ❏ false

52. A typical surface type filter would be a mesh strainer.

❏ true   ❏ false

53. When low micron filtration is required, a strainer is usually used.

❏ true   ❏ false

54. *Most depth type filters can be reused by washing.*
    ❏ true   ❏ false

55. *The pressure drop through a filter and housing is independent of the flow rate.*
    ❏ true   ❏ false

56. *Which type of line is most likely to return fluid to the reservoir with no filtration?*
    ❏ return
    ❏ drain
    ❏ pilot
    ❏ pressure

57. *What is the best way to add fluid to the system?*
    Answer: _____
    _____

58. *Why should a system of regularly taking oil samples for laboratory analysis be set up?*
    Answer: _____
    _____

SECTION THREE

HYDRAULIC PIPING

Pipe

Steel pipe is commonly used as a fluid conductor when large volumes of fluid are involved, or where its lower cost relative to tubing, is a factor. There are various methods of manufacturing pipe. For general hydraulic purposes, seamless carbon steel pipe is recommended. It must be free from dirt, rust, scale and any machining debris, before being installed into any hydraulic system.

The standard finish given to steel pipe is a lacquer coating that is intended to prevent corrosion during shipping and storage. This is referred to as "black iron pipe". The preferred finish for hydraulic systems is either "pickled and oiled" or "pickled only". Galvanized pipe should never be used in any hydraulic system.

Sizes and Schedule Numbers

Nominal pipe size (NPS) is the system used to describe pipe.

For pipe sizes up to and including 12 inches [300 mm] NPS, the outside diameter of the pipe is always a larger dimension than the NPS size (for example a 3 inch [80 mm] NPS has an OD of 3.5 inches [88.9 mm]). For pipe sizes above 12 inches [300 mm], NPS refers to the outside diameter of the pipe (for example a 14 inch [355.6 mm] NPS has an OD of 14 inches [355.6 mm]).

Carbon steel pipe is commercially available in nominal pipe sizes (NPS) ranging from 1/8 inch [6 mm] through to 42 inches [1050 mm]. Each pipe size is available in a variety of wall thicknesses. Because the outside diameter of a specified nominal pipe size must remain constant, any change in wall thickness changes the inside diameter.

The method for sizing pipe (NPS) originates from an earlier system that was developed when there was only one wall thickness for pipe and the pipe was sized according to the inside diameter. Later, pipe was manufactured with three wall thicknesses: standard, extra heavy and double extra heavy. These were referred to as pipe weights. Wall thickness is now expressed as a schedule number. See illustration #75 for the relationship between wall thickness, schedule number and pipe weights for 1 inch [25 mm] NPS pipe. Schedule 40, schedule 80 and schedule 160 are the most common schedule numbers used.

For comparison, wall thicknesses for standard weight pipe and schedule 40 are identical for sizes $1/8$ inch [6 mm] through to 10 inches [250 mm].

Wall thicknesses for extra heavy pipe and schedule 80 pipe are identical for sizes 1/8 inch [6 mm] through to 8 inches [200 mm]. There is no corresponding schedule number for double extra heavy pipe. Generally, double extra heavy pipe has a thicker wall than schedule 160 pipe up to and including 6 inches [150 mm] NPS. Sizes over 6 inches [150 mm] NPS, schedule 160 becomes the thicker walled pipe.

See table #16 for examples of steel pipe dimensions.

Note: See the Appendix for a more comprehensive table of pipe dimensions, pipe and tube pressure ratings, and a table of Stress Values.

NPS inches [mm]	Pipe OD	Pipe Inside Diameter					
	All Schedule Numbers inches [mm]	Schedule 40 inches [mm]	Schedule 80 inches [mm]	Schedule 160 inches [mm]	Standard	Extra Strong	Double Extra Strong inches [mm]
½ [15]	0.840 [21.3]	0.622 [15.80]	0.546 [13.87]	0.466 [11.78]	See schedule 40	See schedule 80	0.252
1 [25]	1.315 [33.4]	1.049 [26.64]	0.957 [24.31]	0.815 [20.70]			0.599
2 [50]	2.375 [60.3]	2.067 [52.50]	1.939 [49.25]	1.689 [42.90]			1.503
4 [100]	4.500 [114.3]	4.026 [102.26]	3.826 [97.18]	3.438 [87.33]			3.152
8 200 mm	8.625 [219.1]	7.981 [202.74]	7.625 [193.70]	6.813 [173.08]			6.875 [174.64]
Note: For a more complete table see the Appendix							

Table #16 – Example of Steel Pipe Dimensions

Schedule 40 pipe is the most commonly available pipe at most plants and is usually the minimum wall thickness used for hydraulic purposes.

If a higher pressure rating for pipe is required, schedule 80, XS, schedule 160 or XXS, may be used.

Nominal Pipe Size (NPS) 1 inch (25mm)

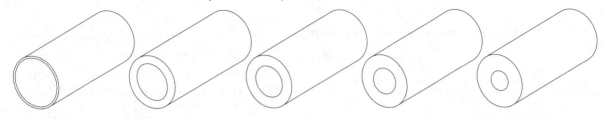

	Light Wall Schedule #10	Standard Schedule #40	Extra Strong Schedule #80	Schedule #160	Extra Extra Strong
Outside Diameter	1.315" [33.4mm]	1.315" [33.4mm]	1.315" [33.4mm]	1.315" [33.4mm]	1.315" [33.4mm]
Inside Diameter	1.097" [27.864mm]	1.049" [26.65mm]	0.957" [24.31mm]	0.815" [20.7mm]	0.599" [15.2mm]
Wall Thickness	0.109" [2.769mm]	0.133" [3.4mm]	0.179" [4.6mm]	0.250" [6.35mm]	0.358" [9.093mm]

$$\text{Wall Thickness} = \frac{\text{Outside Diameter - Inside Diameter}}{2}$$

Illustration #75 — Schedule Numbers and Pipe Weights

Pressure Considerations

The pressure required to produce a specific stress in pipe, or tube, can be calculated using Barlow's formula, which is:

$$\text{Pressure (P)} = 2 \times S \times (T - C) / D$$

Where:
P = pipe internal pressure (psi) [kPa]
T = wall thickness (inches) [mm]
C = allowance for threading (inches) [mm]
D = outside diameter of pipe (inches) [mm]
S = stress on the pipe material (psi) [kPa]

If the piping system is welded (no threading) then:

$$\text{Pressure (P)} = 2 \times S \times T/D.$$

When the maximum allowable stress for the pipe material is used for 'S', the resulting pressure (P) will be the maximum allowable working pressure for that pipe.

When the ultimate tensile strength of the material is used for 'S', the resulting pressure (P) will be the theoretical bursting pressure for that pipe.

Wall thickness and stress values may be found in manufacturers' publications and in various design specifications. See table #16 for examples of pipe dimensions. Table #17 shows the allowance for threading.

Threading Allowance

Pipe Size (NPS)		Allowance	
inches	[mm]	inches	[mm]
½ to ¾	[15 to 20]	0.0571	1.45
1 to 2	[25 to 50]	0.0696	1.77
2½ and larger	[65] and larger	0.100	2.54

Table #17 — General Allowance for Threading

Table #18 shows samples of maximum allowable stress values for seamless carbon steel pipe.

ASTM and API Specification Numbers & Grades		Maximum Allowable Stress (For the listed temp. range)
Specification	Grade	-20 to 650°F. [-29 to 343°C]
Seamless A53	A	12,000 psi [82.7 MPa]
Seamless A53	B	15,000 psi [103.4 MPa]
Seamless A106	A	12,000 psi [82.7 MPa]
Seamless A106	B	15,000 psi [103.4 MPa]
Seamless API 5L	A	12,000 psi [82.7 MPa]
Seamless API 5L	B	15,000 psi [103.4 MPa]
see Section Eleven (page 436) for a more comprehensive table of stress values		

Table #18 — Stress Values for Seamless Carbon Steel Pipe

Using the above formula and values for stress values from table #17, the maximum allowable pressure (P) can be determined for any given pipe. For example:

For 1 inch schedule 40 seamless A53 grade A pipe:

Maximum allowable stress (S) = 12,000 psi (from table #17)

Wall thickness (T) = (OD - ID)/2

T = (1.315 − 1.049)/2 = 0.133 in (from table #16)

Allowance for threading (C) = 0.0696 in (from table #18)

Outside diameter (D) = 1.315 in (from table #16)

Pressure (P) = 2 x S x (T − C) / D

P = 2 x 12,000 x (0.133 − 0.0696) / 1.315

P = 1157 psi (maximum allowable internal pressure)

For 2 inch schedule 40 seamless A53 grade A pipe

Maximum allowable stress (S) = 12,000 psi
(from table #17)
Wall thickness (T) = (OD - ID)/2
T = (2.375 - 2.067)/2 = 0.154 in
(from table #16)
Allowance for threading (C) = 0.0696 in
(from table #18)
Outside diameter (D) = 2.375 in
(from table #16)
Pressure (P) = 2 x S x (T - C) / D
P = 2 x 12,000 x (0.154 - 0.0696) / 2.375
P = 853 psi (maximum allowable internal pressure)

For a specific schedule number, the maximum allowable internal pressure decreases as the pipe size increases.

Pipe Fittings

Note: For more complete information on pipe fittings and standard dimensions, see Sections Four and Five, of IPT's Pipe Trades Handbook.

Pipe fittings are the joining components that make possible the assembly of various lengths of pipe into a functioning piping system.

Pipe fittings are available in a variety of materials (copper, cast iron, malleable iron, forged steel, plastic, etc.). Forged steel fittings are the most suitable for hydraulic purposes.

Fittings may be attached to the pipe by either a welded joint or screw thread joint (maximum recommended pressure for screw thread joints is 2500 psi [17 250 kPa]. The welded joint will be either a socket-welded style or butt welded style.

In situations where pressures are high, vibration is present, or where oil leaks absolutely cannot be tolerated, welded joints are more suitable.

Another advantage that welded joints have over screw thread joints, as shown in illustration #76, is that the transition between the pipe and the fitting is relatively smooth with no change in cross sectional area.

The type of fitting attachments used with pipe may also depend on the pipe size and equipment available.

For welded joints, the socket weld type is usually used for the smaller sizes (2 inch [50 mm] and under). The butt weld is used for the larger sizes.

The screw thread joint is also used on the smaller sizes.

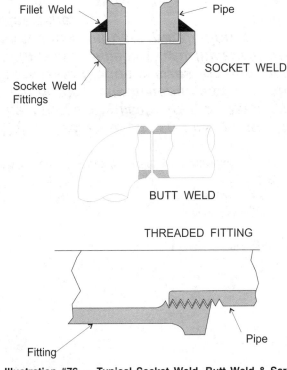

Illustration #76 — Typical Socket Weld, Butt Weld & Screw Thread Fittings

Socket weld fittings are produced in three pressure designations:

- Class 3000
- Class 6000
- Class 9000

Pressure and temperature ratings for each of the pressure class fittings are taken to be equivalent to the following pipe wall thickness designations:

Fitting Class	Schedule No.	Weight
3000	80	XS
6000	160	—
9000	—	XXS

Butt weld fittings are required to have identification markings on each fitting. Illustration #77 shows a typical butt weld fitting and explains the identification markings.

Note: Pressure/temperature ratings for the fittings duplicate that of seamless pipe of the same material, size and wall thickness. Standard sizes for butt weld fittings are available in wall thickness and schedule numbers paralleling that of steel pipe.

Illustration #77 — Butt Weld Fitting Identification

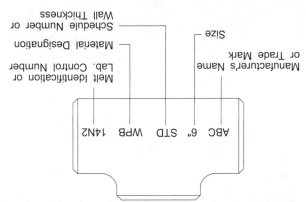

Melt Identification or Lab. Control Number

Material Designation

Schedule Number or Wall Thickness

Size

Manufacturer's Name or Trade Mark

ABC   6"   STD   WPB   14N2

Screw thread joints are common, due to the ease with which pipe can be cut to length, threaded and assembled to form a piping system.

Forged steel threaded fittings are produced in three pressure designations:

- Class 2000
- Class 3000
- Class 6000

Pressure and temperature ratings for each of the pressure class fittings are taken to be equivalent to the following pipe wall thickness designations:

Fitting Class	Schedule No.	Weight
2000	80	XS
3000	160	—
6000	—	XXS

Pipe Flanges

Flanges are used in hydraulic systems for the following two situations:

1. When two pipes are to be connected and pressures are relatively low, standard pipe flanges may be used. Standard steel and alloy pipe flanges are covered under ASME/ANSI specification B16.5 for flange pressure classes of 150 to 2500.

Note: For more complete information on pipe flanges and standard dimensions, see Section Four of IPT's Pipe Trades Handbook.

2. When pressures are high, and/or the pipe is to be connected to a component, SAE 4 bolt solid and split flanges are used. Sealing is accomplished by the use of an O-ring. Illustration #78 shows a socket welded O-ring flange and a pipe threaded O-ring flange. The recommended pipe thread when attaching the threaded flange to pipe is NPTF.

Pipe Threads

Note: The Joint Industrial Council (JIC) recommends that pipe used in service above 2500 psi [17 250 kPa] shall have welded connections. Many companies limit the use of threaded joints to a level much lower than this pressure.

Because the inside diameter of a specific pipe size varies according to the schedule number, pipe can only have male threads. The pipe thread form used for pressure joints in North America is the American National Standard Taper Pipe Thread (NPT).

The American National Standard Taper Pipe Thread (NPT) has a 1 in 16 taper ($^3/_4$ inch per foot) on the diameter and a 60° thread form.

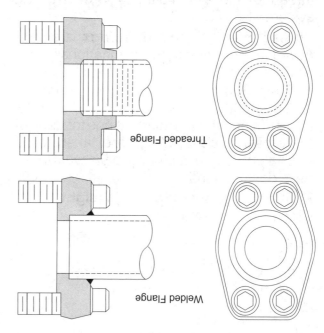

Welded Flange

Threaded Flange

Illustration #78 — SAE 4 Bolt Socket Welded and Pipe Threaded O-ring Flanges

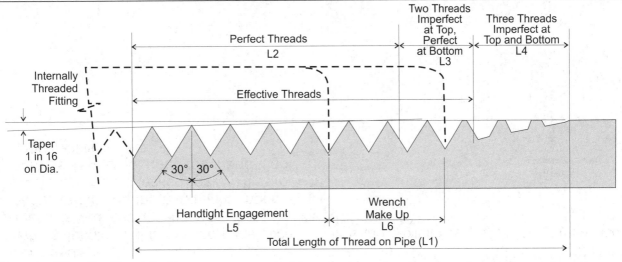

Illustration #79 — Pipe Thread Profile

Referring to the external thread shown in illustration #79, the overall length of the thread consists of the following:

- L1: Overall thread length
- L2: Perfect roots and crests
- L3: Two threads with perfect roots but imperfect crests
- L4: Approximately $3\frac{1}{2}$ threads with imperfect roots and crests.
- L5: Hand tight engagement.
- L6: Wrench make up.

When threads are cut on a pipe, either by hand or machine dies, setting the pitch diameter will determine the engagement length of the internal thread when the thread is cut to the correct length.

When first setting up the pipe dies, a trial cut is made and a fitting with an internal thread is run on hand tight to check the hand tight engagement length. If it is too short, the pitch diameter is reduced on the pipe dies, the thread is re-cut and the hand tight engagement of the fitting is checked again. This procedure is repeated until the hand tight engagement is correct.

Tables #19A and #19B list the various thread dimensions (L1, L2, L3 and L4), the hand tight engagement length (L5) between the internal and external thread and the wrench make up length (L6) for sizes $^1/_8$ inch [6 mm] inch to 6 inches [150 mm] NPS.

The wrench make up length is three full threads for sizes up to and including 2 inch NPS and two full threads for sizes over 2 inch NPS.

NPS	Outside Diameter	Threads per inch	Thread Length L1		L2	L3	L4
inches	inches	number	inches	approx. # threads			
1/8	0.405	27	0.3924	10.6	0.1898	0.0741	0.1285
1/4	0.540	18	0.5946	10.7	0.2907	0.1111	0.1928
3/8	0.675	18	0.6006	10.8	0.2967	0.1111	0.1928
½	0.840	14	0.7815	10.9	0.3909	0.1429	0.2478
3/4	1.050	14	0.7935	11.1	0.4209	0.1429	0.2478
1	1.315	11 ½	0.9845	11.3	0.5089	0.1739	0.3017
1-1/4	1.660	11 ½	1.0085	11.6	0.5329	0.1739	0.3017
1-1/2	1.900	11 ½	1.0252	11.8	0.5496	0.1739	0.3017
2	2.375	11 ½	1.0582	12.1	0.5826	0.1739	0.3017
2-1/2	2.875	8	1.5712	12.6	0.8875	0.2500	0.4337
3	3.500	8	1.6337	13.1	0.9500	0.2500	0.4337
3-1/2	4.000	8	1.6337	13.5	1.0000	0.2500	0.4337
4	4.500	8	1.7337	13.9	1.0500	0.2500	0.4337
5	5.563	8	1.8400	14.7	1.1563	0.2500	0.4337
6	6.625	8	1.9462	15.6	1.2625	0.2500	0.4337

Table #19A — Pipe Thread Dimensions

Table #19B — Pipe Thread Dimensions

NPS	Outside Diameter	Threads per inch	Thread Length L1		Hand Tight Engagement Length L5		Wrench Makeup Length L6	
inches	inches	number	inches	approx. # threads	inches	approx. # threads	inches	approx. # threads
1/8	0.405	27	0.3924	10.6	0.1615	4.4	0.1111	3
1/4	0.540	18	0.5946	10.7	0.2278	4.3	0.1667	3
3/8	0.675	18	0.6006	10.8	0.240	4.5	0.1667	3
1/2	0.840	14	0.7815	10.9	0.320	4.5	0.2143	3
3/4	1.050	14	0.7935	11.1	0.339	4.8	0.2143	3
1	1.315	11 ½	0.9845	11.3	0.400	4.6	0.2609	3
1-1/4	1.660	11 ½	1.0085	11.6	0.420	4.8	0.2609	3
1-1/2	1.900	11 ½	1.0252	11.8	0.420	4.8	0.2609	3
2	2.375	11 ½	1.0582	12.1	0.436	5.0	0.2609	3
2-1/2	2.875	8	1.5712	12.6	0.682	5.5	0.2500	2
3	3.500	8	1.6337	13.1	0.766	6.1	0.2500	2
3-1/2	4.000	8	1.6337	13.5	0.821	6.6	0.2500	2
4	4.500	8	1.7337	13.9	0.844	6.8	0.2500	2
5	5.563	8	1.8400	14.7	0.937	7.5	0.2500	2
6	6.625	8	1.9462	15.6	0.958	7.7	0.2500	2

Due to the clearance between the root of the internal thread and the crest of the mating external thread, as shown in illustration #80, there may be a spiral clearance along the length of the thread; therefore, a sealant must be used on NPT threads. The sealant should be applied to the external threads only, avoiding the first one or two threads, to reduce the possibility of system contamination. The sealant will also act as a lubricant and reduce the chance of galling.

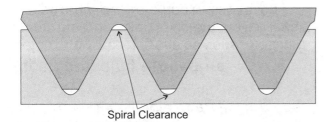

Spiral Clearance

Illustration #80 — Spiral Clearance Around NPT Threads

A variation of the NPT thread that is used for hydraulic purposes is the Dryseal ANSI Standard Taper Pipe Thread (NPTF). This thread has the same form and dimensions as the NPT thread, except that the truncation of the crests and roots is changed to ensure that the spiral clearance around the thread is eliminated.

Note: The Joint Industrial Council (JIC) recommends the use of NPTF threads when taper pipe threads are used for pipe joints. This thread may also be referred to as the National Pipe Tapered Thread For Fuels.

The interference at the crest and root of the mating parts of this thread eliminates the need for a sealant to seal any clearances. Be aware that assembling any thread system without lubrication can lead to galling, especially with materials such as stainless steel or other nickel alloys. A thread sealant should be used with this thread for anti-galling purposes.

Note: Special taps and dies are required for making this type of thread. Unless specially marked, NPTF threads are not easily distinguishable from NPT threads.

Pipe Threading Procedure

Before any threading can be done, measurements must be taken to determine the length of pipe required. Referring to illustration #81, measure the distance between the fittings (dimension 1) and add on two times the thread engagement (dimension 2). This will give the length of pipe required (dimension L). Tables #19A and #19B can be used to estimate the thread engagement (dimension 2). This will be equal to the hand tight engagement length, plus the wrench make up length.

Note: Due to manufacturing tolerances, the thread engagement length of one particular fitting may be different to that of another similar fitting. Because of these manufacturing variations, dimensions from tables #19A #19B are to be used as a guide only.

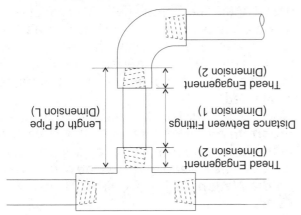

Distance Between Fittings (Dimension 1)

Thread Engagement (Dimension 2)

Length of Pipe (Dimension L)

Thread Engagement (Dimension 2)

Illustration #81 — Pipe Dimensions for Threading.

The pipe may be cut to length using a pipe cutter or a hacksaw. If a hacksaw is used, care must be taken to make the cut square. Use a pipe reamer for removing the internal burr produced by a pipe cutter.

Note: The spiral reamer is for hand use only and should not be used with the power vise.

Straight fluted reamers can be used with the pipe in a fixed or power vise. Any external burrs may have to be filed or ground off.

To ensure that the hand tight engagement is correct, it is advisable to first cut a thread on a piece of scrap pipe. Adjustments can then be made to the dies if required (see tables #19A and #19B for hand tight engagement and overall thread length).

The required pipe can then be threaded. Use liberal quantities of cutting fluid while threading.

When tightening pipe threads, be careful not to over-tighten, especially when assembling an external pipe thread into a cast iron housing. The taper of the thread has a wedging effect and may split or crack housings and fittings.

Note: Because fluid contamination is a major cause of hydraulic system failures, all pipes and fittings are to be absolutely clean when being installed. Steaming, degreasing and pickling are some methods that may be used before installation.

Tubing

Seamless steel tubing is widely used in hydraulic systems. Apart from the cost, it does have a number of advantages over pipe. Because bending is easier, there is a tendency to use fewer fittings. Tubing can be reused many times without sealing problems. Except for high volume applications, tubing can handle most hydraulic requirements with less bulk and weight than a similar piping system.

Sizes

Tubing is sized according to the outside diameter. Each size is available in a variety of wall thicknesses. The wall thickness specified will depend on the application, maximum pressure, material and diameter. Generally, sizes range from:

- $^{1}/_{16}$ inch to 2 inches for fractional sizes. Inch sizes are also sometimes referred to using a 'dash number' system, where the dash number is the OD in sixteenths of an inch. For example, dash 6 (-6) would be $^{6}/_{16}$ or $^{3}/_{8}$ inch OD.
- 3 mm to 25 mm for metric sizes.

Materials

Tubing can be ordered in a variety of materials to suit system requirements. Considerations such as internal pressure, weight, appearance and external environment will influence the decision as to what type of material to use.

It is important that high quality pressure tubing is purchased for hydraulic use. Surface finish, material hardness, concentricity, and ovality are qualities that are important to ensure good sealing when using flared and flareless type fittings.

When using flareless type fittings, it is essential that the tubing is softer than the fitting being used.

For example, carbon steel fittings should not be used with stainless tubing. If the fittings and the tubing are of the same material, the tubing should be in an annealed state.

Carbon Steel Tubing

Seamless carbon steel tubing is probably the most widely used tubing type for hydraulic purposes. Carbon steel tubing has an ultimate tensile strength of approximate 47,000 psi [324 Mpa].

Stainless Steel Tubing

Stainless steel may be used when the external conditions require the use of corrosion resistant material. Most stainless steels have high ultimate tensile strengths (around 70,000 psi [482.6 Mpa]).

Aluminum and other Special Alloyed Tubing

Aluminum alloys and other special alloys are available, if required.

As with all materials, the manufacturer's information is the most reliable and should be used when the allowable stress or allowable working pressures are required.

Plastic Tubing

Many different types of plastic tubing are available for low-pressure purposes.

Tubing Fittings

Threads are not used on the ends of tubing, as they sometimes are with pipe. To attach the ends of a tube to either a component or to another tube, a flared, flareless, or welded type of fitting is used.

Flared Fittings

Flared fittings are suitable for low to medium pressures. The thicker tubing walls that are required for higher pressures reduce the sealing surface and shorten thread engagement when used with conventional flare fittings.

Note: Because the Joint Industrial Council recommends the 37° angle, fittings and couplings using this angle are referred to as JIC fittings or couplings.

The SAE standard J533B covers specifications for both single and double 37° and 45° flares for tube ends, that are to be used with 37° and 45° flared tube fittings. Illustration #82 shows both single and double flared tube ends. The double flare is used with thin walled tubing.

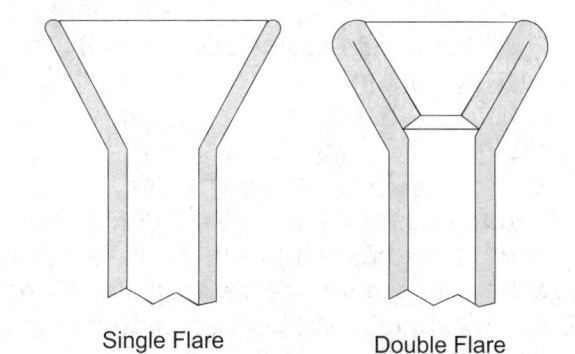

Single Flare   Double Flare

Illustration #82 — Single and Double Flared Tubing

Tubing Size	Maximum Wall Thickness (inches)			
	Single Flare		Double Flare	
	37°	45°	37°	45°
1/8	0.035	0.035	0.025	0.025
3/16	0.035	0.035	0.028	0.028
1/4	0.065	0.049	0.035	0.035
5/16	0.065	0.049	0.035	0.035
3/8	0.065	0.065	0.049	0.049
7/16		0.065		0.049
½	0.083	0.065	0.049	0.049
9/16		0.083		0.049
5/8	0.095	0.095	0.049	0.049
3/4	0.109	0.109	0.049	0.049
7/8	0.109	0.109	0.065	
1	0.120	0120	0.065	
1-1/8	0.120		0.065	
1-1/4	0.120		0.065	
1-1/2	0.120		0.065	
1-3/4	0.120		0.065	
2	0.134		0.065	

Table #20 — Maximum Recommended Wall Thickness for Flaring

The maximum wall thickness recommended by the above SAE standard is shown in table #20.

The SAE 37° flare (JIC) is the standard angle used for hydraulic tubing. A typical example is shown in illustration #83A. The fitting has a short nut, with a sleeve to support the tube. Some designs omit the sleeve, but compensate with a longer nut.

The SAE 45° flare may be used with both regular and inverted flared fittings. The SAE 45° flare is often used with soft copper tubing for applications such as refrigeration, fuel lines and other automotive applications. Illustration #83B shows a 45° inverted flare.

A special tool is required to flare the tubing. The ends of the tubing should be closely inspected and de-burred, both internally and externally, before flaring.

After the flare is made, the flared portion should have no cracks, be concentric to the tubing and the seating surfaces must be free of imperfections that may prevent sealing.

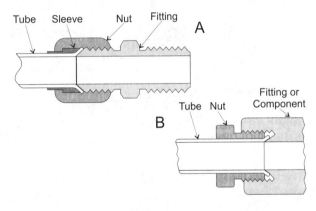

Illustration #83A & B — Threaded Fittings and Flared Connectors

Flareless Fittings

As pressures become higher, the tubing wall thickness must also increase. As indicated in table #20, there is a recommended maximum wall thickness for flaring. This limits the pressure capability of flare type fittings.

Flaleless type fittings were developed for use with the thicker walled tubing, for medium to high pressures. Due to the high clamping pressures exerted by some types, some fitting manufacturers will specify the minimum wall thickness for their particular product.

Flareless type tubing fittings (sometimes referred to as compression fittings) are available in two common styles:

Ferrule or Sleeve Type (illustration #84A): A ferrule is used to seal against the tapered seat of the fitting and the tube. Tightening the nut creates the sealing pressure on both sealing surfaces and deforms the tube.

O-ring Type (illustration #84B): Sealing is achieved by the use of an O-ring mounted in a groove on the inside of the fitting. This type also uses a split ferrule, or sleeve to clamp the tube, so that it will not pull or blow out of the fitting.

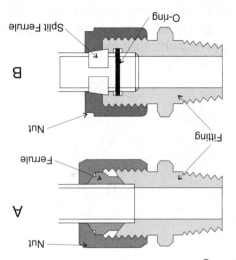

Illustration #84A, B — Flareless Type Tubing Fittings

Note: It is important that these types of fittings are correctly installed. Do not mix fittings from different manufacturers. Refer to the instructions provided by the manufacturer, especially with regards to the amount of tightening.

Welded Fittings

In cases where high pressures and/or vibration is present and frequent disassembly is not required, brazed or welded fittings may be used.

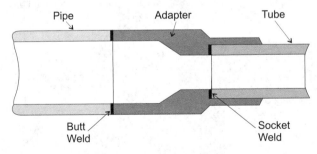

Illustration #85 — Weld or Braze Type Fitting

Illustration #85 shows a fitting (adapter) that connects a tube to a pipe, using both socket and butt welds. Material type, wall thickness and welding skills all have to be taken into account when considering this type of attachment.

The SAE 4 bolt flange fitting is a variation of a welded type fitting. This is similar to the SAE 4 bolt flange pipe fitting shown in illustration #78, except that the socket diameter is machined to suit tubing dimensions instead of pipe OD. A flange is brazed, or silver soldered, on to the end of the tubing. This flange is then clamped to a mating part, using a solid or split flange fitting.

Sealing is accomplished by the use of an O-ring located in a groove in the flange. Illustration #86 shows a cutaway of a typical SAE 4 bolt split flange assembly.

Pressure Rating

Pressure capability can be calculated using a similar formula to that used for calculating pipe pressures. Because tubing is not threaded, the formula does not include an allowance for threading.

Pressure (P) = 2 x S x T / D

Where:

P = pipe internal pressure in psi
T = wall thickness
D = outside diameter of pipe
S = stress on the pipe material in psi

See the Appendix for the pressure ratings of tubing.

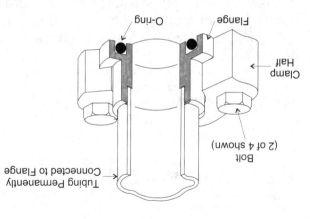

Illustration #86 — SAE 4 Bolt Split Flange Assembly

O-ring

Flange

Clamp Half

Bolt (2 of 4 shown)

Tubing Permanently Connected to Flange

Tubing Installation

The following points should be considered when installing tubing:

- Select a route that is direct.
- Don't box in any doors, mechanical equipment or electrical panels.
- Consider sources of damage (moving equipment, falling objects, flying objects such as rocks on mobile equipment, personnel standing or climbing on the tubing, etc.).
- Use bends to allow for easy assembly/disassembly and to reduce stress on fittings due to thermal expansion and contraction. For bend examples, see illustration #87).
- Use high quality tubing that is round, has consistent wall thickness and is free from scratches, nicks and other damage.
- Use a tube cutter to cut the tubing (de-burr both inside and outside of the cut end).
- Don't put too much tension on the tightening handle of the tube cutter, especially with thin wall tubing.
- Use as few fittings as possible (one of the main advantages of tubing is that it can be easily bent, which reduces the use of elbows).
- Tubing can be bent by hand, hand benders and production benders (make sure that there are no kinks, wrinkles or flattening on the finished bend. For good and bad bend examples, see illustration #88.
- Bends must not be too close to fittings (fitting manufactures will specify the minimum straight tube length required from the end of the tube to the start of the bend).
- Use the appropriate matching hydraulic fittings.

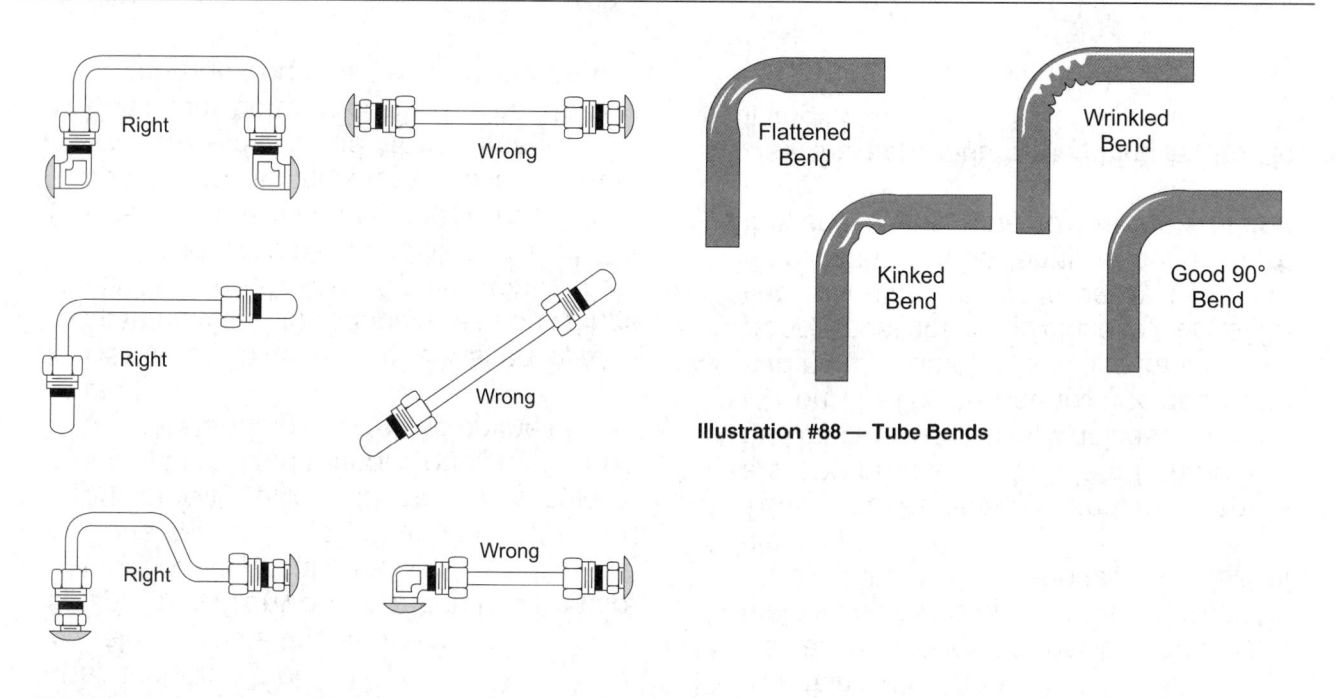

Illustration #88 — Tube Bends

Illustration #87 — Tube Routing

Flexible Hose

Piping and tubing are rigid fluid conductors and are therefore not suitable in situations where one end of the conductor moves independently of the other.

Other advantages of hose over rigid conductors are:

- Simple to route and set in place
- Can withstand vibration
- No problems with thermal expansion or contraction

A flexible hose consists of: an inner tube, reinforcement and an outer protective cover.

When a length of hose has the appropriate end fittings attached, it is referred to as a hose assembly. Illustration #89 shows a typical hydraulic hose assembly.

Inner Tube

The inner tube is made from either oil resistant synthetic rubber (usually neoprene) or an oil resistant thermoplastic material.

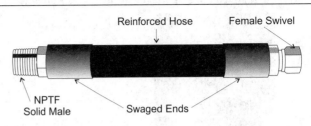

Illustration #89 — Typical Hydraulic Hose Assembly

It should be able to withstand temperatures of -40° to 200° F (-40° to 93°C).

Reinforcement

The amount and type of reinforcement will determine the pressure rating for the hose (see table #22 for typical examples). The type of reinforcement ranges from single and multiple fibre braid for low-pressure applications, to 6-Spiral steel wire reinforcement for very high pressures.

As the amount of reinforcement increases, the hose becomes less flexible.

Outer Protective Cover

The outer cover is usually manufactured from an oil and weather resistant thermo-plastic, or synthetic rubber material.

Hose End Fittings

There are two main types. One is a crimped or swaged on type, that is not re-usable. These fittings are discarded with the hose when the hose has to be replaced. The second type is re-usable. Assembly and dis-assembly is accomplished using common hand tools (see "Making up Flexible Hose Assemblies".

There is a wide variety of stems available that allow hydraulic hose to be attached to any fitting or connector.

Flexible Hose Standards

There is a standard set by the Society of Automotive Engineers (SAE) for hydraulic hose specifications.

The SAE J517 standard covers general, dimensional and performance specifications for hydraulic hose.

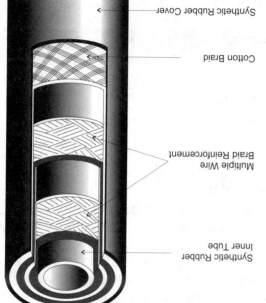

Synthetic Rubber Inner Tube

Multiple Wire Braid Reinforcement

Cotton Braid

Synthetic Rubber Cover

Illustration #90 — Typical Construction of SAE 100R2A

Under this standard, the hose is classified using 100R numbers.

For example, SAE 100R5 has a hose construction consisting of an inner tube of oil resistant synthetic rubber and two textile braids separated by a high tensile steel wire braid. All braids are to be impregnated with an oil and mildew resistant synthetic rubber compound (see table #22 for working pressures). Illustration #90 shows the typical construction of SAE 100R2A, which is a two wire braid hose.

Flexible Hose Sizes

As with tubing, flexible hose is sized using a dash number system. The dash number represents the inside diameter of the hose in $\frac{1}{16}$ inch for all hose types except for SAE 100R3. For SAE 100R3, the dash size denotes the hose inside diameter equal to the equivalent tube outside diameter. Refer to table #21.

Dash Number	Hose ID Inches	
	All Except SAE 100R3	**SAE 100R3**
-3	3/16	
-4	1/4	3/16
-5	5/16	1/4
-6	3/8	5/16
-8	1/2	3/8
-10	5/8	1/2
-12	3/4	5/8
-14	7/8	
-16	1	7/8
-20	1 1/4	1 1/8
-24	1 1/2	1 3/8
-32	2	1 13/16

Table #21 — Dash Numbers and Hose ID

The SAE J513 standard also lists the maximum OD for each hose size and R100 number.

Due to modern manufacturing techniques and materials, most manufacturers produce hose that meets or exceeds the SAE J513 requirements, yet are smaller than the maximum OD specified.

Note: Because of this, it is extremely important to carefully match the end fittings to the hose being used.

Flexible Hose Pressure Considerations

The pressure capability of flexible hose depends on the amount and type of reinforcement and the hose diameter. As with pipe and tubing, the recommended working pressures become less as the hose diameter increases.

Generally, fibre reinforced hose is used for low pressures, single and two wire braid are for medium pressures and 4 and 6 spiral wraps are considered high pressure hose.

Table #22 gives a comparison of the working pressures required by SAE J513, for a selection of wire reinforced hoses.

When selecting a hose for a specific application, pressure charts or tables supplied by the hose manufacturer should be consulted. Many hoses exceed the pressure requirements of SAE J513.

Dash No	SAE 100R5 Single Wire Braid	SAE 100R2A Two Wire Braids	SAE 100R10 4 Spiral Wire Wrap	SAE 100R11 6 Spiral Wire Wrap
-4	3000	5000	8700	11250
-6	2250	4000	7500	10000
-8	2000	3500	6250	7500
-10	1750	2750		
-12	1500	2250	5000	6250
-16	800	1850	4000	5000
-24	500	1250	2500	3000
-32	350	1125	2500	3000

Table #22 — Pressure Rating (psi) of Selected SAE Specification Hoses

Flexible Hose Installation

The following points should be considered when installing flexible hose:

- The hose should not be twisted as it is being tightened up on the fittings (illustration #91).
- Never use a bending radius less than that recommended by the hose manufacturer (illustration #92).
- Ensure that there is adequate slack (illustration #93). Hose under pressure may elongate up to 2% of its length or contract up to 4% of its length, depending on pressure, the type of hose and size.

- Make sure a vibrating or moving hose is not rubbing on a fixed object, or that moving parts do not rub on or trap flexible hose.
- Route the hose away from high heat sources. If this cannot be done, either shield or insulate the hose. Make sure that it is possible to access each end of the hose for installation and removal purposes.

Flexible Hose Installation

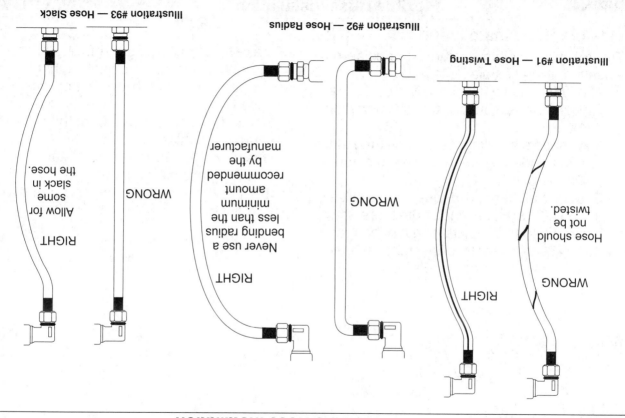

Illustration #91 — Hose Twisting

WRONG — Hose should not be twisted.

RIGHT

Illustration #92 — Hose Radius

RIGHT — Never use a bending radius less than the minimum amount recommended by the manufacturer.

WRONG

Illustration #93 — Hose Slack

RIGHT — Allow for some slack in the hose.

WRONG

Making up Flexible Hose Assemblies

Some hydraulic hose is designed to have the outer protective layer removed at the ends where the fittings are located; this is referred to as "skiving". It is important that the fittings are correctly selected as "skive", or "no skive" types, to suit the type of hose being used.

Hydraulic hose assemblies can be one of two types, either permanent ends or reusable ends.

Permanent ends are swaged onto the ends of the hose, using a hand, or power operated swager. Illustration #94 shows a cutaway through a non-skive swaged hose end.

Reusable ends are assembled onto the ends of the hose using simple hand tools and a vise. Illustration #95 shows a reusable socket and nipple end fitting.

To avoid leaks, or end fittings blowing off, use the manufacture's recommended fittings for their particular hose.

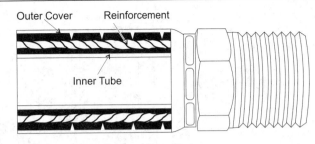

Illustration #94 — Swaged Hose End

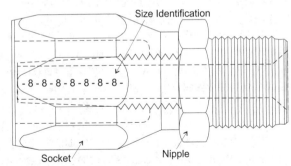

Illustration #95 —- Reusable Hose End

Connecting Components

Fluid conductors are attached to hydraulic components by either a threaded, or a flanged fitting. Fitting manufacturers provide a large number of fittings and adapters to connect the various ends supplied on the conductors, to the specific type of connection provided on the component.

NPT and NPTF Connections

The ports of many low, to medium pressure, components are often provided with taper pipe threads. Although the Joint Industrial Council (JIC) recommends the use of NPTF for tapered pipe threads, some manufacturers use NPT for hydraulic purposes (see "Pipe Threads" for more information). Pipe ends that are threaded (NPT or NPTF) can be installed directly into the component if they are of the same nominal size as the port thread.

Pipe of a different nominal size, tubing and hose will require some type of adapter fitting to be connected to the tapped port.

When installing male taper threaded pipe or fittings to components, do not over-tighten, especially if the housing is cast iron. If possible, use a straight fitting rather than an elbow. Elbows often require orientation to a particular direction. This may cause over or under tightening. Illustration #96 shows a NPTF to SAE male 37° flare (JIC) adapter, which is only one of many adapter fittings on the market today.

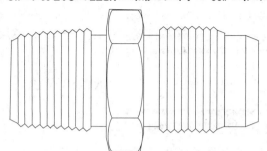

Illustration #96 — Adapter fitting, NPTF to SAE Male JIC

Note: Some connectors may use a parallel form of the NPT and NPTF threads. These are referred to as NPSM (National Pipe Straight Thread for Mechanical Joints) and NPSF (National Pipe Straight Thread for Fuels). There is no sealing accomplished by the threads. In this case, a 30° seat located at the end of the thread seals the connection.

SAE Straight Thread (O-Ring Boss)

American Standard Unified Thread Form is used for attaching adapters to ports on various hydraulic components. When the adapter is attached to a port, the sealing is accomplished by the use of an O-ring that is compressed into a tapered seat. Two styles of adapters are common. The solid type is used when no orientation is required (as with the straight nipple shown in illustration #97A).

The locknut type uses a nut and washer above the O-ring, which allows orientation of such fittings as the elbow (shown in illustration #97B). Both adapters shown in illustrations #97A and #97B, convert from the SAE O-ring port to SAE male 37° flare (JIC). A wide variety of adapters are available to convert from the SAE parallel port thread, to the appropriate type to fit the conductor being attached.

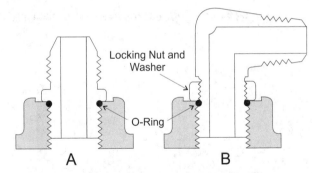

Illustration #97A, B — SAE Straight Thread Fittings

Table #23 lists the dash number, nominal tube OD, thread size (OD), thread ID and minimum spot face diameter for SAE ports (see illustration #98 for these dimensions).

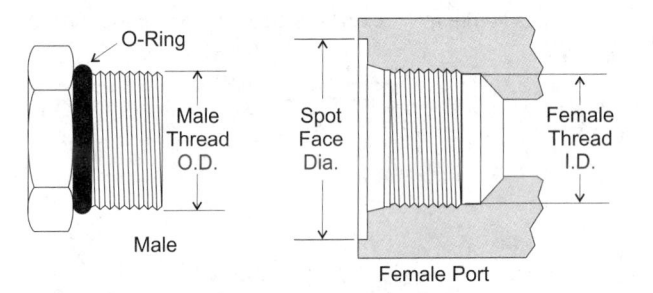

Illustration #98 — SAE Straight Thread O-ring Port

Tube		Thread Size	Female Thread	Male Thread	Spot Face Dia. (ins.)
Dash No.	Noml. Size (ins.)		I.D. (ins.)	O.D. (ins.)	
-2	1/8	5/16 -24	0.267	5/16	0.672
-3	3/16	3/8 -24	0.330	3/8	0.750
-4	1/4	7/16 -20	0.383	7/16	0.828
-5	5/16.	½ -20	0.446	½	0.906
-6	3/8	9/16 -18	0.502	9/16	0.969
-8	½	3/4 -16	0.446	3/4	1.888

Table #23 — SAE Straight Thread Port Dimensions

O-Ring Flange Connection

The O-Ring 4 bolt flange, which is available in both solid and split flange configurations, is a common connection to pumps and motors. When the O-ring flange is bolted to the machined surface of the component, the O-ring makes the seal.

The split flange is shown in illustration #86. SAE dimensions are covered by the SAE code J518, which has two sizes, code 61 and 62. A slight variation to SAE code J518 is the "Caterpillar" flanges, which are basically the same as code 62, except for a thicker flange head.

Examples of solid flanges are shown in illustration #78. They are connected to the conductor by either screw thread or welding. The bolt hole dimensions and bolt size will depend on the pressure rating and the nominal flange size.

Other Threads

Due to the large number of countries that manufacture hydraulic components, the possibility of encountering other types of threads is high.

Some of the more common foreign threads are:

British Standard Pipe Tapered (BSPP) (ISO 7/1)

Similar to NPT but should not be mixed, due to different thread angle (55° for BSPT, 60° for NPT) and threads per inch. As with NPT threads, the seal is made on the threads.

British Standard Pipe Parallel (BSPP) (ISO 228/1)

As with all parallel threads, the threads do not perform any sealing action. When used as a connector, the seal is on a 30° seat. This thread is also popular for port connections and is used in conjunction with a soft metal sealing ring that seals on a spot face.

SECTION THREE QUESTIONS
Hydraulic Piping

1. What type of pipe finish is preferred for hydraulic systems?

   Answer: _____

   _____

2. At what size does NPS refer to outside diameter of the pipe?
   - ❏ above 8 inch
   - ❏ above 10 inch
   - ❏ above 12 inch
   - ❏ above 15 inch

3. As the wall thickness of pipe changes the inside diameter changes.
   - ❏ true   ❏ false

4. The wall thickness for 10 inch schedule 40 pipe is identical to 10 inch standard weight pipe.
   - ❏ true   ❏ false

5. The wall thickness for 10 inch schedule 80 pipe is identical to 10 inch extra heavy pipe.
   - ❏ true   ❏ false

6. What is the corresponding schedule number for double extra heavy pipe?
   - ❏ 60
   - ❏ 80
   - ❏ 160
   - ❏ there is no corresponding schedule number

7. What is the maximum allowable pressure for a 1/2 inch, threaded, schedule 160 pipe if the maximum allowable stress is 15,000 psi?
   - ❏ 3920 psi
   - ❏ 4639 psi
   - ❏ 4835 psi
   - ❏ 5115 psi

8. What is the maximum allowable pressure for a 2 inch, threaded, schedule 80 pipe if the maximum allowable stress is 15,000 psi?
   - ❏ 1239 psi
   - ❏ 1427 psi
   - ❏ 1875 psi
   - ❏ 2130 psi

9. What is the maximum allowable pressure for a 50 mm, threaded, schedule 80 pipe if the maximum allowable stress is 103 420 kPa?
   - [ ] 12 880 kPa
   - [ ] 14 990 kPa
   - [ ] 15 550 kPa
   - [ ] 16 770 kPa

10. What is the maximum allowable pressure for a 15 mm, threaded, schedule 80 pipe if the maximum allowable stress is 103 420 kPa?
    - [ ] 26 880 kPa
    - [ ] 28 495 kPa
    - [ ] 30 456 kPa
    - [ ] 32 143 kPa

11. What is the recommended maximum pressure for screw thread pipe joints?

    Answer: _____

12. List three situations where a welded pipe joint would be preferred over a threaded joint:

    Answer: _____

13. What are the three pressure designations for forged steel fittings?

    Answer: _____

14. The American National Standard Taper Pipe Thread (NPT) has a 1 in 16 ($^{3}/_{4}$ inch per foot) taper on the diameter and a 60 degree thread form.
    - [ ] true
    - [ ] false

15. All pipe threads have the same number of threads per inch.
    - [ ] true
    - [ ] false

16. How does the NPTF thread differ from the NPT thread?

    Answer: _____

17. Why should a thread sealant be used with the NPTF thread?

    Answer: _____

18. Which type of reamer should be used in a power vise to remove internal burrs after cutting a pipe off to length:
    - [ ] spiral reamer
    - [ ] straight fluted reamer

19. The spiral reamer can be used to remove external burrs.
 ❏ true   ❏ false

20. Over-tightening pipe threads in a housing:
 ❏ is recommended to prevent leaks
 ❏ may split or crack the housing
 ❏ is necessary when vibration is present
 ❏ will ensure that the pipe is all the way up to the shoulder

21. Tubing is sized according to the:
 ❏ outside diameter
 ❏ inside diameter

22. The wall thickness of tubing is specified by a schedule number similar to iron pipe.
 ❏ true   ❏ false

23. Tubing sized as dash 12 (-12) would be 1-1/2 inch tubing.
 ❏ true   ❏ false

24. Carbon steel is the only available material for tubing.
 ❏ true   ❏ false

25. When using flareless type fittings it is important that the tubing is soft relative to the fitting material.
 ❏ true   ❏ false

26. NPT threads are used when tubing is to be threaded.
 ❏ true   ❏ false

27. When using flared fittings, the double flare is used:
 ❏ when extremely high pressures are expected
 ❏ for the thicker wall thicknesses
 ❏ when using thin walled tubing
 ❏ only with 45 degree angles

28. The 37 degree flare is the standard angle used for hydraulic tubing.
 ❏ true   ❏ false

29. What is the maximum allowable pressure of dash 8 carbon steel tubing with a wall thickness of 0.065 inches if the maximum allowable stress for this material is 11,750 psi?
 ❏ 2563 psi
 ❏ 2621 psi
 ❏ 2844 psi
 ❏ 3055 psi

30. List three advantages that flexible hydraulic hose has over rigid conductors:

 Answer: _____

 _____

31. List the three main components of flexible hydraulic hose:

Answer: _____

32. For a given size, what determines the pressure rating of flexible hydraulic hose?
☐ the length of the hose
☐ The reinforcement
☐ the end fittings
☐ the thickness of the cover

33. The swaged on type of hydraulic hose end is not reusable.
☐ true   ☐ false

34. The dash number used to size hydraulic flexible hose refers to the inside diameter of the hose for most hose types.
☐ true   ☐ false

35. A dash 5 flexible hydraulic hose is what size in inches?
☐ 5/32
☐ 5/16
☐ 5/8
☐ 5/4

36. A 1-1/4 inch hydraulic hose is what dash size?
☐ -5
☐ -10
☐ -20
☐ -40

37. For a specific reinforcement, the working pressure of hydraulic hose will become less as the size is increased.
☐ true   ☐ false

38. As a hose is pressurized its length will become:
☐ shorter
☐ longer
☐ remain same length

SECTION FOUR

FOUR

ACCESSORIES

Reservoirs

Functions

A hydraulic reservoir should be designed to perform the following functions:

- Hold sufficient oil to meet system demands.
- Act as a heat exchanger (the oil cools in the reservoir before being pumped back into the system).
- Act as a fluid conditioner. Air entrained in the oil will rise to the surface and escape, while some of the heavier solid contaminants will settle to the bottom of the reservoir and remain there until the reservoir is cleaned out.

Size

Ideally, the reservoir should be large enough to provide sufficient fluid to:

- Hold two to three times the pump output per minute.

Note: This is not usually applicable to reservoirs on mobile equipment where the reservoirs are often considerably smaller.

- Ensure a high enough fluid level so that when all the actuators are fully extended, there will not be a whirlpool effect at the pump suction. If this occurs, air may be drawn into the pump suction.
- Have enough air space when all the actuators are fully retracted to allow for thermal expansion.

Shape

A tall narrow profile is preferable to a wide flat shape. This will provide a larger area on the sides rather than top and bottom, as this is more efficient for heat dissipation. Also, if the pump is mounted level with, or lower than, the bottom of the tank there will be a higher head of oil on the pump suction.

Connections and Fittings

The following points should be considered regarding any line connections and fittings attached to the reservoir.

- The pump inlet line should be flanged so it is possible to remove the suction strainer for cleaning purposes.
- Lines into the top of the reservoir should be screwed onto raised fittings so they are above accumulated dirt and fluid that often covers the top of the reservoir.
- All lines returning oil to the reservoir should terminate below fluid level to prevent foaming. Return lines are terminated about 2 inches [50 mm] above the bottom of the reservoir. The line ends should be cut off at 45° and oriented so the returning fluid is directed towards the sides of the reservoir. Drain lines should terminate just below the lowest fluid level.

Note: For components that are particularly sensitive to drain line back pressure, the drain line may be above fluid level.

Features

Oil Level Indicator: A vertical sight glass, or float controlled indicator, will allow the amount of fluid in the reservoir to be easily checked. With this method, there is no possibility of introducing contaminants, as there is when using a dipstick.

Filler: This may be part of the breather opening. Many systems have a simple screen to prevent large objects from entering the reservoir as it is being filled or topped up. A more preferable method is to also have an opening with a quick connect fitting attached and use a filtering transfer system. This will allow clean filtered oil to be pumped into the tank at any time without opening up the tank. See Section Two for a view of a typical transfer system that could be used to top up or fill a reservoir.

Temperature Gage: A temperature gage is often installed on a reservoir to monitor the oil temperature.

One type of reservoir with standard features is shown in illustration #99.

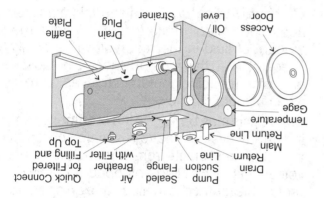

Illustration #99 — Reservoir Features

Breather: The opening, which allows air in and out of the reservoir as the oil level rises and falls, should be equipped with a filter to prevent dirt from entering with the air. This filter should be easily replaceable and have a low micron rating. See Section Two for a view of a typical filler/breather.

Internal Access Doors: Access plates or doors are required for cleaning and maintenance purposes. These should be positioned and sized to allow complete access to the inside of the reservoir.

Baffles: One or more baffle plates are provided to prevent the returning fluid from flowing directly to the pump suction.

Drain Plug: The bottom of the reservoir should be dished down, so that a drain plug can be installed at the lowest point in the reservoir.

Accumulators

Accumulators are used to store pressurized hydraulic fluid. When system fluid enters the accumulator, it acts against a load, either to raise a weight, or compress a spring or gas charge. When the system demands more flow than the pump can deliver (this will cause the pressure to drop), fluid from the accumulator is forced back into the system by the load. Accumulators also dampen pulsations and reduce hydraulic shock loads in the system.

There are three basic types of accumulators in use. These are:

- Weight loaded
- Spring loaded
- Gas loaded

 Accumulator Graphic Symbol

Weight Loaded

The weight loaded accumulator, as shown in illustration #100, is essentially a vertical cylinder with weights acting against the rod.

When the pressure in the system becomes high enough, the piston will move up, raising the weights.

The weight loaded accumulator differs from the spring and gas loaded accumulators, in that it will maintain a constant pressure as it is discharging fluid into the system. Weight loaded accumulators tend to be large and bulky and are only used in situations where large quantities of fluid are needed at constant pressure. The cylinder is normally positioned vertically with the weights directly attached.

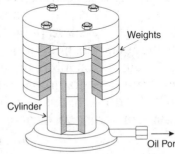

Illustration #100 — Weight Loaded Accumulator

Spring Loaded

Spring loaded accumulators are similar to the weight loaded, in that a cylinder is used. Instead of weights, a spring is used for the load. Spring loaded accumulators do not produce a constant pressure, due to the fact that the spring force changes, relative to the amount of compression of the spring. This type of accumulator can be mounted in any position. See illustration #101 for an example of a spring loaded type.

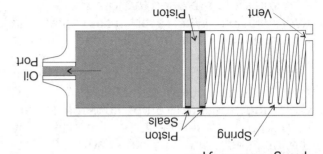

Illustration #101 — Spring Loaded Accumulator

Gas Loaded

The gas loaded accumulator uses a compressed gas (usually nitrogen) to maintain a load on the hydraulic fluid in the accumulator. When the accumulator is empty of oil, the gas chamber is filled with nitrogen to a pre-determined pressure. This is referred to as the precharge pressure. The amount of precharge pressure will depend on the minimum operating pressure and maximum system pressure. Gas loaded accumulators do not produce a constant pressure, due to the fact that the gas pressure changes, relative to the amount of oil in the accumulator.

Most manufacturers recommend that "dry nitrogen" be used for the precharge gas. If a gas not recommended by the manufacturer is being considered, consult the manufacturer.

Caution: Oxygen must not be used for precharging.

Gas loaded accumulators are rated according to their maximum operating pressure and total gas capacity.

There are three main types of gas loaded accumulators, they are:

- Piston type
- Bladder type
- Diaphragm type

Piston Type

Illustration #102 shows a cross section through a gas charged piston type accumulator. The design is essentially a cylinder containing a free floating piston with seals. One side of the piston is open to the system and contains hydraulic fluid. The other side of the piston is precharged with gas. When the system pressure exceeds the precharge pressure, oil enters the cylinder and moves the piston towards the precharged side of the cylinder. If the system pressure drops, the force on the piston from the gas pressure pushes oil back into the system.

The main disadvantage of piston type accumulators compared to the other gas loaded accumulators is that response is slow (due to inertia and friction). Piston seals are also subject to wear and eventual leakage. Because of this last point, the precharge pressure should be regularly checked.

The main advantages of this type are:

- There is no limit to the gas compression ratio.
- The accumulator can be fully discharged without fear of damage.

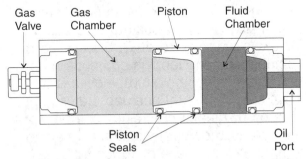

Illustration #102 — Gas Loaded Piston Type Accumulator

Bladder Type

The bladder type accumulator is the most common type in use. The gas precharge is separated from the oil by a rubber bladder that is mounted inside a metal chamber. The system fluid connection is in the bottom of the chamber. A poppet valve prevents the bladder from extruding into the bottom opening when the accumulator is being precharged. This valve also prevents extrusion, should the minimum operating pressure drop too low, causing the accumulator to completely discharge.

Taking the following precautions may prevent possible damage to the bladder:

• Ensure that the bladder does not contact the anti-extrusion valve when the system is at minimum pressure. There are two methods that may be used to achieve this:

1. The precharge pressure is set at 90% of the minimum operating pressure.
2. The accumulator is oversized so that the system demand for fluid is less than that available from the accumulator.

• Ensure that the bladder does not contact the anti-extrusion valve when precharging the accumulator. This is accomplished by introducing a small quantity (enough to cover the anti-extrusion valve) of hydraulic fluid, before adding the precharge gas.

• Ensure that the bladder cushion is not over compressed when the system is at maximum pressure. This is achieved by ensuring that the maximum pressure is not more than three times the minimum operating pressure.

Illustration #103 shows the various stages of the bladder type accumulator operation.

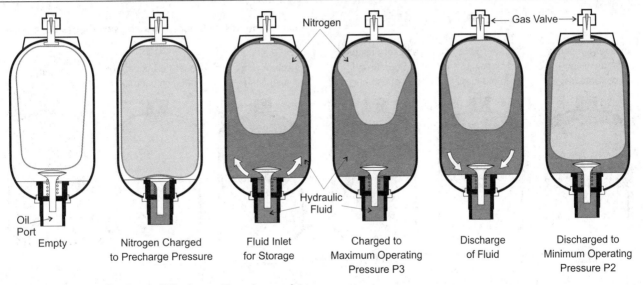

Nitrogen

Gas Valve

Hydraulic Fluid

Oil Port

Empty

Nitrogen Charged to Precharge Pressure

Fluid Inlet for Storage

Charged to Maximum Operating Pressure P3

Discharge of Fluid

Discharged to Minimum Operating Pressure P2

Illustration #103 — Gas Loaded Diaphragm Type Accumulator

Diaphragm Type

A diaphragm type accumulator may be selected when lightweight and compactness is a concern.

The diaphragm type accumulators are similar in design to the bladder type, except a diaphragm is used instead of a bladder, to separate the hydraulic fluid from the gas charge. Illustration #104 shows the various stages of operation.

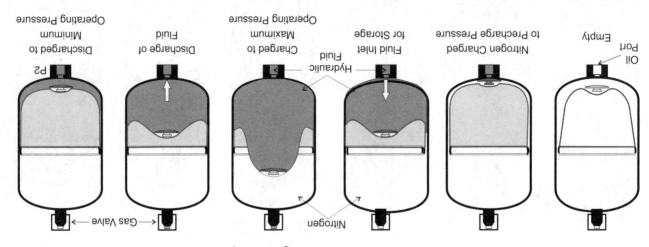

Illustration #104 — Gas Loaded Diaphragm Type Accumulator

Empty
Oil Port

Nitrogen Charged to Precharge Pressure

Fluid Inlet for Storage

Charged to Maximum Operating Pressure

Discharge of Fluid

Discharged to Minimum Operating Pressure
P2

Hydraulic Fluid

Nitrogen

Gas Valve

Intensifiers

An intensifier is a device used to generate a pressure at its outlet that is higher than that at its inlet. The fluid at the inlet and outlet may be the same type, such as hydraulic fluid, or they may be different, such as compressed air at the inlet and hydraulic fluid at the outlet.

The pressure increase is achieved by using a large piston area on the inlet side and a small piston area on the discharge (see illustration #105). The amount of pressure increase is proportional to the piston area ratio (inlet piston/outlet piston). It should be realized that when fluids with virtually no compressibility (such as hydraulic fluids) are used, the volume of fluid from the outlet, will be proportionately less than the amount of fluid applied to the inlet.

If a relatively low pressure (Pin) such as 200 psi [1.379 MPa] were applied to the inlet of the intensifier shown in illustration #105, the outlet pressure (Pout) would be:

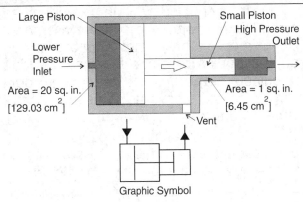

Illustration #105 — Intensifier

Pout = Pin x area ratio
Pout = 200 x 20/1 = 4000 psi
[Pout = 1.379 x 20/1 = 27.58 MPa]

Note: The calculation does not take into account friction between the piston, seals, and the cylinder walls, therefore the actual output pressure will be slightly less than the calculation value.

Pressure Gages

The most common instrument used to measure pressure is the Bourdon tube type pressure gage, as shown in illustration #106. This type of pressure gage uses a closed end curved tube (Bourdon tube) to convert pressure changes to rotary movement. The open end of the Bourdon tube is attached to a fitting that allows it to be connected to the pressure source. The other end is closed off and is attached, via a mechanical linkage, to a gear segment. When the pressure on the inside of the tube is atmospheric (equal pressures on both inside and outside of the tube), the pressure gage pointer is set to read zero degrees. If the pressure inside the tube becomes greater than atmospheric pressure, the tube tends to straighten, causing the gear segment to pivot, rotating the center gear and the pointer indicates a positive pressure.

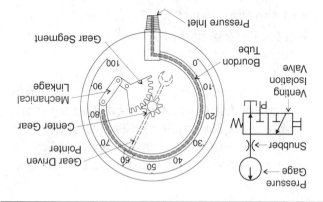

Illustration #106 — Bourdon Tube Type Pressure Gage

The amount of pointer movement will depend on the pressure change, tube stiffness and the linkage and gear dimensions.

The pressure gage will be calibrated against known pressures. Pressure gages of this type will be most accurate when reading at approximately half scale, for example if the pressure gage scale is from 0 to 145 psi [1000 kPa] the most accurate readings would be at approximately 72 psi [500 kPa].

It is for this reason that a single pressure gage will not suffice for all occasions. If the pressure drop across a return line filter is being checked and pressures in the 0 to 72 psi [500 kPa] range are expected, a pressure gage calibrated to maximum of 2900 psi [20 MPa] would not be recommended.

Pressure pulsations and fluctuations can quickly damage a pressure gage, and pointer vibration may prevent an accurate reading. There are two methods used to alleviate this problem.

One is to fill the casing with a fluid, usually glycerine. The second is to control the flow into and out of the Bourdon tube with some type of restriction in the pressure inlet. This restriction is often referred to as a snubber and may be built into the pressure gage, or attached separately. Two types of snubbers are shown in illustration #107.

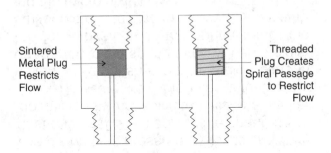

Sintered Metal Plug Restricts Flow

Threaded Plug Creates Spiral Passage to Restrict Flow

Illustration #107 — Typical Snubber Arrangements

When installing pressure gages, maximum life will be obtained if:

- Full scale pressure on the gage is 1 1/2 to 2 times the expected maximum operating pressure
- A snubber is either built in or installed
- A venting isolation valve is installed

The graphic symbol for the venting isolation valve is shown in illustration #106. This valve ensures that the pressure gage is only subject to pressure when a reading is taken.

If the pressure gage is directly connected to the system, it will be continually subject to the varying pressures and pressure shocks from the system and will lose accuracy after a period of time. If a simple shut off valve is installed, the pressure gage will be protected from the pressure shocks, but will continually be subject to the last pressure tested unless some means of venting is installed.

Pressure Switches

A pressure switch may be used to start or stop a pump or actuate a valve by opening or closing a set of electrical contacts. Either a pressure increase or decrease may be used to activate a pressure switch. Two types of pressure switches are shown. These are the piston type, and the Bourdon tube type. To prevent transient pressure surges from damaging a pressure switch, a snubbing arrangement similar to those shown in illustration #107 may be used.

The piston type pressure switch is shown in illustration #108. An adjustable spring holds the micro switch activated via the striker plate. Pressure from the inlet actuates the piston, which pushes on the striker plate in opposition to the spring force. When the piston force overcomes the spring force, the striker plate is moved to the right, deactivating the micro switch.

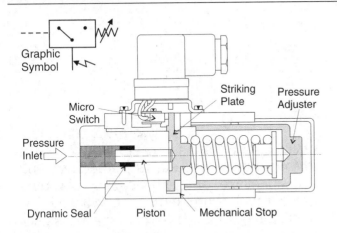

Graphic Symbol

Micro Switch

Striking Plate

Pressure Adjuster

Pressure Inlet

Dynamic Seal

Piston

Mechanical Stop

Illustration #108 — Piston Type Pressure Switch

A mechanical stop prevents excessive piston movement. Adjusting the spring tension will change the pressure at which the micro switch is activated and deactivated. The piston type pressure switch is suitable in situations where there are high switching rates and the possibility of heavy pressure pulsations and/or mechanical vibration.

As the name suggests, the Bourdon tube type of pressure switch shown in illustration #109 uses a Bourdon tube in conjunction with a micro switch. An increase in pressure in the Bourdon tube will cause the end of the tube to move to the left, deactivating the micro switch. Pressure adjustment is made by moving the micro switch toward or away from, the end of the Bourdon tube. The micro switch housing is spring loaded to prevent the Bourdon tube from exerting excessive force on the micro switch.

Some of the advantages of the Bourdon tube pressure switch are:

- High accuracy
- Long life
- Can be used with any type of liquid or gas
- No dynamic seals or leakage problems
- No problems with contaminants.

One of the main disadvantages of the Bourdon tube pressure switch is the fact that it is essentially a coiled spring, and mechanical vibrations or hydraulic pulsations may be amplified, especially if the excitation frequency approaches the natural frequency of the tube. This may cause unwanted activation of the micro switch.

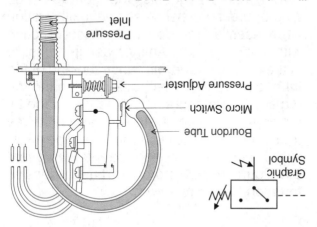

Graphic Symbol

Bourdon Tube

Micro Switch

Pressure Adjuster

Pressure Inlet

Illustration #109 — Bourdon Tube Type Pressure Switch

Heat Exchangers

Hydraulic fluids will provide their designed sealing and lubricating qualities with a minimum resistance to flow when they are operated within a specific temperature range.

Operating the hydraulic system below this temperature range results in a high resistance to flow, which in turn causes large pressure drops throughout the system and in extreme cases may cause starvation at the pump inlet.

Operation at temperatures above the specified range reduces the viscosity, which adversely affects the sealing and lubricating qualities of the fluid. Internal component leakage rates and metal to metal contact will increase, which will reduce efficiency, cause excessive wear and increase the temperature even further.

The fluid will also oxidize and break down at a faster rate, causing sludge, varnish and other damaging contaminants to form.

A well designed hydraulic system will normally dissipate enough heat from the components and reservoir to ensure that fluid temperatures do not rise above the recommended level. When a smaller than recommended reservoir must be used, or when much of the system is in close proximity to high ambient temperatures, a cooler may be required to remove heat.

Separate units such as the shell and tube heat exchanger or the radiator type are usually located in the return line to cool the hydraulic fluid flowing from the system to the reservoir. On some systems, the cooling water flow or the cooling fan drive, may be controlled by a thermal device located in the reservoir.

Note: *The recommended operating and maximum temperatures will depend on the type of fluid being used. The best source of these recommended temperatures is the manufacturer of the particular product. As a general guide, it is considered good practice to keep the operating temperature of petroleum based oils below 55°C (130°F).*

Depending upon the type of application, climate, or location of equipment, the operating temperature of the fluid may have to be increased, rather than cooled.

When ambient temperatures are low, heaters may be required to increase the temperature of the hydraulic fluid before start up. An immersion type heater would be submerged in the reservoir, preferably in the vicinity of the pump suction.

Note: *The lowest start up temperature of a particular system will depend on the system components (especially the pump) and the low temperature viscosity characteristics of the hydraulic fluid being used. For more information on low temperature start up, see Section Two "Choosing the Correct Viscosity".*

The three basic types of heat exchange units are:

- Shell and tube heat exchanger
- Radiating type heat exchanger
- Immersion type heat exchanger

Shell and Tube Heat Exchangers

The shell and tube type of heat exchanger as shown in illustration #110, is an external liquid to liquid heat exchanger used for industrial hydraulic systems. Although this type of heat exchanger can be used as either a heater or cooler, it is normally used as a cooler to remove heat from the hydraulic fluid.

The shell and tube heat exchanger consists of a cylindrical shell containing a bundle of tubes. Hydraulic fluid usually flows through the shell around the outside of the tubes (shellside) and the heating or cooling medium flows through the tubes (tubeside). In most industrial hydraulic systems, cold water is used as the cooling medium.

There are various designs of shell and tube heat exchangers, however illustration #110 is a typical fixed tube sheet type.

As the cooling fluid makes a single pass through the tubes, the hot hydraulic fluid passes through the shell circulating around the outside of the tubes. Baffles in the shell ensure that the hydraulic fluid does not flow directly across the top of the shell, but circulates past all areas of the tubes.

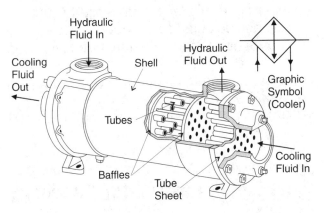

Illustration #110 — Shell and Tube Type Heat Exchanger

Radiating Type Heat Exchangers

The radiating type heat exchanger is an external liquid to air heat exchanger and is used as a cooler to remove heat from the hydraulic fluid. An example is shown in illustration #111. This type, which may resemble the coolant radiator found in automobiles and trucks, or may be composed of a series of individual finned tubes, is most often found on mobile equipment but may also be used in industrial applications. The hydraulic fluid is passed through the finned tubes, where cooling takes place. The fins help with the heat transfer by providing a larger surface area. A fan is used to blow air past the finned tubes to increase the cooling effect.

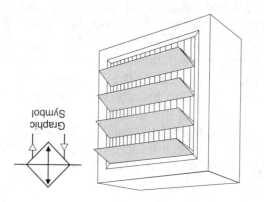

Graphic
Symbol

Illustration #111 — Radiator Type Heat Exchanger

Immersion Type Heat Exchanger

Immersion type heat exchangers are located in direct contact with the hydraulic fluid in the reservoir. There are two main types of immersion heat exchangers. They are electric immersion shown in illustration #112, and steam or water coils, shown in illustration #113. The electric immersion type is used as a heater; whereas, the steam or water coils can be used as either heaters or coolers. This type of heat exchanger is positioned in the reservoir in direct contact with the hydraulic fluid. Due to possible fluid damage or degradation when exposed to high temperatures, it may be necessary to provide a positive means of circulating the fluid close to the heating element or coils. This prevents local overheating of the fluid when the immersion exchanger is used as a heater. Limiting the power input to electric heaters, or controlling steam temperatures to steam coils is also possible.

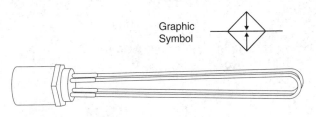

Graphic Symbol

Illustration #112 — Electric Immersion Type

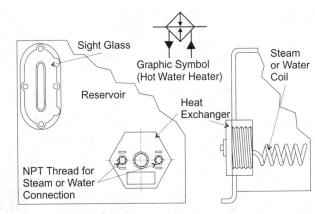

Sight Glass

Graphic Symbol
(Hot Water Heater)

Reservoir

Heat Exchanger

Steam or Water Coil

NPT Thread for Steam or Water Connection

Illustration #113 — Steam/Water Coil Immersion Type

SECTION FOUR QUESTIONS

Accessories

1. Compared to the pump displacement per minute, what is the recommended size for reservoirs?
   - ❏ 1 to 2 times
   - ❏ 2 to 3 Times
   - ❏ 3 to 4 times
   - ❏ the recommended size has nothing to do with pump displacement

2. Return lines to the reservoir should terminate below the fluid level.
   - ❏ true   ❏ false

3. List 5 common features found on reservoirs:
   Answer: _____
   _____

4. A vertical sight glass is preferable to a dipstick for monitoring the reservoir fluid level because:
   - ❏ it provides greater accuracy
   - ❏ it provides another method of checking for contamination
   - ❏ there is no possibility of introducing contaminants

5. List the three basic accumulator types:
   Answer: _____
   _____

6. Of the three basic types of accumulators, which one will produce a constant pressure when discharging fluid?
   Answer: _____
   _____

7. The spring loaded accumulator can only be mounted in a vertical position.
   - ❏ true   ❏ false

8. One factor that affects the precharge pressure on a gas loaded accumulator is the displacement of the hydraulic pump.
   - ❏ true   ❏ false

9. What is the usual type of gas used for precharging gas loaded accumulators?
   Answer: _____
   _____

10. Which type of gas must not be used for precharging gas loaded accumulators?
    Answer: _____
    _____

11. List three types of gas loaded accumulators:

Answer: _____

12. List two of the disadvantages the piston type accumulator has when compared to the other gas loaded types:

Answer: _____
_____

13. If the piston area ratio of an intensifier is 8 to 1, what is the output pressure if 4000 kPa is applied to the input (large piston end)?
□ 500 kPa
□ 4000 kPa
□ 10 000 kPa
□ 32 000 kPa

14. If the piston area ratio of an intensifier is 6 to 1, what is the output pressure if 500 psi is applied to the input (large piston end)?
□ 6000 psi
□ 3000 psi
□ 1000 psi
□ 500 psi

15. An intensifier with an area ratio of 8 to 1 requires 16 litres of hydraulic fluid at the inlet when moving through a full stroke. What amount of fluid will be discharged from the outlet?
□ 128 litres
□ 64 litres
□ 16 litres
□ 2 litres

16. An intensifier with an area ratio of 6 to 1 requires 1-1/2 gallons of hydraulic fluid at the inlet when moving through its full stroke. What amount of fluid will be discharged from the outlet?
□ 9 gallons
□ 1-1/2 gallons
□ 3/4 gallon
□ 1/4 gallon

17. The major advantage of the Bourdon tube type pressure gage is that it has no moving parts.
□ true □ false

18. A Bourdon tube type of pressure gage is calibrated from 0 to 2000 psi. Which of the following readings would be most accurate?
□ 10 psi
□ 1000 psi
□ 1800 psi

19. List two devices that should be installed with the pressure gage to increase pressure gage life:

Answer: _____

_____

20. List two types of pressure switches:

Answer: _____

_____

21. Which type of pressure switch does not have any possibility of dynamic seal leakage?

Answer: _____

_____

22. The operating temperature of petroleum based oils should normally not be higher than:
   ❏ 30°C (86°F)
   ❏ 40°C (104°F)
   ❏ 55°C (130°F)
   ❏ 70°C (158°F)

23. Heat exchangers used with hydraulic systems are always used to remove heat from the system.
   ❏ true   ❏ false

24. The shell and tube cooler uses liquid as a medium to transport heat away from the system.
   ❏ true   ❏ false

25. Immersion type heat exchangers can only be used as heaters to add heat to the hydraulic system:
   ❏ true   ❏ false

SECTION FIVE

HYDRAULIC PUMPS

Pumping Principles

The purpose of a hydraulic pump is to convert the mechanical energy of the prime mover into hydraulic energy. The pump accomplishes this by simply pushing hydraulic fluid into the discharge line (creating flow).

The majority of hydraulic pumps used for power hydraulic services are the positive displacement type. These pumps operate on the principle of having an expanding pumping chamber on the suction part of the stroke and a contracting pumping chamber on the discharge part of the stroke.

Illustration #114 shows a simple positive displacement pump. When the piston is moving out of the cylinder, as in illustration #114A (expanding pumping chamber), the cylinder pressure is reduced until it is lower than the pressure on the reservoir side of the suction check valve.

This pressure differential induces hydraulic fluid to flow into the cylinder. Fluid cannot enter from the discharge side, due to the discharge check valve.

When the piston is moving into the cylinder, as in illustration #114B (contracting pumping chamber), the pressure in the cylinder rises until it is higher than the pressure in the discharge. This pressure differential causes the fluid to move into the discharge. Fluid cannot move back into the suction, because of the suction check valve. The pump only produces flow. Any pressure in the discharge is the result of resistance to flow.

Hydraulic fluid is virtually non-compressible. Should there be a blockage or closed line in the discharge, the limiting factors on the pressure developed by the pump (assuming negligible internal leakage) are, the amount of force available to push the piston down and the strength of the pump parts.

In an actual system, the pump drive may stall or something will break or burst, if the discharge is blocked and there is no provision for limiting the pressure. It is for this reason, that relief valves or pressure compensation must be used with positive displacement pumps.

All positive displacement hydraulic pumps operate on the principle of having an expanding pumping chamber to create the suction and a contracting pumping chamber to cause the discharge. Some pumps will be designed with a porting system to control the flow of hydraulic fluid into and out of the pumping chamber, instead of the suction and discharge check valves shown in illustration #114A and #114B. Other pumps will rely on the clearance between the moving parts to seal between the suction and discharge.

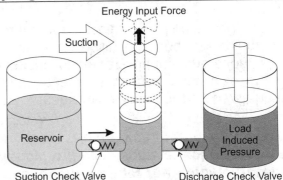

Illustration #114A — Simple Hydraulic Pump - Suction Stroke

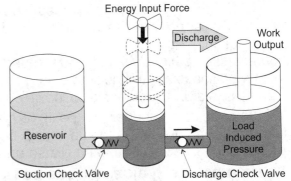

Illustration #114B — Simple Hydraulic Pump - Discharge Stroke

Displacement

The total volume displaced in the pumping chamber, or chambers, as the drive shaft completes one complete revolution, is a common method of specifying the size of a hydraulic pump. This is referred to as the "displacement per revolution".

Another method of specifying the size of a hydraulic pump is to specify the volumetric output per minute, or second, for a particular pump rotating speed. For example, gallons or litres per minute at 1725 rpm. When a pump is tested for its actual volumetric output, it is important that the test be carried out at the pressure at which the pump will operate (see "Pump Volumetric Efficiency" below).

Fixed and Variable Displacement

Pumps will have two classifications regarding displacement. They will be regarded as either "fixed" or "variable" displacement.

The fixed displacement pump will have a fixed volumetric output at a specified rotating speed. The flow from fixed displacement pumps may be varied by changing the driven rpm, as is often the case on mobile equipment.

Note: Changes in operating pressure that consequently effect the volumetric efficiency, will have some effect on the output (see "Pump Volumetric Efficiency" below).

The variable displacement pump will have some means of changing the size of the pumping chambers during operation. This results in the ability to change the volumetric output for a specified rotating speed.

Pump Volumetric Efficiency (Ev)

Due to internal leakage within the pump, the actual volumetric output will be less than the theoretical volumetric output (refer to illustration #115).

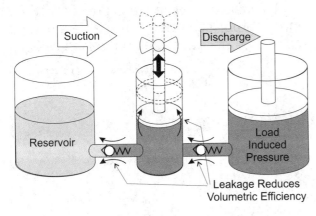

Illustration #115 — Volumetric Losses

Ev = (Actual output/theoretical output) x 100

Because the leakage takes place across the clearance spaces within the pump, the amount of leakage will be dependent to a large extent on the pressure being developed.

Higher pressures will result in a lower volumetric efficiency because of the greater pressure difference across the clearance spaces (see Section One, "Flow Through an Orifice"). The volumetric efficiency must be quoted for the pressure at which the pump will operate for it to be of any practical use. The actual output can then be calculated.

Actual output
= displacement/revolution x rpm x Ev

Mechanical Efficiency (Em)

All moving machines create losses due to friction between (refer to illustration #116), the moving parts. Due to these losses, the actual amount of torque or force required to drive a pump is greater than the theoretical torque required to produce the pressure and flow.

If the actual power P(in) required to drive the pump at a specified pressure and flow rate is known, the hydraulic power P(out) can be calculated from the pressure and flow. The overall efficiency can be calculated using:

$$Eo = (P(out)/P(in)) \times 100$$

The overall efficiency is also a product of the mechanical and volumetric efficiencies and can be calculated using:

$$Eo = Ev \times Em$$

Inefficiencies in the pumping system result in heat being added to the hydraulic fluid (see Section One, "Heat Generation"). As pump wear occurs (increasing internal clearances), the volumetric efficiency will become lower due to an increase in internal leakage.

The volumetric efficiency increases with increased speed and reduced discharge pressures, while the mechanical efficiency increases with decreased speed and higher pressures.

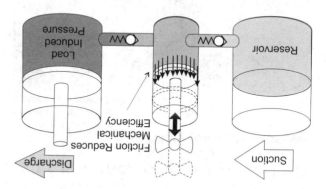

Illustration #116 — Mechanical Losses

If the actual torque T(in) is measured on a dynamometer, and the theoretical torque T(out) calculated, the mechanical efficiency (Em) can be determined by using the following formula:

$$Em = (T(out)/T(in)) \times 100$$

Overall Efficiency (Eo)

The overall efficiency takes into account both the mechanical and volumetric efficiencies.

Pump Pressure Rating

The maximum pressure rating for a pump, which the manufacturer specifies, is usually the maximum pressure that the pump will withstand without damage. Due to a lack of industry standards regarding maximum operating pressures, it is advisable to select a pump with a maximum pressure rating higher than the maximum expected system pressure. Operating a pump beyond its maximum pressure rating will reduce service life and may cause catastrophic failure.

Hydraulic Pump Classification

The majority of positive displacement hydraulic pumps will fall under one of three types:
* Gear
* Vane
* Piston

Illustration #117 is a chart showing the relationship of the most common types of hydraulic pumps to these three classifications.

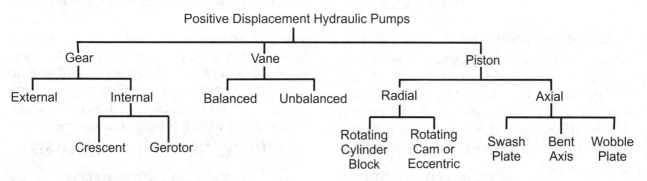

Illustration #117 — Hydraulic Pump Classification

Gear Type Hydraulic Pumps

The most common types of gear pumps consist of a housing in which two meshed gears operate. The sides of the gears are contained by side plates, which are sometimes referred to as wear or pressure plates. A drive shaft is attached to one gear, which drives the idler gear.

Gear type hydraulic pumps are fixed displacement pumps. Because the gears and bearings have to cope with unbalanced forces acting on them from the suction and discharge pressure difference, they are referred to as unbalanced pumps. Illustration #118 shows the direction of load on the bearings of an external gear pump. The strength of the housing, bearings and shaft are the limiting factors for the maximum pressure capability of the gear pump.

Any internal leakage on this pump will be from the discharge back to the suction.

Because case drains are not used on gear pumps, either the shaft seal is designed to withstand the discharge pressure, or the shaft seal area is drained back to the suction. Gear pumps can be divided into two basic designs, the external gear pump and the internal gear pump.

External Gear Pump

Spur gears are the most economical to manufacture and are consequently the most common design for external gear pumps. Helical and herringbone gears are quieter and smoother in operation. Helical gears are limited to low pressure applications because of axial loading on the gears. Herringbone may also be used, but are more expensive to manufacture and can operate in one direction of rotation only.

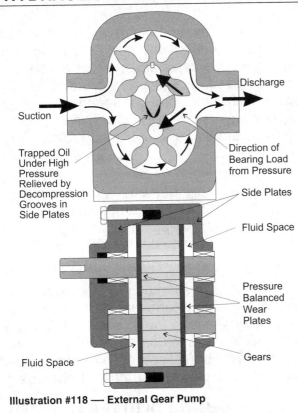

Suction

Trapped Oil Under High Pressure Relieved by Decompression Grooves in Side Plates

Discharge

Direction of Bearing Load from Pressure

Side Plates

Fluid Space

Pressure Balanced Wear Plates

Fluid Space

Gears

Illustration #118 — External Gear Pump

Maximum pressures for most general purpose external gear pumps are normally up to 1500 psi [10 342 kPa], but some high pressure designs are capable of over 4000 psi [27 579 kPa].

Illustration #118 shows the fluid flow path through an external gear pump. Fluid flows into the suction area, due to the drop in pressure as the gear teeth unmesh. As the gears rotate, fluid that occupies the space between adjacent gear teeth and the pump housing is carried towards the discharge. When the gear teeth remesh in the discharge area, the fluid is forced out from between adjacent teeth and has no other place to go but out the discharge. Any pressure build up from oil that may be trapped under the meshed teeth is relieved via decompression grooves machined into the side plates.

On high pressure gear pumps, pressure balanced wear plates may be incorporated, as shown in illustration #118.

Discharge pressure is ported between the wear plates and the side plates, so that an increase in pressure tightens the wear plate against the sides of the gears. This feature reduces internal leakage at high pressures, and automatically compensates for wear.

Internal Gear Pump

The internal gear pump consists of inner and outer gears rotating inside a stationary housing. The smaller inner gear is mounted off center to the outer gear to allow the gears to be completely in mesh on one side and out of mesh at the other.

The internal gear pump is manufactured in two designs. One has a crescent seal and the other has a generated rotor, which is referred to as a gerotor pump. Both pumps operate on a principle similar to the external gear, in that the unmeshing and consequent remeshing of the gears create the pumping action.

Illustration #119 shows the main components of the crescent seal pump, which are the internal and external gears and the crescent seal, that is part of the housing.

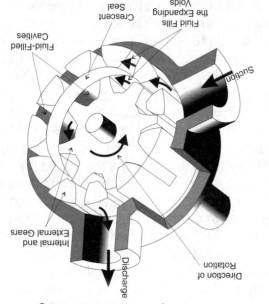

Illustration #119 — Crescent Seal Internal Gear Pump

Fluid-Filled Cavities

Crescent Seal

Fluid Fills the Expanding Voids

Suction

Direction of Rotation

Discharge

Internal and External Gears

As the gears are rotated by the input drive (which may be on either gear), fluid enters the suction area and fills the voids between the adjacent teeth on both gears as they unmesh. It is then carried on both sides of the crescent seal, to the discharge area. As the gears mesh back together, fluid is forced out of the cavities and can only pass into the discharge.

The gerotor pump in illustration #120 operates in a similar manner to the crescent seal pump. The main difference is that each tooth of the inner gear teeth maintains constant contact with the outer gear as they rotate, eliminating the need for a crescent shaped seal. The input drive is on the inner gear, which has one tooth less than the outer gear. The outer gear rotates in the housing.

The cavities exposed to the suction port are increasing in volume as the two gears rotate and become unmeshed, the induced low pressure causes fluid to flow from the suction and fill the expanding cavities. The gears then begin to remesh, reducing the size of the cavities. This forces the fluid out through the discharge port to the discharge line.

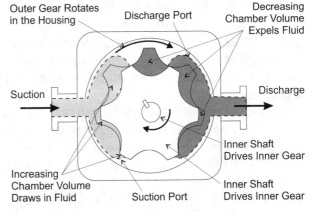

Illustration #120 — Gerotor Internal Gear Pump

Sliding Vane Hydraulic Pumps

Vane pumps are capable of pressures up to approximately 3000 psi, depending on the design and manufacturer.

A slotted rotor that contains sliding vanes rotates inside a cam ring (refer to illustration #121). Close fitting port plates enclose the sides to direct the fluid into and out of the pumping chambers. The pumping chambers increase in size as they progress from the suction, to the mid point between suction and discharge. The expanding volume lowers the pressure and causes fluid to enter the chambers. From this mid point, the pumping chambers begin to decrease in size and fluid is forced into the discharge.

The width of the shape of the rotor and cam ring ultimately control the displacement of the pump. The vanes are held against the cam ring by a combination of centrifugal and hydraulic pressure. A minimum of 600 rpm is required on most pumps to force the vanes out to the cam ring on start up. Adequate sealing between the vane and the cam ring is essential for efficient pump operation.

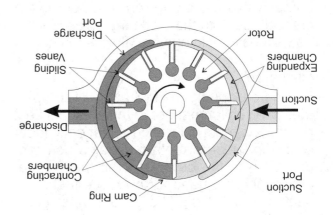

Illustration #121 — Sliding Vane Pump Principle

As discharge pressures increase, the pressure between the vane and the cam ring must also increase. This is accomplished by porting discharge pressure under the vane to force it out against the cam ring. At high pressures a simple square ended vane with discharge pressure pushing it against the cam ring would develop too much force against the cam ring, which would result in excessive friction, wear and short vane and cam ring life.

There are a number of vane designs that are used in high performance pumps, that provide for adequate sealing between the vane and the cam ring, yet do not cause excessive wear and friction. These vane designs used on high performance pumps (as shown in illustration #122) make use of system pressure under the vanes, but provide some means of hydraulically balancing the resulting force so that the vanes are only partially loaded.

The type of vane used will depend on the manufacturer and intended service.

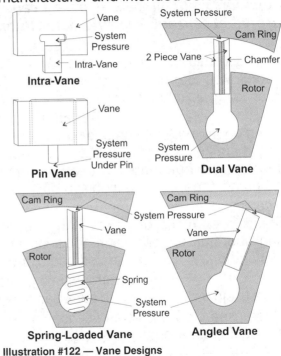

Illustration #122 — Vane Designs

Fixed Displacement Vane Pumps

The fixed displacement vane pump is a balanced design. Referring to illustration #123, the cam ring is elliptical in shape and allows the use of two diametrically opposed intake and discharge ports.

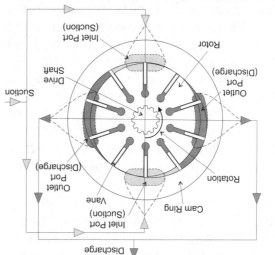

Illustration #123 — Balanced Vane Pump

This feature balances the forces generated by the suction and discharge pressures.

Balanced vane pumps are available in a variety of configurations.

Double pumps are essentially two pumps in one housing, which require only one drive motor. They have two separate discharge lines and may have one or two inlet lines.

Cartridge designs allow for easy pump servicing. The main pumping parts (rotor, vanes, cam ring, port plates etc.) are pre-assembled and can be changed out on a worn pump in minutes.

If it is required that the pump be driven in the opposite direction, the correct flow through the pump can be maintained, simply by rotating the cam ring 90°.

Note: Some vane designs may require the vanes to be turned in the rotor slots, should the direction of rotation be changed. If in any doubt, check with the manufacturer.

Variable Displacement Vane Pumps

The variable displacement vane pump has the disadvantage of having an unbalanced design that limits the pressure capability to somewhat less than that of the fixed displacement (balanced) vane pump, but has the advantage of variable volume capabilities. The cam ring is circular in shape, which provides for one intake and one discharge port.

Illustration #124 shows the basic components of a simple pressure compensated unbalanced vane pump.

Note: A pressure compensated pump will reduce its flow rate, or stop flow, when the system pressure reaches a predetermined value.

The cam ring is pushed over to the maximum volume position by the compensator spring.

Note: The maximum volume can be changed from this maximum position to a lesser volume by adjusting the volume adjustment screw. This volume adjustment allows the pump's maximum volume output to be matched to the system requirements.

The pump internal pressure pushes the cam ring towards the thrust bearing and compensator spring. If pressure increases sufficiently, the force on the cam ring will overcome the compensator spring and allow the cam ring to become almost centered (as shown in illustration #125). In this condition, the pump output (flow) is just sufficient to maintain that pressure.

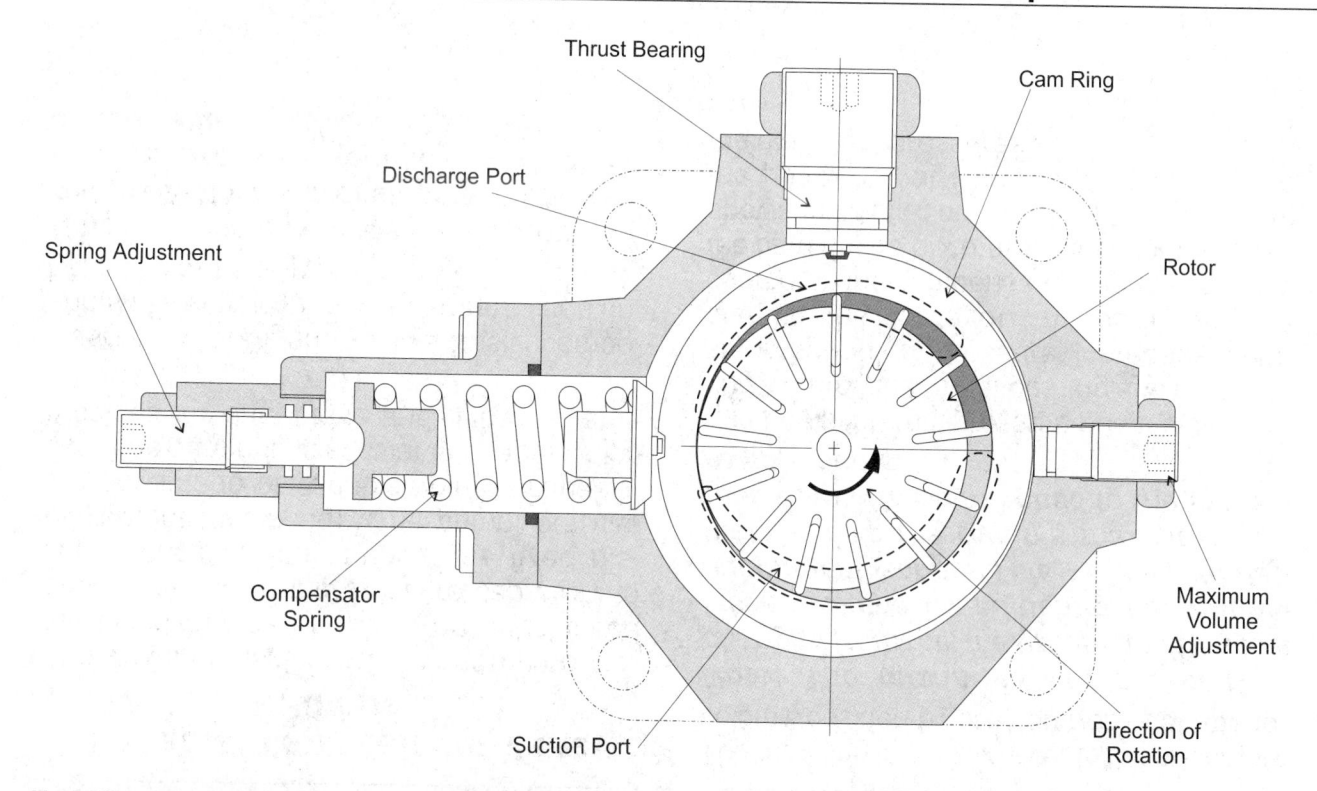

Illustration #124 — Unbalanced Vane Pump, Full Volume

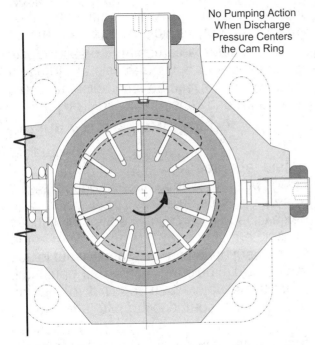

No Pumping Action
When Discharge
Pressure Centers
the Cam Ring

Illustration #125 — Unbalanced Vane Pump, Compensating

If there is a demand for more fluid from the system, the pump internal pressure will drop. Spring pressure will then force the cam ring back, creating an increased flow, which will keep the pressure up to the compensator spring setting. More tension on the compensator spring increases the pressure at which the pump will compensate.

Note: Generally, vane pump internal leakage is drained back to suction. In the case of pressure compensated vane pumps, an external case drain is required to drain the high temperature leakage oil back to the reservoir, to prevent heat build up.

There are various other controls available, both manual and automatic for adjusting the flow from this pump.

Piston Type Hydraulic Pumps

Piston type pumps have the highest pressure capability of all pumps.

Piston type hydraulic pumps consist of a number of cylinder and piston assemblies contained in a single housing. The orientation of the cylinders, in relation to the rotation of the drive shaft, will determine the classification (illustration #117). Either check valves (illustration #114), or port plates (illustration #126), will be used to control the fluid flow in and out of the cylinder, as the piston reciprocates.

In-Line Axial Piston Pump

The in-line type axial piston pump has pistons that reciprocate parallel to the axis of rotation of the cylinder block. The drive shaft, also rotates on the same centerline.

The reciprocating action is shown in illustration #126 with a single piston in a cylinder block.

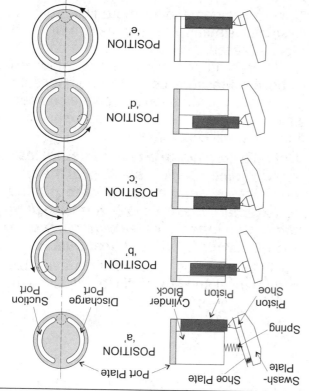

Illustration #126 — In-Line Axial Piston Pump Principle

The piston shoe, which is attached to the piston on a ball joint, is held against the angled swash plate by spring force.

The suction stroke starts from piston position 'a' and continues as the cylinder barrel rotates on its centerline to position 'c'. The swash plate does not rotate. The piston, which has to follow the swash plate angle, is drawn out of the cylinder to the end of its stroke. The cylinder continues to rotate and the piston is pushed back into the cylinder by the angled swash plate, to complete the discharge stroke at position 'e'.

In an actual pump, the cylinder barrel has multiple pistons, usually an odd number, such as seven, nine, or eleven. The drive shaft, which is usually splined to the cylinder block, may enter the pump housing from either the swash plate side (most common), or the port plate side of the housing.

In-line axial piston pumps are susceptible to piston shoe/piston separation problems if they are subjected to high suction vacuums and high case drain pressures. On the suction stroke, the shoe plate pulls the piston out of the cylinder by exerting force on the piston shoe.

If excessive force is required the swaged piston shoe may separate from the piston ball.

It is important that case drains have an unrestricted flow back to the reservoir. The pump housing should be oriented so that the case drain is out of the top of the pump. This will keep the casing full of fluid for lubrication purposes. After a pump has been changed out, the case should be filled with clean oil before start up.

Fixed Displacement In-Line Axial Piston Pumps

As shown in illustration #126, the angle of the swash plate determines the length of the piston stroke, which in turn determines the displacement per revolution. Fixed displacement pumps have a constant swash plate angle.

Illustration #127 is a cutaway of a typical fixed displacement, in-line axial piston pump. Referring to illustration #127:

- The drive shaft, cylinder block, pistons, and shoe plate rotate when the pump is driven.
- The pump housing, port plate, and swash plate are stationary.
- The spring inside the cylinder block pushes the shoe plate away from the cylinder block, which in turn keeps the piston shoes up to the swash plate on the suction stroke.

- The port plate separates the suction and discharge fluids and provides an open passage from the pistons to the appropriate suction and discharge connections.
- The case drain allows all internal leakage to be ported back to the reservoir.

A typical piston, piston shoe and shoe plate are shown in illustration #128. The piston shoe is swaged over the ball end of the piston to form a ball joint.

Lubrication for the ball joint, and the swash plate/piston shoe interface, is accomplished by providing a small diameter hole through the piston and piston shoe. Pressurized oil is fed into these two areas on the pressure part of the stroke (pistons being pushed into the cylinder). If the lubricating hole through the piston or piston shoe becomes partially or fully blocked, damage to the piston ball, piston shoe and swash plate will quickly occur.

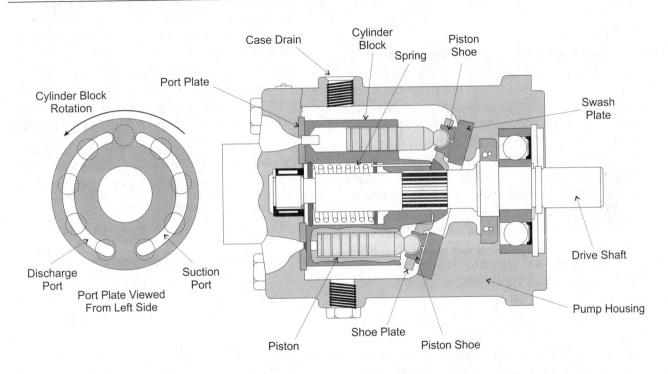

Illustration #127 — Fixed Displacement In-Line Axial Piston Pump

Variable Displacement In-Line Axial Piston Pumps

The variable displacement in-line axial piston pump is similar to the fixed displacement pump, with one main exception. The swash plate, as shown in illustration #129, is mounted on a pivoting yoke that allows for adjustment of the swash plate angle. This change in the swash plate angle will change the displacement.

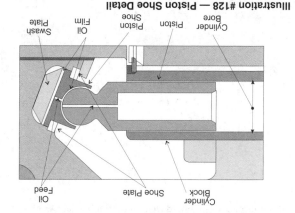

Illustration #128 — Piston Shoe Detail

Cylinder Bore
Piston
Piston Shoe
Oil Film
Swash Plate
Cylinder Block
Shoe Plate
Oil Feed

Depending on the intended application, yoke angle can be controlled manually, or by a variety of automatic devices.

The pump in illustration #129 is a pressure compensated in-line axial piston pump. The yoke is held at maximum angle by the yoke spring. When the discharge pressure reaches the compensator setting, the compensator directs fluid from the discharge to the yoke piston. This moves the swash plate towards the perpendicular (when the swash plate is perpendicular to the rotating axis, flow is zero), reducing the flow output to prevent any further pressure rise. If pressure begins to fall, fluid is bled from the yoke piston and the yoke spring changes the swash plate angle to increase the flow. The compensator pressure will be maintained, as long as the fluid demand is less than the maximum pump output.

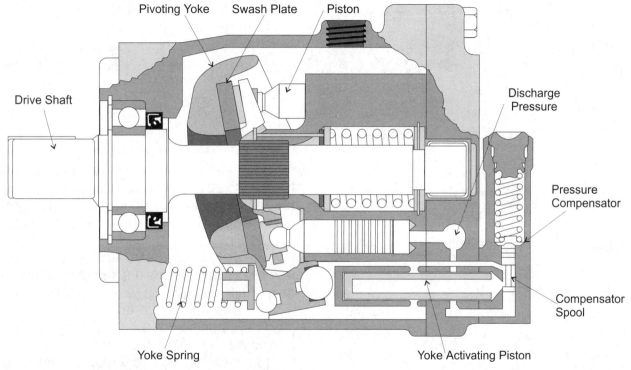

Illustration #129 — Variable Displacement In-Line Axial Piston Pump

Another variation of the variable volume in-line axial piston is the over-center design. This enables the yoke to position the swash plate on either side of the perpendicular, to reverse the fluid flow though the pump. Illustration #130A has the swash plate positioned to use port B as the discharge port. When the swash plate is perpendicular, as in illustration #130B, there is zero flow. When the swash plate goes over-center, as in illustration #130C, the flow is reversed and port A is the discharge port.

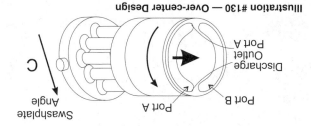

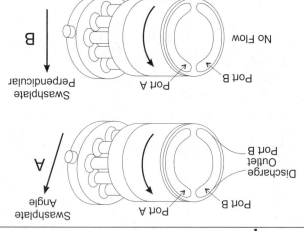

Illustration #130 — Over-center Design

Bent Axis Axial Piston Pump

A bent axis axial piston pump consists of a rotating cylinder block that is driven by a flanged shaft, the rotating axis of which is at an angle to the rotating axis of the cylinder block. The pistons are connected to the flanged drive shaft via piston rods. The force required to reciprocate the pistons is transmitted directly from the drive shaft flange, to the pistons by the piston rods. The port plate separates the suction and discharge fluids and provides an open passage from the pistons to the appropriate suction and discharge connections. The method used to transmit the torque required to rotate the cylinder block (overcoming the frictional resistance) depends on the design and manufacturer.

Some of the methods used are:

- Through the piston rods and pistons.
- Through a central universal link.
- Through bevel gears that are built into the drive shaft flange and the cylinder block.

Note: The bent axis pump is a more robust design than the in-line axial piston pump. This type of pump is not only generally more capable of generating higher pressures and flow rates, but it will also tolerate lower suction pressure and higher case drain pressures.

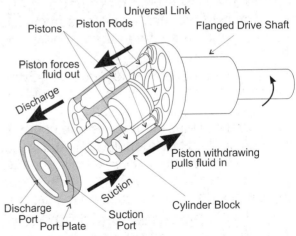

Illustration #131 — Bent Axis Axial Piston Pump Principle

Illustration #131 shows that the length of piston stroke, and consequently the displacement, will be dependent on the angle between the drive shaft and the cylinder block.

The bent axis pump can be either fixed or variable displacement.

The angle of the fixed displacement pumps will be up to approximately 30°.

Variable displacement pumps have the cylinder block mounted on a yoke, which allows the cylinder block angle to be adjusted. Some variable displacement bent axis pump designs also have over-center capability for reversible flow. The method of adjustment may be by manual, or automatic means.

Radial Piston Pumps (Rotating Cylinder Block)

This type of pump is similar in principle to the unbalanced sliding vane pump. An off-center rotor turns inside a circular reaction ring. The rotor contains cylinders and pistons (instead of vanes and slots) that radiate out from the center. In the center of the rotor is a stationary pintle that contains the suction and discharge ports. Centrifugal force holds the pistons out against the cam ring.

This type of pump may be fixed or variable displacement. Some variable displacement pump designs also have over-center capability, for reversible flow. Either a manual, or automatic mechanism, is used to change reaction ring eccentricity in the variable displacement designs.

Referring to illustration #132A, the pistons in the lower half are moving out of the cylinders and are on the intake stroke (clockwise rotation).

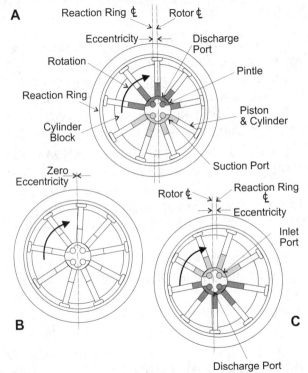

Illustration #132 — Radial Piston Pump (Rotating Cylinder Block)

At the same time, the pistons in the upper half are being forced into the cylinders, thereby pushing the oil out towards the center and into the discharge port, located in the pintle.

The number of pistons, the diameter of the pistons, and the length of stroke, determine the displacement of this pump. The length of the stroke is governed by the rotor/reaction ring eccentricity.

When the rotor and reaction ring are centered, as shown in illustration #132B, there is zero flow. The flow is reversed when the reaction ring is moved over to the right, as in illustration #132C.

Radial Piston Pumps (Rotating Cam or Eccentric)

This type of pump is basically a number of simple piston type pumps arranged radially around a central eccentric drive shaft. The number of pistons used will depend on the size, manufacturer and application for which it is intended. Because the cylinders are stationary, check valves are required to control the flow into and out of the cylinder as the pistons reciprocate.

The direction of shaft rotation does not affect the direction of fluid flow through the pump.

This type of pump is capable of higher pressures than any of the other types of pumps discussed. When required pressures approach 5,000 psi (34 000 kPa) and greater, this type of pump is the only one that is capable of this pressure.

Illustration #133 is a three piston example of this type of pump. The oil enters the pump casing at the bottom and completely fills the housing. Three pistons, with integral inlet check valves, reciprocate as the central cam is rotated. Outlet check valves allow oil to pass into the discharge chamber when the pistons are forced outward, and prevent back flow when the pistons are on the suction stroke.

Because the flow is controlled by check valves and not a port plate, this pump may be operated in either direction.

The inlet check valves allow fluid that passes up through the center of the pistons into the pumping chambers on the intake stroke, and prevents the same fluid from returning down the piston on the discharge stroke.

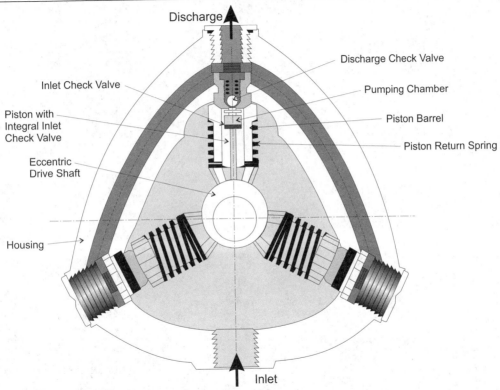

Illustration #133 — Radial Piston Pump (Rotating Cam or Eccentric)

SECTION FIVE QUESTIONS

Hydraulic Pumps

1. *The majority of hydraulic pumps used for power hydraulic service are:*
   - ❏ positive displacement
   - ❏ centrifugal

2. *What causes the fluid to flow from the suction line into the cylinder in a piston type hydraulic pump?*

   Answer: _____

   _____

3. *The consequence of a blockage or closed line between a positive displacement pump and the relief valve may be:*
   - ❏ a stalled motor
   - ❏ a burst discharge line
   - ❏ a broken pump or coupling
   - ❏ all of the above

4. *Each of the pistons in a 9 cylinder axial piston pump displaces 0.01 litres. What is the displacement per revolution?*
   - ❏ 0.01 litres
   - ❏ 0.09 litres
   - ❏ 1.0 litres
   - ❏ 9.0 litres

5. *What is the volumetric output at 1800 rpm of the pump in the above question?*
   - ❏ 123 litres per min
   - ❏ 146 litres per min
   - ❏ 162 litres per min
   - ❏ 180 litres per min

6. *A variable displacement pump will have some means of changing the rpm in order to change the displacement.*
   - ❏ true   ❏ false

7. *Why does the volumetric output of a hydraulic pump become less as the discharge pressure rises?*

   Answer: _____

   _____

8. *If the power input to a hydraulic pump is 32 HP and the calculated output HP (from the discharge pressure and flow rate) is 39 HP, what is the overall efficiency of the pump?*
   - ❏ 75%
   - ❏ 80%
   - ❏ 82%
   - ❏ 89%

9. What are the three major positive displacement pump classifications?

    Answer: _____

    _____

10. Herringbone gear pumps can only operate in one direction of rotation.

    ❑ true   ❑ false

11. What would be the result of excessive clearance between the gear teeth and the pump housing in an external gear pump?

    Answer: _____

    _____

12. What are the two types of internal gear pump?

    Answer: _____

    _____

13. What creates the pumping action in a gear pump?

    Answer: _____

    _____

14. What is the approximate minimum start up speed of a sliding vane pump?

    ❑ 200 rpm
    ❑ 400 rpm
    ❑ 500 rpm
    ❑ 600 rpm

15. Centrifugal force and sometimes springs are used to provide an outward force on the vanes of a vane pump. What other method is used to provide adequate force for sealing between the cam ring and the vane at higher pressures?

    Answer: _____

    _____

16. What is the difference between the fixed displacement and the variable displacement vane pump?

Answer: _____
_____

17. Which vane pump provides a balanced design?
❏ fixed displacement
❏ variable displacement

18. Which type of pump would be used as a pressure compensated pump?
❏ fixed displacement
❏ variable displacement

19. Piston type hydraulic pumps always have suction and discharge valves to control the flow into and out of the pump.
❏ true   ❏ false

20. The drive shaft of an in-line axial piston pump is connected to, and drives the:
❏ piston shoes
❏ swash plate
❏ port plate
❏ cylinder block

21. When installing a pump the casing should be oriented so that the case drain fitting is at:
❏ 12:00 o'clock
❏ 6:00 o'clock

22. The length of piston stroke in the in-line axial piston pump is determined by the:
❏ crankshaft throw
❏ length of the pistons
❏ swash plate angle
❏ piston diameter to length ratio

23. On an in-line axial piston pump, the swash plate rotates with the cylinder block.
❏ true   ❏ false

24. On an in-line axial piston pump, the case drain directs the drain oil back into the suction.
❏ true   ❏ false

25. On an in-line axial piston pump, the piston shoe ball joint and the piston shoe to swash plate interface lubrication is provided by:
❏ splash
❏ a separate lubrication pump
❏ the surrounding fluid
❏ a small hole through the end of the piston and piston shoe

26. If the swash plate angle of a variable displacement in-line axial piston pump is perpendicular to the rotating axis of the cylinder block there will be:
   ❏ maximum flow
   ❏ intermediate flow
   ❏ minimum flow
   ❏ zero flow

27. With some variable displacement in-line axial piston pumps it is possible to reverse the flow through the pump without changing the direction of shaft rotation.
   ❏ true   ❏ false

28. The bent axis axial piston pump incorporates suction and discharge valves to control the flow of fluid into and out of the pumping chambers.
   ❏ true   ❏ false

29. The bent axis axial piston pump can only be a fixed displacement unit.
   ❏ true   ❏ false

30. The radial piston pump with rotating cylinder block requires the use of suction and discharge valves to control the flow of fluid into and out of the cylinders.
   ❏ true   ❏ false

31. The radial piston pump with stationary cylinder block requires the use of suction and discharge check valves to control the flow of fluid into and out of the cylinders.
   ❏ true   ❏ false

32. Changing the direction of shaft rotation of a radial piston (stationary cylinder block) pump will change the direction of fluid flow through the pump.
   ❏ true   ❏ false

SECTION
SIX
HYDRAULIC ACTUATORS

Function of Hydraulic Actuators

The function of a hydraulic actuator is the opposite to that of a hydraulic pump. Hydraulic actuators convert the hydraulic power produced by the pump back to mechanical power. The power produced by the actuator will be either:

- A force and linear motion, such as that produced by a hydraulic cylinder
- A torque and rotary motion, such as that produced by a hydraulic motor

The magnitude of the force or torque produced by the actuator will be dependent on the resistance to movement and the maximum available system pressure. The speed at which the cylinder piston moves, or the motor rotates, will depend on the flow rate to the actuator and the displacement of the actuator.

Linear Actuators (Cylinders)

Cylinder Rating and Performance

The manufacturer's ratings for the cylinder should include:

- Maximum pressure
- Cylinder diameter
- Piston rod diameter
- Length of stroke

The maximum pressure is limited by the strength of the cylinder assembly and the types of seals used for the piston and piston rod.

If the cylinder is to be used in a meter out situation at the rod end, check that the piston rod seals are capable of pressures higher than system pressure.

1. For more information on metering the flow out of a cylinder, see Section Seven "Actuator Speed Control Methods".

2. For more information on hydraulic principles, including pressure intensification, force, pressure, velocity and flow rate calculations. See Section One "Pressure Intensification."

The effective piston area will determine the force output available and the speed of operation for a specified pressure and flow rate.

Single Acting Cylinder

A single acting cylinder has one port and is operated hydraulically in one direction only. When fluid is pumped into the port, pressure creates a force on the ram or piston and the ram or piston rod extends. To retract the cylinder, the oil is released from the cylinder and the plunger or piston returns because of the weight of the load or spring pressure.

Illustration #134A shows a single acting cylinder with a spring return. Illustration #134B shows a ram, which is a single acting cylinder with a piston rod and piston of the same diameter.

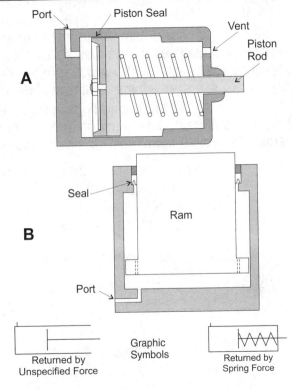

Illustration #134 — Single Acting Cylinder

Double Acting Cylinder

The double acting cylinder has port connections at both ends of the cylinder. This allows the cylinder to be extended and retracted using hydraulic power.

When fluid is introduced into the cap end, the piston will extend, providing that fluid is allowed to exit from the rod end of the cylinder. To retract the piston, the flows are reversed. The majority of double acting cylinders have a piston rod extending out of the cylinder on one side only, as shown in illustration #135. This creates unequal piston areas and consequently, these are classified as differential cylinders.

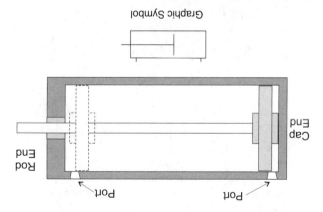

Graphic Symbol

Illustration #135 — Double Acting Cylinder

When the piston is extending, fluid is pumped into the cap end of the cylinder, and pressure acts on the full piston area.

While retracting, fluid enters the rod end of the cylinder, but due to the attached piston rod the effective area of the piston rod is reduced by the area of the piston rod, as shown in illustration #136.

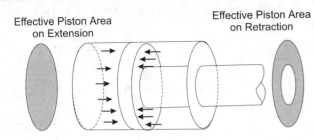

Illustration #136 — Unequal Piston Areas

If the piston is being extended (pressure to the larger area), the available force from the piston is greater and the speed is slower than when the piston is being retracted (pressure to the smaller area).

If the cap area of the piston is two times that of the rod side, the cylinder is referred to as having a 2 - 1 ratio, or simply as a 2 - 1 cylinder.

The extension speed of a 2 - 1 cylinder is one half of the retraction speed. The force available on extension is two times that available on retraction.

A double rod cylinder is shown in illustration #137. A piston rod extends from both ends of the cylinder. This type is classified as a non-differential cylinder. Double rod cylinders will provide equal forces and speeds when the piston is moving in either direction.

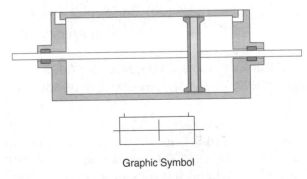

Graphic Symbol

Illustration #137 — Double Rod Cylinder

Cylinder Design Variations

Telescoping Cylinder

Telescoping cylinders may be single or double acting, and for the graphic symbols for both single and double acting telescoping cylinders. The telescoping cylinder provides for a much longer stroke than is available from a standard cylinder of the same retracted length.

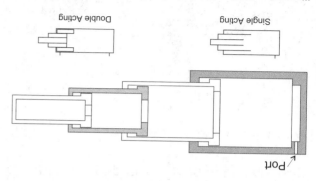

Illustration #138 — Single Acting Telescoping Cylinder

The force available from a telescoping cylinder is greatest when the cylinder is fully retracted (greatest area) and is the least when the last sleeve is being extended (smallest area).

The speed will also vary. It will be a relatively slow speed when starting from the retracted position and faster when the last sleeve is being extended.

Tandem Cylinder

The tandem cylinder consists of at least two in line attached cylinders (refer to illustration #139). The pistons are also attached by a piston rod to form to a single unit. This cylinder arrangement allows larger forces to be generated from a small diameter cylinder. The main disadvantage is the increased length of the assembly.

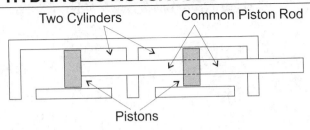

Illustration #139 — Tandem Cylinder

Duplex Cylinder

The duplex cylinder is similar in construction to the tandem in that two or more cylinder bodies are joined together. The difference being that where the tandem cylinders are of equal stroke and the pistons are connected by a piston rod, the duplex cylinders have unequal strokes and the two pistons are not connected. The pistons may be oriented in the same direction (see illustration #140A), or they may be oriented in opposite directions (see illustration #140B).

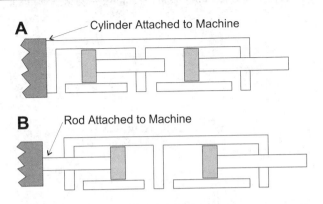

Illustration #140 — Duplex Cylinders

Cylinders are often used to achieve accurate mechanical positioning. A double acting cylinder, standard or tandem, will have two exact positions (fully extended and fully retracted) in which valve or seal leakage will have no effect.

Illustration #141 shows a duplex cylinder with three exact mechanical positions and illustration #142 shows a duplex cylinder with four exact mechanical positions.

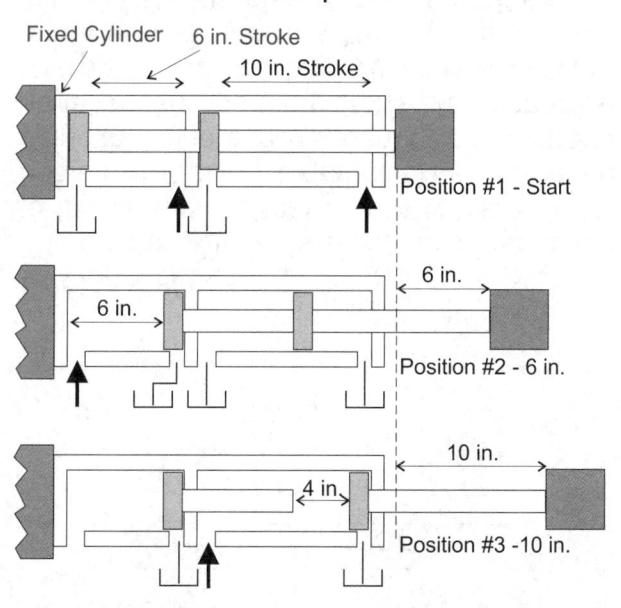

Illustration #141 — Duplex Cylinder, Three Position

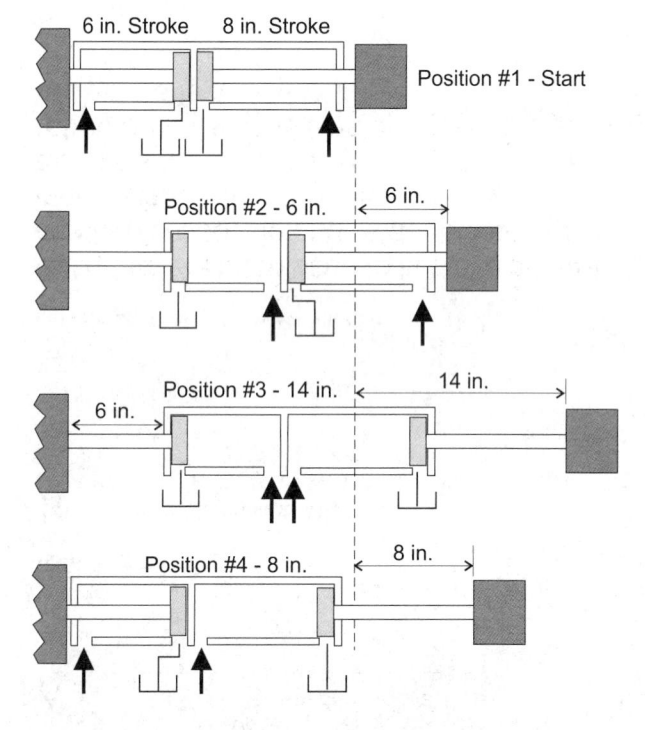

Illustration #142 — Duplex Cylinder, Four Position

Cylinder Features

Cushions

To prevent mechanical shock when a piston has reached the end of the cylinder, hydraulic cushions are often incorporated into the cylinder design. A hydraulic cushion slows the piston down at the end of the stroke by restricting the flow out of the cylinder. The cushions may be at one or both ends of the stroke and may be adjustable or non adjustable. Adjustable cushions allow the speed of the piston to be regulated as it approaches the end of the stroke. Non adjustable cushions slow the piston down by a fixed amount at the end of the stroke.

In illustration #143A, the fluid flows unrestricted out of the port, as the piston approaches the cylinder cap end head. When the plunger enters the head (illustration #143B), it cuts off the main flow path and the piston decelerates due to the flow restriction at the adjustable orifice.

Adjusting the orifice, controls the final speed. A similar cushion arrangement is used at the rod end when the piston is being extended.

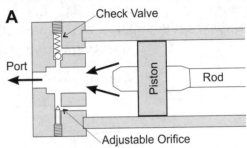

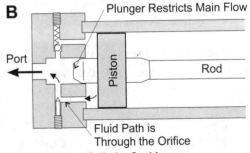

Illustration #143 — Cylinder Cushions

Whether or not a stop tube should be used will depend on the length and the diameter of the cylinder and the application to which the cylinder is to be used. Cylinder manufacturers supply charts that indicate when stop tubes should be used and the required stop tube length for their particular cylinders.

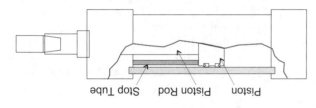

Illustration #144 — Stop Tube

- Piston
- Piston Rod
- Stop Tube

Rod Wiper/Scraper

The removal of contaminants such as dirt, mud, ice, etc, from an extended piston rod, as it is being retracted back into the cylinder, is extremely important to overall system cleanliness, as well as to the life of the rod seals and bushing.

To ensure that the full flow and force is available when the cylinder is to be extended from a fully retracted position, a check valve located at the cap end bypasses the adjustable orifice and allows the flow of oil into the cylinder. A check valve at the rod end and head serves a similar purpose.

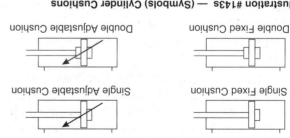

Illustration #143s — (Symbols) Cylinder Cushions

- Double Fixed Cushion
- Double Adjustable Cushion
- Single Fixed Cushion
- Single Adjustable Cushion

Stop Tube

To prevent excessive piston rod/bushing and piston/cylinder wear on extra long cylinders, a stop tube is often specified. The stop tube prevents the piston from traveling all the way to the end of the cylinder.

Most cylinders incorporate a piston rod scraper/wiper arrangement, as shown in illustration #145, which is often combined with the piston rod bushing. Some conditions may warrant the use of a rubber boot that completely shields the piston rod from the environment.

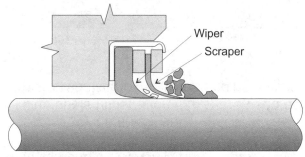

Illustration #145 — Rod Wiper Scraper

Dynamic Cylinder Seals

The two areas that require sealing are:
- Between the piston and cylinder
- Between the piston rod and the rod end head

The most common seals for these applications are described below and are pressure actuated. A pressure actuated seal is initially held against the sealing surface by material springiness or elasticity. Pressure inside the sealed chamber acts on the seal area and forces the seal tighter against the sealing surface. An increase in the sealed pressure increases the sealing force. Four types of pressure actuated seals are described below.

- Cast iron piston rings, as shown in illustration #146, are used as hydraulic cylinder piston seals.

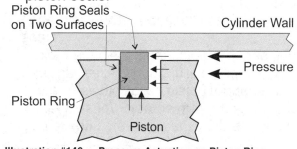

Illustration #146 — Pressure Actuation on Piston Ring

Durability, low frictional resistance, and the ability to withstand very high pressures make this a very common seal. Due to the required groove clearance and end gap, a small amount of leakage will occur and cause the piston to drift in some situations. If this is undesirable, elastomer type seals may be specified.

- Cup seals (illustration #147) are used as piston seals and can withstand high pressures.

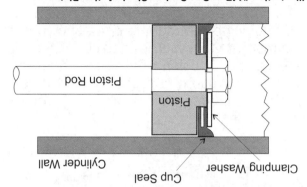

Illustration #147 — Cup Seal on Single Acting Piston

The piston acts as a backing plate and a large washer clamps the cup seal in place. A single acting piston requires only one cup seal as shown in illustration #147, while a double acting piston requires two seals.

- U-Section rings (sometimes referred to as U-cups) (illustration #148) may be used as piston or rod seals. A single endless ring is used to seal in one direction only and is installed in an individual ring groove.

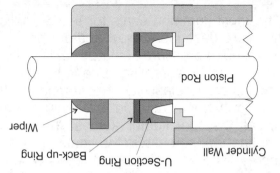

Illustration #148 — U-Section Ring Seal on Piston Rod

If used on a double acting piston, two rings mounted in two separate grooves will be required.

- V-Rings, sometimes referred to as Chevron packings (illustration #149), may be used as piston rod and piston seals. They are used in sets of three or more and are suitable for very high pressures.

The rings may be endless, or where it is required for installation purposes, of a split design.

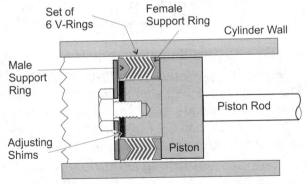

Illustration #149 — V-Ring Seal on Single Acting Piston

When installing split rings the joints should be staggered to reduce the possibility of leakage. The ring sets are sandwiched between male and female support rings. The amount of compression is usually adjusted by loosening or tightening a gland follower or clamping plate. An alternative design uses spring tension to set the compression and automatically adjust for wear. The V-ring set, shown in illustration #149, is adjusted by adding or removing the adjusting shims. Too much compression will cause premature wear and excessive frictional losses. Too little will allow leakage, especially at low pressures.

Piston Rod Bushing

Piston rod alignment and support is achieved by the use of a bushing mounted in the rod end head. Materials for this bushing will typically be brass, bronze, or cast iron.

Cylinder Mounting Features

There is a wide variety of mounting methods available for anchoring the cylinder. The type used will depend on the application. Some applications will require that the cylinder be solidly anchored, while some will be pivoting. Common cylinder mounting methods are:

- Flanges
- Extended tie rods
- Side, centerline and end lugs
- Tapped holes

Common pivoting mounting methods are:

- Fixed clevis at cap end
- Rod end trunnion
- Cap end trunnion
- Intermediate trunnion

As with cylinder mounting, the piston rod end is chosen to suit the application or the intended attachment.

Standard rod ends include:

- Male thread on a reduced diameter
- Male thread on the full diameter
- Female thread
- Plain end

Most manufacturers will also produce rod ends to customer specification.

It is extremely important to ensure that the piston rod to cylinder alignment is maintained, as the piston is extended and retracted.

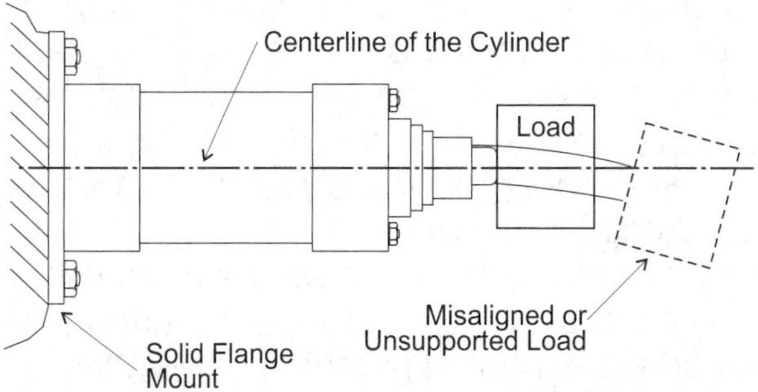

Illustration #150 — Cylinder or Load Misalignment

Side loading due to load misalignment or an unsupported load on a solidly mounted horizontal cylinder (see illustration #150) will cause accelerated wear to the piston rod, piston rod bushing, cylinder, piston, and all seals.

Cylinder Sealing Problems

Piston Rod Seal Leaks

Any leakage at the piston rod seal will be readily apparent. If the rod is not worn or damaged, installing a new seal will usually cure the problem. The clearance between the piston rod and bushing and the condition of the rod wiper/scraper, should be checked at this time. Any excess clearance in the bushing (rod radial movement) may reduce the seal efficiency and cause premature seal leakage. An inefficient wiper/scraper will cause premature seal, bushing, and rod wear and may also allow contaminants to enter the system.

Piston to Cylinder Leaks

Fluid leakage at the seal, between the piston and cylinder, is not as apparent as rod leakage. The symptoms of a piston seal leak will vary depending on the operating conditions and the circuitry.

Some of the symptoms of piston seal leakage may be:
- Piston drift or creep (slowly lowering under load)
- Pressure intensification
- Piston speed decrease
- Piston speed increase

Piston Drift (Creep)

Illustration #151A shows a raised cylinder supporting a load. When the direction control valve (DCV) is in the neutral position, the check valve prevents oil from leaving the bottom of the cylinder and the load stays in the raised position.

The load is supported by the area of the piston; therefore, pressure under the piston (P) will be equal to the load divided by the piston area, (see Section One "Pressure to Support a Load").

Illustration #151 — Piston Drift

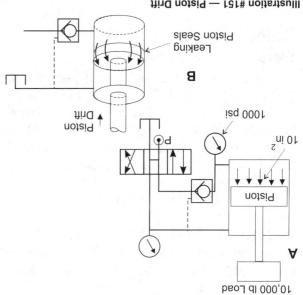

$P = 10,000 \text{ lb}/10 \text{ in}^2 = 1000 \text{ psi}$

$[P = 44.482 \text{ kN}/0.0064516 \text{ m}^2 = 6895 \text{ kPa}]$

The rod side of the piston is open to the reservoir; therefore, the pressure difference across the piston is 1000 psi [6 895 kPa]. Any leakage of fluid past the piston rings (see illustration #151B) will reduce the volume of fluid under the piston, causing the piston to lower (drift). The leaked oil will be returned to the reservoir through the neutral position of the DCV. A greater load on the rod will increase the pressure difference, the rate of leakage, and piston drift.

Pressure Intensification

The circuit, shown in illustration #152A, has two check valves installed. One is placed in each line to the cylinder. The check valve in the line to the rod end of the cylinder is installed to prevent cylinder creep.

Note: See Section One for more information on pressure intensification.

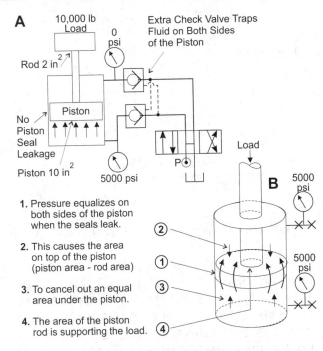

1. Pressure equalizes on both sides of the piston when the seals leak.

2. This causes the area on top of the piston (piston area - rod area)

3. To cancel out an equal area under the piston.

4. The area of the piston rod is supporting the load.

Illustration #152 — Pressure Intensification

When the DCV is centered (see illustration #152A), fluid is trapped in both the rod side and the cap side of the cylinder. The 10,000 lb [44.482 kN] load is supported by the area of the piston, similar to the previous example. If the piston seals leak, pressure will equalize on both sides of the piston (see illustration #152B). When this happens, the area on the rod side of the piston offsets the same amount of area on the cap side of the piston. This leaves an area the size of the piston rod (2 in^2 [0.001 29 m^2]), to support the load. The pressure developed both above and below the piston will be:

10,000 lb/2 in^2 = 5000 psi

[44.482 kN/0.001 29 m^2 = 34 482 kPa]

Note: 5000 psi = 34 473.79 kPa. The difference is due to the number of decimal places used in the calculation.

Compare this pressure with the pressure required to support the load when the piston seals do not leak (1000 psi [6 895 kPa], as shown in illustration #151A).

Piston Speed Decrease

Consider the schematic shown in illustration #153. If there is no leakage at the piston seals, the speed at which the piston extends will be fixed by the diameter of the cylinder and the flow rate (Q) into the cylinder. Any fluid leakage past the piston seals will reduce the amount of fluid available to fill the space behind the piston, hence, the speed will be reduced.

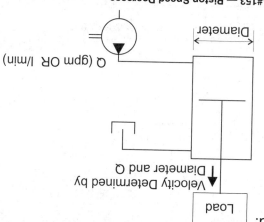

Illustration #153 — Piston Speed Decrease

Because the flow rate across an orifice is determined be the size of the orifice, and the pressure difference across the orifice, increasing the load on the rod (increase in pressure) will increase the amount of seal leakage and consequently cause a greater speed reduction. A speed reduction will also occur on the return stroke, as long as there is a load causing a large enough pressure difference across the piston to cause appreciable leakage. If there is no load and very little pressure difference, there will be negligible leakage, unless the seals are extremely worn or damaged.

Note: *See Section One for more information on flow through an orifice.*

Piston Speed Increase

Illustration #154 shows a double acting, 2 - 1 cylinder being extended. There is a pressure compensated flow control valve restricting the fluid coming out of the cylinder, thereby controlling the speed of extension. This is referred to as a "meter out" circuit. For the purpose of this example, there is no load on the rod.

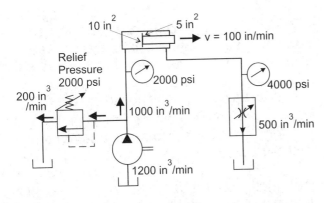

Illustration #154 — No Seal Leakage

The system relief valve is set at 2000 psi [13 800 kPa] and the flow control valve is set to allow 500 in³/min [8200 cm³/min] from the rod end of the cylinder to the reservoir.

Note: The piston speed is controlled by the volume of fluid leaving the rod side of the piston. See Section One for more information on piston speed calculations.

The theoretical piston speed and flows are calculated as follows:

Piston speed:

$(500$ in³/min$)/5$ in² $= 100$ in/min

$[(8194$ cm³/min$)/32.26$ cm² $= 254$ cm/min$]$

The amount of fluid required to fill the cap end of the cylinder:

100 in/min x 10 in² $= 1000$ in³/min

$[254$ cm/min x 64.516 cm² $= 16\ 387$ cm³/min$]$

Amount of fluid over the relief:

1200 in³/min $- 1000$ in³/min $= 200$ in³/min

$[19\ 680$ cm³/min $- 16\ 387$ cm³/min $= 3277.5$ cm³/min$]$

The pressure in the cap end of the cylinder will be at the relief setting of 2000 psi [13 789.5 kPa].

Due to pressure intensification, the pressure in the rod end of the cylinder will be 4000 psi [27 579 kPa] (2 - 1 ratio cylinder).

Calculate the piston speed when there is seal leakage as shown in illustration #155:

Note: Fluid will always flow from a high pressure area to a lower pressure area (see Section One "Flow Through an Orifice").

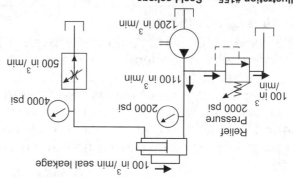

Illustration #155 — Seal Leakage

The cylinder in question has a higher pressure at the rod end of the piston than at the cap end; therefore, any leakage at the piston seals will be from the rod end to the cap end.

The cylinder in illustration #155 has a serious leak at the piston seals (100 in³/min) [1640 cm³/min]). The volume of fluid leaving the rod side of the cylinder is equal to the volume passing through the flow control, plus the volume leaking past the piston seals.

Fluid leaving rod side of piston:
500 in³/min + 100 in³/min = 600 in³/min
[8194 cm³/min + 1638.7 cm³/min = 9832 cm³/min]

Piston speed:
(600 in³/min)/5 in² = 120 in/min
[(9832 cm³/min)/32.26 cm² = 304.7 cm/min]

Due to piston seal leakage, the piston speed changed from 100 to 120 in/min [254 to 305 cm/min].

Note: Any load on the piston will reduce the pressure difference across the piston, and therefore reduce the leakage past the piston seals.

Checking for Piston Seal Leaks

Whether or not the following tests can be done will depend on the cylinder, piping, and load configuration.

Piston seal leaks may occur in both directions across the piston (although not always equally), or in one direction only (when the appropriate pressure difference is applied across the piston). Cast iron rings usually leak in both directions. Cup seals and U-section rings may leak in one direction, if only one of the seals is damaged. The intended application for the cylinder will determine if the leakage across the piston has to be checked in one or both directions.

Cast iron piston rings will leak a small amount due to ring end clearance. This will cause the cylinder to drift under load. Ideally, this type of cylinder would be checked for leakage when new for comparison purposes.

When testing for piston seal leaks, a pressure difference across the piston must be generated.

Method One

This method requires an external load exerted on the cylinder and uses piston drift to determine if the seals are leaking.

To complete this test, it must be possible to exert a constant force on the piston rod. Modifications to the piping may also be required.

Often, the first indication that piston seals are leaking, is when a load will not maintain a raised position, but slowly lowers back down.

The piston seals in illustration #156A are leaking from the cap end and to the rod end. The piston seals in illustration #156B are leaking from the rod end and to the cap end.

If attempting to simulate these conditions, note that a pressure gage is used to measure the pressure difference across the piston, and that the low pressure side of the piston is open to the reservoir. This allows fluid to flow towards the reservoir in illustration #156A and be drawn from the reservoir in illustration #156B.

A shut off valve should be used on the high pressure side to prevent any possible leakage back to the reservoir (do not rely on spool type DCV).

Accurate measurements for drift can be obtained by using a stopwatch to time the movement over a specified distance. A number of observations should be made at intervals along the stroke.

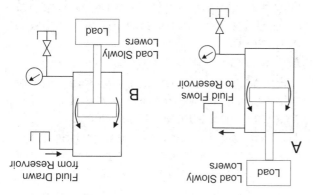

Illustration #156 — Checking for Piston Seal Leakage, Load Method

Method Two

Method Two uses pressure intensification to create the pressure difference across the piston.

This test may be accomplished without placing an external load on the piston rod, but it only checks for leakage in one direction (from the rod end to the cap end of the cylinder).

To check on the amount of leakage past the piston seals, a shut off valve (needle or globe) should be piped into the rod end cylinder line. See illustration #157.

Locate the piston at the cap end of the cylinder and close the shut off valve. When system pressure (2000 psi [13 789.5 kPa] in this example) is applied to the cap end of the piston, pressure intensification causes 4000 psi [27 579 kPa] to be generated at the rod end of the cylinder.

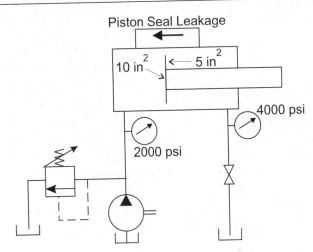

Illustration #157 — Checking for Piston Seal Leakage, Intensification Method

Due to this 2000 psi [13 789.5 kPa] pressure difference, fluid will migrate from the rod side to the cap side of the piston if there is any seal leakage.

This will cause the piston to drift out. The rate of drift is an indication of the amount of leakage. Due to uneven wear or damage, leakage and consequently the rate of drift may not be constant for the whole stroke. Therefore the amount of drift should be checked at various points along the cylinder stroke.

The rate of drift measured in this test is the speed reduction that the cylinder would encounter when operating with that same pressure difference across the piston.

The cylinder shown in illustration #157 had a rate of drift of 15 in/min [38.1 cm/min] when the above test was performed. The actual amount of fluid leaking past the piston seals is:

$$15 \text{ in/min} \times 5 \text{ in}^2 = 75 \text{ in}^3/\text{min}$$
$$[38.1 \text{ cm/min} \times 32.26 \text{ cm}^2 = 1229 \text{ cm}^3/\text{min}]$$

Rotary Actuators (Motors)

Uni-directional Fixed Capacity

Bi-directional Fixed Capacity

Uni-directional Variable Capacity

Bi-directional Variable Capacity

Illustration #158 — (Symbols) Hydraulic Motors

As discussed at the start of this section, hydraulic motors convert the hydraulic power produced by the pump into mechanical power in the form of torque and rotary motion. Graphical symbols for some of the more common hydraulic motors are shown in illustration #158.

Motor Performance Ratings

Manufacturers provide information regarding the performance of their particular hydraulic motors. The following is an explanation of some of the more common information topics.

Displacement:

Hydraulic motors are usually sized according to their displacement per revolution (in^3/rev or cm^3/rev). Motors may be fixed or variable displacement, depending on the design.

Flow and Speed:

Some manufacturers will specify two flow rates and two maximum speeds (continuous and intermittent).

Note: See Section One for more information on hydraulic motor speed calculations.

Torque:

Torque is expressed in inch pounds (in lb), foot pounds (ft lb) or newton metres (N•m).

The torque developed by a motor is a function of the pressure difference across the motor and the displacement per revolution. Increasing the pressure difference and/or motor displacement will increase the torque developed.

- **Theoretical torque** assumes a 100% motor efficiency
- **Running torque**, in reference to a motor, is the torque that is available to keep a load turning. It takes into account the motor efficiency, which for most common motors is around 90%. If it is referenced to a load, it is the torque required to keep the load turning. The motor running torque must be greater than the load running torque
- **Breakaway torque** is the initial torque required to start a stationary load turning.
- **Starting torque** is the torque available from a motor to start a load turning, and is usually expressed as a percentage of the theoretical torque.

- This may range from 60 to 90 percent of the theoretical torque. The starting torque must be higher than the breakaway torque for the motor to be able to start a stationary load turning.

- **Torque/100 psi** (ft lb or in lb/100 psi) is the theoretical torque available per 100 psi pressure difference across the motor. This may be expressed as $N \cdot m/1000$ kPa if metric terms are used.

- **Torque at rated pressure and flow** is usually the actual running torque available. It takes into account the motor efficiency.

Note: See Section One for more information on ''Energy Torque and Power''.

Maximum Pressure:

The manufacturer may list a number of maximum pressures:

- **Maximum continuous pressure:** This is sometimes referred to as the maximum pressure when continuous or intermittent pressures are not specified.

- **Maximum intermittent pressure**

- **Maximum peak pressure:** Some motors may be subject to a pressure higher than the maximum continuous pressure for short periods.

An example illustrating these three maximum pressure ratings may be: a pump with a maximum continuous pressure rating of 3000 psi [20 684 kPa], a 10% per minute intermittent pressure rating of 3750 psi [25 855 kPa] and a 1% per minute peak pressure rating of 4250 psi [29 303 kPa].

The maximum pressures that can safely be applied to this pump are:

- 3000 psi [20 684 kPa] continuously
- 3750 psi [25 855 kPa] for no more than 6 seconds(10%) in any minute
- 4250 psi [29 303 kPa] for no more than 0.6 seconds(1%) in any minute

- *Maximum back pressure:* This is the maximum pressure allowed in the return line.
- *Maximum drain pressure:* This is the maximum pressure allowed in the drain line.
- *Maximum case pressure:* Some motors may have this pressure specified for situations when the case drain is not being used.

Gear Motors

The two types of gear motor designs are:
- External gear motor
- Internal gear motor

External Gear Motor

The external gear motor consists of two meshing gears contained in a close fitting housing (see illustration #159). It is similar to the external gear pump. One gear is connected to the output shaft.

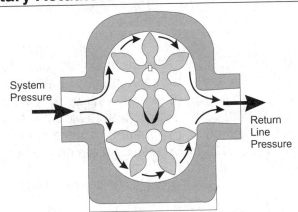

Illustration #159 — External Gear Motor

Fluid enters the inlet port and, acting on both gears, causes them to rotate in opposite directions. The fluid trapped in the spaces between adjacent teeth and the housing is carried to the discharge side of the motor. A close fit between the housing and the gear teeth is essential to keep the internal leakage to a minimum. The sides of the gears are also contained by close fitting side plates for the same reason.

Internal Gear Motor

The internal gear motor is of the gerotor type, where an inner gear operates inside an outer gear.

The inner gear has one tooth less than the outer gear. There are two distinct designs:

- Direct drive gerotor motor
- Orbiting gerotor motor

Direct Drive Gerotor Motor

The direct drive internal gear motor consists of an internal/external gear set, both of which rotate relative to the housing. As the gears rotate, the chambers between the inner and outer teeth increase in size for the first half of rotation and then decrease in size (see illustration #160). The tooth shape maintains a seal between the chambers to prevent fluid bypassing from inlet to discharge.

The outer gear is constrained radially by the housing. The inner gear, which is eccentric to the outer gear, is attached to the output shaft.

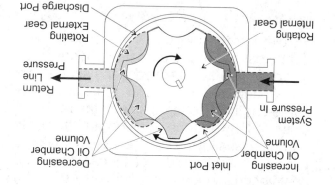

Illustration #160 — Direct Drive Gerotor Motor

Rotating External Gear

Rotating Internal Gear

Discharge Port

Return Line Pressure

System Pressure In

Inlet Port

Increasing Oil Chamber Volume

Decreasing Oil Chamber Volume

Side plates are also used to contain the fluid. A porting arrangement in the housing controls the flow of fluid. Pressurized fluid is admitted from the intake to the expanding chambers, while at the same time, fluid from the contracting chambers is discharged to the return line.

Orbiting Gerotor Motor

The orbiting internal gear motor is similar to the direct drive gear motor, except the outer gear is stationary. This causes the rotating inner gear to make an orbit as it circles inside the outer gear (see illustration #161).

This design also requires the fluid into and out of the motor to be controlled by a rotating port plate, sometimes referred to as a commutator or disc valve, which is driven at the same speed as the inner gear. The rotating motion from the inner gear is transmitted to the drive shaft, via a splined coupling.

Ducts in the casing (numbered 1 through 7 in illustration #161A), channel fluid between the port plate and the cavities formed between the outer and inner gears. The port plate has twelve openings that are connected to either the inlet (pressure) or discharge ports and is timed to deliver fluid to or from the gear cavities at the appropriate time.

Consider illustration #161A as the starting point with tooth 'A' in full engagement with the cavity 1. The port plate is directing inlet fluid to cavities 1, 5, 6 and 7 causing the inner gear to rotate anti-clockwise. Cavities 2, 3 and 4, which are decreasing in volume as the inner gear rotates, are open to the discharge port.

Illustration #161B shows the position of the inner gear and the port plate after the drive shaft has been driven $1/14$ of a revolution. Teeth 'A', 'B' and 'C' have been in full engagement and are now being pushed away from cavities 1, 2 and 3 by inlet fluid. Tooth 'D' is in full engagement with cavity 4 and is also exposed to inlet pressure. Cavities 5, 6 and 7 are open to the discharge.

Illustration #161C shows the position of the inner gear and port plate after the drive shaft has been driven $1/7$ of a revolution.

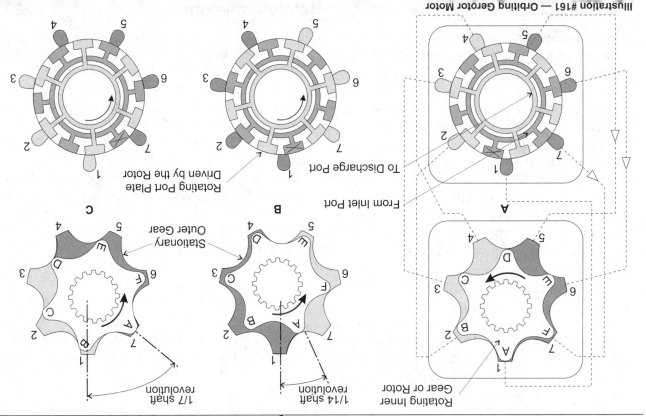

Illustration #161 — Orbiting Gerotor Motor

From Inlet Port

To Discharge Port

Rotating Port Plate
Driven by the Rotor

Stationary
Outer Gear

Rotating Inner
Gear or Rotor

1/14 shaft
revolution

1/7 shaft
revolution

A

B

C

Tooth 'A' is again in full engagement, but now is in cavity 7. At this point the inner gear has made $^6/_7$ of a revolution, while the drive shaft has made $^1/_7$.

For the drive shaft to make one complete revolution there will be 42 tooth engagements and disengagements. This can be considered as 42 power strokes per shaft revolution, which is the reason that this hydraulic motor provides high torque at low rpm.

Vane Motors

As with vane pumps, vane motors are available in either balanced or unbalanced configurations. The unbalanced type uses a round cam ring eccentric to the rotor, which provides for one inlet and one discharge area. The balanced type uses an elliptical cam ring, which is centered to the rotor and provides for two inlet and two discharge areas.

These are diametrically opposed, balancing the radial forces on the rotor.

The majority of vane motors used in industry are of the balanced design (see illustration #162).

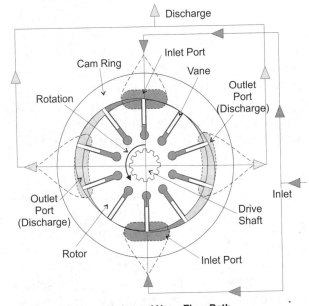

Illustration #162 — Balanced Vane Flow Path

Torque is developed as each vane passes an inlet port and becomes subject to high inlet pressure on one side and low outlet pressure on the other side (see illustration #163).

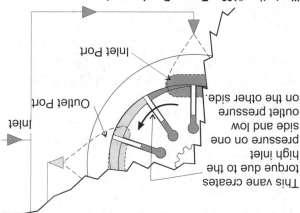

This vane creates torque due to the high inlet pressure on one side and low outlet pressure on the other side.

Inlet

Outlet Port

Inlet Port

Illustration #163 — Torque Development

Inlet pressure is also ported under the vanes to provide a variable force dependent on the load. Many balanced vane motors may be operated in either direction of rotation, simply by reversing the fluid flow to and from the motor.

Some provision must be made to hold the vanes out to the cam ring on startup; otherwise, fluid may bypass directly from the inlet port to the discharge port without acting on the vanes. Springs or rocker arms are two common mechanical methods. Hydraulic methods include inlet check valves or an external pressure source to provide the initial pressure to load the vanes.

In-Line Axial Piston Motors

The in-line axial piston motor has a rotating group that consists of a cylinder block with pistons that reciprocate parallel to the axis of rotation, and an output drive shaft that rotates on the same axis as the cylinder block. The stationary parts consist of a housing, a port plate that directs fluid to and from the cylinders, and a swash plate that is at an angle to the face of the cylinder block.

To demonstrate how the torque is developed, illustration #164 shows two pistons assembled in a cylinder block. The cylinder containing piston 'A' is open to inlet pressure. The cylinder containing piston 'B' is open to discharge. The piston shoes are in contact with the angled swash plate. When inlet pressure forces piston 'A' out of the cylinder, the shoe plate slides down the angle of the swash plate, causing the cylinder block to rotate.

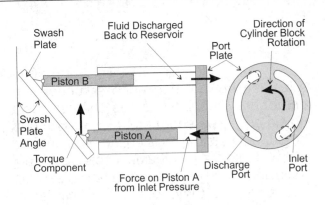

Illustration #164 — In- Line Piston Motor Principle

This rotation will cause piston 'B' to be pushed back into the cylinder by the angled swash plate, returning the fluid through the discharge port back to the reservoir. The theoretical torque developed will depend on the swash plate angle, the inlet pressure, the piston diameter, and the number of pistons.

The stationary port plate directs fluid to and from the cylinders.

Referring to illustration #165, torque is developed when oil from the inlet port acts on piston 'A' and force is transferred to the shaft flange via the piston rod. The torque component causes the assembly to rotate as piston 'A' moves out of the cylinder.

Piston 'B' will be pushed back into the cylinder by the shaft flange as the assembly rotates, discharging the return oil through the discharge port to the outlet. This design eliminates the side loading on the pistons that is encountered by the swash plate type motor, and makes it a more robust unit. The piston displacement, and consequently the torque developed, is dependent on the bent axis angle.

In-line axial piston motors may be fixed or variable displacement. The variable displacement motor will have the swash plate mounted on a yoke that allows the angle to be adjusted. Increasing the swash plate angle will increase the amount of torque available, but reduce the speed, due to the increased piston displacement. Decreasing the angle will decrease the torque available, but increase the speed. A minimum angle (maximum speed) stop is usually provided, to limit the speed to the designed maximum.

Bent Axis Axial Piston Motor

The bent axis axial piston motor has a rotating group that consists of a cylinder block, pistons, piston rods and an output shaft. The pistons reciprocate parallel to the axis of the cylinder block rotation. The piston rods connect pistons to the output shaft. The axis of the cylinder block is at an angle to the axis of the output shaft.

The bent axis axial piston motor may be fixed or variable displacement. The variable displacement has the cylinder block mounted on a yoke, which allows the angle between the cylinder block and the output shaft to be adjusted.

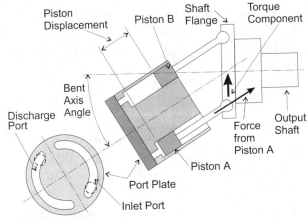

Illustration #165 — Bent Axis Axial Piston Motor

Radial Piston Motor (Rotating Cylinder Block)

An off center rotor turns inside a circular cam or reaction ring (see illustration #166). The rotor contains cylinders and pistons that radiate out from the center. In the center of the rotor is a stationary pintle that contains inlet and discharge ports. When the cylinders are in the lower quadrant (90° to 270°), they are open to inlet pressure, and when in the upper quadrant (270° to 90°) they are open to discharge.

Fluid from the inlet port creates an outward force on the pistons causing the cylinder block to rotate as the piston shoes react against the eccentric reaction ring.

The pistons are pushed back into the cylinder by the reaction ring as they travel from 270° to 90°.

The amount of torque available depends on the number and diameter of the pistons, the maximum system pressure and the eccentricity of the reaction ring.

This type of motor may be fixed or variable displacement. The variable displacement motor will have a means of adjusting the eccentricity of the reaction ring. Increasing the eccentricity increases the piston displacement, slowing the speed and increasing torque capability. The maximum speed is controlled by limiting the minimum eccentricity.

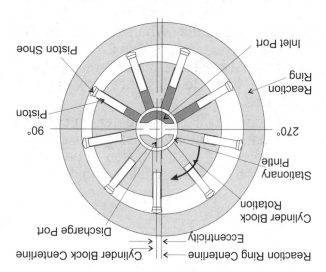

Illustration #166 — Radial Piston Motor (Rotating Cylinder Block

Piston Shoe

Inlet Port

Reaction Ring

Piston

90°

270°

Stationary Pintle

Cylinder Block Rotation

Discharge Port

Eccentricity

Reaction Ring Centerline

Cylinder Block Centerline

Radial Piston Motor (Stationary Cylinder Block)

This type of motor comprises of a number of cylinders mounted radially around a crank or eccentric, which is part of the output shaft. System fluid is directed to the appropriate pistons, through a commutator, or distributor valve (see illustration #167).

The pressurized fluid causes the pistons to move inwards, pushing on the crank or eccentric, causing the output shaft to rotate. The exhausting pistons are pushed outward by the rotating crank, discharging the fluid through the distributor valve to the discharge.

A hole through the piston and connecting rod supplies lubricating fluid to the connecting rod slipper pad.

Direction of Rotation

Almost all hydraulic motors used in industrial applications are designed to be bi-directional (the output shaft can rotate in two directions). By reversing the direction of fluid flow through the motor, the rotation of the output shaft will be reversed.

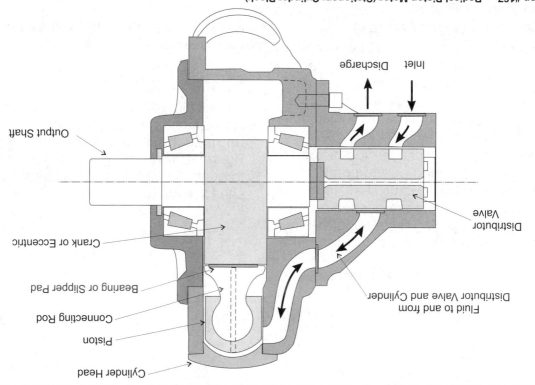

Output Shaft

Crank or Eccentric

Bearing or Slipper Pad

Connecting Rod

Piston

Cylinder Head

Discharge

Inlet

Distributor Valve

Fluid to and from Distributor Valve and Cylinder.

Illustration #167 — Radical Piston Motor (Stationary Cylinder Block)

Hydraulic Motor Wear

All hydraulic motors use close fitting clearances, to seal between moving and stationary parts. When a motor is new, some leakage will occur. The amount will be dependent on the pressure difference across the clearances and the size of the clearances.

Pressure is created by the load on the motor shaft; therefore, the maximum leakage will occur when the motor is at full load and consequently, maximum pressure.

As wear occurs, the amount of leakage for a specific load will increase. This will cause the shaft speed to decrease (assuming that the motor is supplied with the same amount of input flow). If the motor is equipped with a case drain line, the amount of flow through the drain line will increase. On motors that do not have a case drain, the leakage passes to the discharge.

To check for hydraulic motor wear, it is advisable to make some initial observations when the motor is still in a new condition. For piston motors that have a case drain, observe the amount of flow through the drain line when the motor is operating at a specific pressure (use the operating pressure, if possible). This may be accomplished by either using a flow meter, or by opening the drain line and measuring the time it takes to fill a known container. If there is no case drain line, check the shaft speed at a specific pressure and flow rate. The motor may then be checked for wear at any time by completing the same test and comparing with the original readings.

Note: Some gear and vane motors may have a drain from the shaft seal area, but the majority of leakage may be occurring due to wear at the vanes and gears, etc. These motors should be checked for wear by checking for a speed reduction under full load or load pressure.

SECTION SIX QUESTIONS

Hydraulic Actuators

1. The force available from a single rod double acting cylinder is greater when the piston is being extended than when it is being retracted.

   ❑ true   ❑ false

2. Any double acting cylinder can be referred to as a non-differential cylinder.

   ❑ true   ❑ false

3. A non-differential cylinder will provide equal force and equal speeds in both directions.

   ❑ true   ❑ false

4. It is not possible to have a double acting telescoping cylinder.

   ❑ true   ❑ false

5. The force available from a telescoping cylinder is the greatest when the last sleeve is being extended.

   ❑ true   ❑ false

6. The extension speed of a telescoping cylinder will be constant throughout the length of the stroke.

   ❑ true   ❑ false

7. What type of cylinder arrangement would provide a high force output while maintaining a low diameter profile?

   Answer: _____
   _____

8. What type of cylinder arrangement would provide a number of exact mechanical positions?

   Answer: _____
   _____

9. What feature would be used to prevent mechanical shock when a cylinder reaches the end of its stroke?

   ❑ pillows
   ❑ springs
   ❑ air shocks
   ❑ cushions

10. Stop tubes are sometimes used to reduce bushing and cylinder wear. What is affect does the stop tube have on cylinder operation?

    Answer: _____
    _____

11. What type of device could be installed on a cylinder to shield the piston rod/bushing opening from contaminants?

    Answer: _____
    _____

12. *What are the two areas that require dynamic seals on double acting cylinders?*

    Answer: _____

    _____

13. *Describe how a "pressure activated" dynamic seal works:*

    Answer: _____

    _____

14. *Cast iron piston rings are suitable for use as piston to cylinder seals.*

    ❏ true   ❏ false

15. *Cast iron piston rings will allow a small amount of leakage.*

    ❏ true   ❏ false

16. *If a single endless U-Section sealing ring is used, it will seal in:*

    ❏ a single sealing ring will not seal
    ❏ two directions
    ❏ one direction only

17. *V-Rings are used in sets and are suitable for high pressures.*

    ❏ true   ❏ false

18. *Piston rod alignment and support where it leaves the cylinder is usually provided by the rod seals.*

    ❏ true   ❏ false

19. *List the possible cylinder wear points if the piston rod is side loaded:*

    Answer: _____

    _____

20. *List some of the symptoms of piston to cylinder seal leakage:*

    Answer: _____

    _____

21. *The illustration shows an extended vertical cylinder with the load pushing in the retract direction. The port at the cap end of the cylinder is blocked off. The port at the rod end is open to the reservoir. The result of any leakage past the piston seals would be that:*

    ❏ the load would remain static
    ❏ the pressure on the rod side of the piston would increase
    ❏ the pressure on the cap side of the piston would increase
    ❏ the load would slowly lower

22. The illustration shows an extended vertical cylinder with the load pushing in the retract direction. Both ports to the cylinder are blocked off. The result of any leakage past the piston seals would be that:
   - ❏ the load would remain static and the pressure on the rod side of the piston would increase
   - ❏ the pressure on the cap side of the piston would increase
   - ❏ the load would slowly lower

23. The illustration shows a loaded cylinder being extended. The result of any leakage past the piston seals would be that:
   - ❏ the extension speed would increase
   - ❏ the extension speed would decrease
   - ❏ there would be a decrease in the force available to raise the load

24. The illustration shows an unloaded differential cylinder being extended. The extension speed is controlled by a flow control valve in the line from the rod end of the cylinder (meter out). The result of piston seal leakage would be:
   - ❏ the extension speed would increase
   - ❏ the extension speed would decrease
   - ❏ there would be a decrease in the force available to raise the load

25. The type of cylinder piston seal most likely to leak slightly is:
   - ❏ V-Rings
   - ❏ U-Cup
   - ❏ cast iron
   - ❏ O-Rings

26. To check the piston seals in a hydraulic cylinder, a pressure difference across the piston must be created. Describe two methods that may be used to create this pressure difference:

   Answer: _____

   _____

27. Hydraulic motor are usually sized by:

☐ overall diameter
☐ diameter of the output shaft
☐ displacement per minute
☐ displacement per revolution

28. Hydraulic motors are only available in fixed displacement designs.

☐ true   ☐ false

29. Both the inner and outer gears rotate on the direct drive gerotor motor.

☐ true   ☐ false

30. Fluid into and out of the orbiting gerotor motor is controlled by a timed rotating port plate (commutator).

☐ true   ☐ false

31. Both the inner and outer gears rotate on the orbiting gerotor motor.

☐ true   ☐ false

32. Fluid into and out of the orbiting gerotor motor is controlled by a timed rotating port plate (commutator).

☐ true   ☐ false

33. What would probably happen on start up if there were no provision for holding the vanes out to the cam ring on vane motors?

Answer: _____

_____

34. What are two common mechanical methods of pushing the vanes out to the cam ring on vane motors?

Answer: _____

_____

35. Changing the swash plate angle of an in-line axial piston motor will change the speed without affecting the available torque.

☐ true   ☐ false

36. The speed of a variable speed radial piston motor (rotating cylinder block) will decrease as the eccentricity of the reaction ring is increased.

☐ true   ☐ false

37. Observing or measuring the fluid flow from the case drain of a hydraulic motor is one way of checking for wear.

☐ true   ☐ false

SECTION SEVEN

BASIC CONTROL VALVES

Introduction

In a basic hydraulic circuit the pump supplies fluid to the actuator. A variety of valves are placed in the circuit to ensure that the actuator provides adequate force or torque, and operates in the required direction and at the correct speed.

There are three basic control functions for these valves. They are:

1. Pressure Control
2. Direction Control
3. Flow Control

Pressure Control

Pressure control valves are used in hydraulic circuits to function as one of the following:

- Relief Valves
- Unloading Valves
- Sequence Valves
- Counterbalance Valves
- Brake Valves
- Pressure Reducing Valves

Relief Valves

Relief valves are used to limit the maximum pressure developed. These are normally closed valves. When the pressure reaches a preset value the relief valve opens and directs the fluid to a low pressure area, usually the reservoir, preventing any further significant rise in pressure.

System relief valves are the most common relief valve application and direct the flow of oil to the reservoir when relieving pressure. There are three terms associated with the opening of the relief valve. They are:

- *Cracking Pressure:* The pressure at which the valve first starts to open and bleed fluid to the reservoir.
- *Full Flow Pressure:* The pressure that is required to pass the total amount of flow through the valve to the reservoir.
- *Pressure Override:* The difference between the cracking pressure and the full flow pressure.

There are two types of relief valves. They are direct acting and pilot operated.

Direct Acting Relief Valves

The direct acting relief valve uses a main spring, acting on a ball or poppet, to directly oppose the hydraulic force.

Illustration #168 shows a ball type direct acting relief valve. The spring holds the ball against the seat, thereby sealing the system pressure from the tank port.

When system pressure exceeds the spring force, the ball unseats, allowing fluid to flow to the reservoir. If the system pressure decreases, the spring will force the ball back on to the seat to close the valve. High pressure override, noisy operation, limited flow capacity and a narrow pressure adjustment range, limits the use of this type of relief valve.

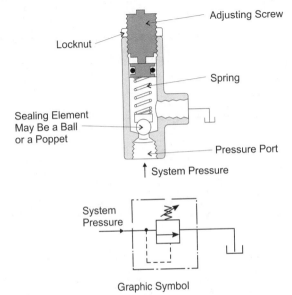

Illustration #168 — Direct Acting Relief Valve

Pilot Operated Relief Valves

Pilot operated relief valves do not have the inherent limitations or disadvantages of the direct acting relief valve.

The pilot operated relief valve consists of two direct acting relief valves (a main valve and a pilot valve) built into one valve body. The main valve is large and will handle high flow rates at low pressure differentials. The pilot valve is small and controls low flow rates at high pressure differentials.

Two common pilot operated relief valve designs are explained below.

Pilot Operated Poppet Relief Valve

Illustration #169 shows a pilot operated poppet relief valve. The basic operation is as follows:

- System pressure is ported through an orifice, to the pilot valve and the spring side of the main poppet valve, by an interconnecting passage.

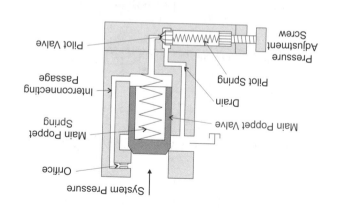

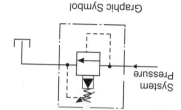

Graphic Symbol

Illustration #169 — Pilot Operated Poppet Relief Valve

- This equalizes the pressure on both sides of the main poppet as long as the pilot valve remains closed.
- When the system pressure is less than the pilot spring setting, the main poppet spring (light pressure) holds the main poppet on its seat.
- When system pressure reaches the pilot spring setting, the pilot valve unseats, limiting the pressure on the spring side of the main poppet (flow through the interconnecting passage is limited by the orifice).
- Any further rise in system pressure will unbalance the forces acting on the main poppet, causing it to unseat and allow system fluid to the reservoir.
- When system pressure falls, the pilot valve closes, allowing the pressure to equalize on both sides of the main poppet. The main poppet spring will then close the main poppet.

Pilot Operated Balanced Piston Relief Valve

Illustration #170 shows a pilot operated balance piston relief valve. The basic operation is as follows:

- System pressure is ported through an orifice, to the upper side of the balanced piston and to the pilot valve.
- Pressure is equalized above and below the balanced piston.
- When the system pressure is less than the pilot spring setting, the hydraulic forces above and below the balanced piston are equal. This allows the light main spring to hold the main valve on its seat.
- When system pressure reaches the pilot spring setting, the pilot valve unseats, limiting the pressure above the balanced piston.

Pressure Control

- Fluid from the pilot valve is bled down through the center of the balanced piston stem, to drain back to the reservoir.

- Any further rise in pressure will unbalance the forces acting on the balanced piston, causing it to move up, unseating the main valve and allowing system fluid to flow to the reservoir.

- The hole through the balanced piston (orifice) limits the flow to the upper side of the piston.

- When system pressure falls, the pilot valve closes, allowing the pressure to equalize on both sides of the balanced piston. The light spring will then close the main valve.

Note: *The pilot operated relief valve is often represented by the graphic symbol shown in illustration #168. The detailed symbol (illustration #169 and #170) is used when circuit design requires it, as in illustration #171.*

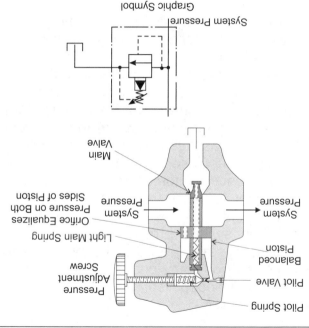

Illustration #170 — Pilot Operated Balanced Piston Relief Valve

Graphic Symbol

System Pressure

Main Valve

Orifice Equalizes Pressure on Both Sides of Piston

System Pressure

System Pressure

Light Main Spring

Balanced Piston

Pressure Adjustment Screw

Pilot Valve

Pilot Spring

Venting the Relief Valve

It is often required for the total output of a hydraulic pump to be returned to the reservoir under little or no pressure.

This allows the pump output to be accessible whenever required, but the input power to the pump driver is very low, as is the heat input into the system when the valve is being vented.

Pilot operated relief valves can be used for this purpose. Illustration #171 shows a pilot operated poppet relief valve. The chamber on the spring side of the main poppet is connected to the reservoir via a solenoid operated directional valve.

With the directional valve in the position shown (solenoid not energized), the pressure on the spring side of the main poppet will be at reservoir pressure and the system pressure will vent to the reservoir at a pressure set by the light spring above the main poppet. Usually it requires less than 50 psi [345 kPa] to overcome this spring.

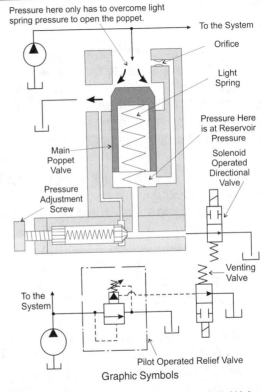

Illustration #171— Venting a Pilot Operated Relief Valve

If higher pressure is required for pilot operation, a 75 psi [517 kPa] spring may be installed.

Unloading Valves

The unloading valve is used to allow a system to reach a predetermined pressure, at which time the pump output will be directed back to the reservoir at close to zero pressure.

Two Pump Unloading

Applications that require an initial high volume of low pressure fluid and then require a low volume of high pressure fluid to complete the process, often use a two pump (one high volume low pressure, one low volume high pressure) system. Both pumps supply fluid for the high volume low pressure phase. When low volume high pressure fluid is required, the high volume pump output is directed to the reservoir at almost zero pressure. The low volume high pressure pump then completes the operation.

Illustration #172 shows a direct acting spool valve connected to unload the high volume pump when the system pressure reaches the value set at the valve.

The valve is shown in its normally closed position with the system pressure lower than the valve setting. When system pressure rises to the valve setting, the pressure from the external pilot line will raise the spool against the spring pressure. This will connect the primary port to the secondary port, thus venting the high volume pump to the reservoir.

The output from the low volume pump is prevented from venting, due to the isolating check valve between it and the unloading valve. The valve will continue to vent the high volume pump, as long as the system pressure remains above the unloading valve setting.

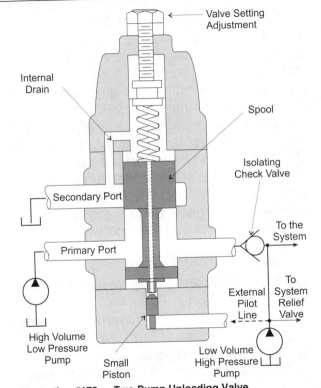

Illustration #172 — Two Pump Unloading Valve

Labels in illustration #172:
- Valve Setting Adjustment
- Internal Drain
- Spool
- Isolating Check Valve
- Secondary Port
- Primary Port
- To the System
- To System Relief Valve
- External Pilot Line
- High Volume Low Pressure Pump
- Small Piston
- Low Volume High Pressure Pump

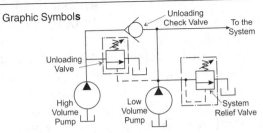

Graphic Symbols

Labels in graphic symbols:
- Unloading Check Valve
- To the System
- Unloading Valve
- High Volume Pump
- Low Volume Pump
- System Relief Valve

Accumulator Charging (Unloading Relief)

Some circuits containing accumulators and fixed displacement pumps may be designed with a special relief valve that will unload the pump (direct the pump output to tank at low pressure), when the accumulator has been charged to full pressure (refer to Section Four for more on accumulators).

As the accumulator supplies oil to the circuit, the system pressure will fall until the unloading relief directs the pump flow back into the circuit to recharge the accumulator. Spool, poppet, or balanced piston designs may be used. The type shown in illustration #173 is the balanced piston.

Note: The maximum pressure setting of the relief valve must be matched to the maximum charging pressure required by the accumulator.

Referring to illustration #173, when system pressure is low, fluid from the pump is directed into the system through the isolating check valve. As the pressure rises and the accumulator becomes fully charged, the pilot poppet will crack open, limiting the pressure above the balance piston, and on the right side of the unloading piston. As the pressure rises further, the balanced piston moves up, opening the pump and system to the reservoir. The isolating check valve will immediately close when fluid attempts to drain from the system. This will maintain the fluid in the system and accumulator. The unloading piston will now have system pressure acting on the left side and tank pressure on the right side and will continue to hold the pilot poppet wide open.

The pump output will be directed to the reservoir at a low pressure (the value of this low pressure is set by the light spring on top of the balanced piston).

As the system demands fluid, the system pressure will fall as fluid is discharged from the accumulator. The system pressure will fall to a level much lower than the relieving pressure before the pilot valve resets and pump output is directed back into the circuit (recharging).

This pressure differential (difference between the relieving and recharging pressures) is set by the difference in the unloading piston area and the pilot poppet seat area. This will typically be approximately 15%. Recharging will occur when the system pressure has dropped to 85% of the relieving pressure. This arrangement ensures that the pump is not continually cycling between loading and unloading at each slight rise or fall in pressure.

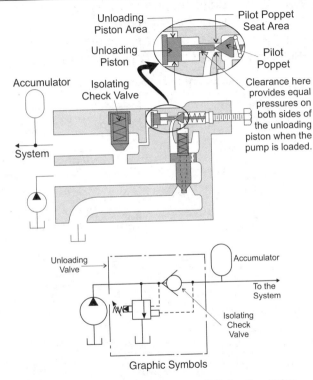

Unloading Piston Area

Pilot Poppet Seat Area

Unloading Piston

Pilot Poppet

Accumulator

Isolating Check Valve

Clearance here provides equal pressures on both sides of the unloading piston when the pump is loaded.

System

Unloading Valve

Accumulator

To the System

Isolating Check Valve

Graphic Symbols

Illustration #173 — Accumulator Circuit Unloading Valve

Note: If a bladder or diaphragm type accumulator is used, the gas precharge pressure should be set at no more than 90% of the recharging pressure (minimum circuit pressure). Refer to Section Four for more on accumulators.

Sequence Valves

The role of this sequence valve is to ensure that the clamping cylinder extends and exerts a minimum clamping force before the work cylinder is extended. A sequence valve is used in a circuit when two or more actions are to be carried out in a specific order. A typical arrangement would be a two cylinder, clamp and work circuit.

Illustration #174 shows a direct acting spool valve connected into a circuit as a sequence valve. When hydraulic fluid is directed to the cap end of the two cylinders, the clamping cylinder will operate first, due to the normally closed sequence valve preventing flow to the work cylinder.

When the clamping cylinder meets resistance, the circuit pressure will rise and the small piston under the sequence spool in the sequence valve will raise the spool to allow fluid to the work cylinder.

Illustration #174 — Sequence Valve (Cylinders Extending)

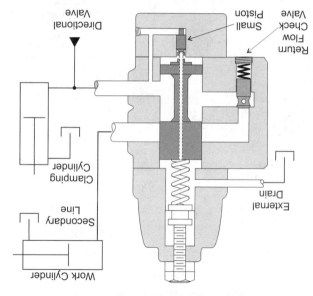

Clamping force will be maintained because the minimum pressure in the circuit when the work cylinder is operating will be at least the pressure setting of the sequence valve.

The sequence valve is fitted with an external drain due to the pressure in the secondary line (an internal drain would drain the top of the spool to the secondary line).

When the cylinders are to be retracted, the return flow check valve, which bypasses the spool, allows hydraulic fluid to flow freely in the reverse direction, allowing the work cylinder to retract.

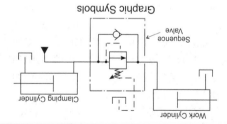

Graphic Symbols

Counterbalance Valves

Counterbalancing is a general term used when a valve arrangement creates a back-pressure on an actuator to prevent the load from overrunning and increasing the speed of actuator.

There are two different valve applications, they are:

- Counterbalance
- Overcenter

Counterbalance Valves

A counterbalance valve is required when the load on an actuator exerts a continual force that tends to move the actuator faster than the designed hydraulic speed.

Illustration #175 shows a direct acting spool valve acting as a counterbalance valve controlling the extension of a cylinder. In this circuit the counterbalance valve is internally drained and piloted. The load on the cylinder is acting in the direction of extension.

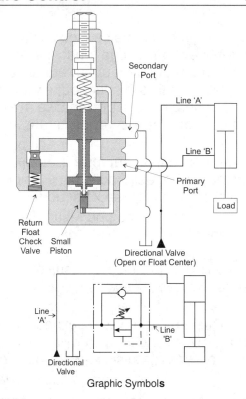

Illustration #175 — Counterbalance Valve

The counterbalance valve creates a back-pressure in line 'B' to "counterbalance" the overrunning load on the cylinder when it is being extended.

A built in check valve allows a free flow in the opposite direction when the cylinder is to be retracted. The pressure setting on the valve must be slightly greater than the highest pressure generated by the overrunning load.

Three major disadvantages to this arrangement are:

- Unexpected load surges could cause the cylinder to overrun.
- The continual hydraulic back pressure reduces the available cylinder force.
- In certain situations substantial amounts of energy from the pump are released into the system as heat (e.g. if the load in illustration #175 were removed and the cylinder was extended).

Overcenter Valves

An overcenter valve is required when an actuator load will vary from resistive to overrunning or when the maximum force available is required from the cylinder.

Illustration #176 shows an overcenter valve controlling the extension of a cylinder that has an overcenter load attached. The valve in this example is a direct acting spool valve with the primary port connected to line 'B'. The pilot port is externally connected to line 'A' (which is the supply line to the cap end of the cylinder) and the valve is internally drained.

When the cylinder starts the extension stroke, maximum pressure is required in line 'A' to move the load. The overcenter valve, located in the return from the rod end of the cylinder will open, due to the pressure from the pilot line connected to line 'A'.

As the load goes overcenter, it will attempt to pull the piston out of the cylinder, reducing the pressure in line 'A'. When the pressure in line 'A' drops to the overcenter valve setting, the valve will start to close, creating a restriction in line 'B' and consequently a hydraulic load on the cylinder. The hydraulic load will prevent the load from cavitating the cap side of the cylinder and pulling the piston ahead of the oil supply, as there must be pressure in line 'A', equal to the setting of the overcenter valve.

When the overcenter valve is piloted as shown, its pressure setting can be quite low (100 to 200 psi [690 to 1380 kPa]).

A built in check valve allows a free flow in the opposite direction when the cylinder is to be retracted.

To control the overrunning load when the cylinder is being retracted, a second overcenter valve would be installed in line 'A'.

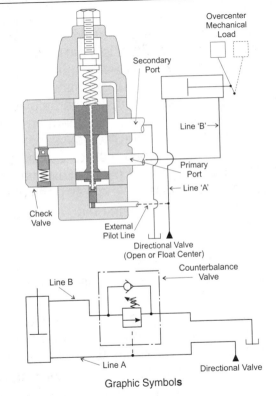

Illustration #176 — Overcenter Valve

Brake Valves

Instead of using an overcenter valve and cross port relief to control the deceleration of a high inertia load, a brake valve may be used.

The brake valve will also control any tendency for the load to drive the actuator and can therefore be used as an overcenter valve. Illustration #177 shows a direct acting spool valve being used as a brake valve.

When used as a brake valve, the spool valve is fitted with a solid spool (no center drain hole) and a remote pilot line (from line 'A') that accesses the underside of the spool (large diameter of the spool). An internal pilot (small diameter piston) senses the pressure from the motor discharge (line 'B'). With this arrangement, a relative low pressure from the external pilot, or a high pressure from the internal pilot, will raise the spool and open the valve.

Note: If the load shown in illustration #176 is fast moving with high inertia, problems will arise if the load is suddenly stopped. When the fluid supply to line 'A' is cut off the drop in pressure will cause the counterbalance valve to quickly close (the pilot line is connected to line 'A'), causing a dangerous rise in pressure in line 'B'. A cross port relief (between lines 'A' and 'B') could be used to solve this.

The advantages of this arrangement over the counterbalance valve are:

- The valve is independent of the load induced pressure which allows it to be used with varying loads.
- Full cylinder force is available.
- Will not substantially add to the heat being generated from the lowering load.

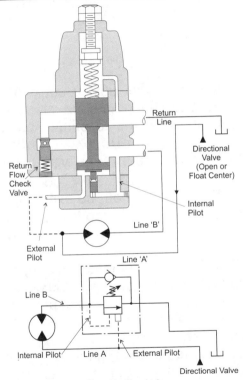

Return
Line

Directional
Valve
(Open or
Float Center)

Return
Flow
Check
Valve

Internal
Pilot

Line 'B'

External
Pilot

Line 'A'

Line B

Internal Pilot

Line A

External Pilot

Directional Valve

Graphic Symbols

Illustration #177 — Brake Valve

Line 'A' is the supply line to the motor. The brake valve is connected into the return line from the motor, which is line 'B'.

When fluid is supplied to drive the motor, the pressure in line 'A' (which is the result of the load on the motor) opens the brake valve (raises the spool) via the external pilot line, allowing a free flow of fluid out of the motor back to the directional valve. The valve will stay open as long as there is sufficient load on the motor.

If the load tries to overrun, the pressure drops in line 'A' and the brake valve starts to close, causing the pressure to rise in line 'B', putting a hydraulic load on the motor (controlling the overrun). The combination of the pilot pressure from line 'B' on the small piston, and the pilot pressure from line 'A' on the underside of the spool, positions the spool to allow the correct amount of fluid to maintain a constant motor speed.

Pressure Reducing Valves

Pressure reducing valves are used to limit the pressure in a portion of the hydraulic circuit to a value less than the main relief valve setting. These are normally open valves. They may be either direct acting or pilot operated and will have an external drain, due to the fact that both inlet and outlet ports are pressurized. The graphic symbols are shown in illustration #179.

Illustration #178 shows a pilot operated pressure reducing valve. The outlet pressure is ported to the upper side of the spool and to the pilot relief via a balance hole through the center of the spool. The spool is hydraulically balanced as long as the outlet pressure is below the pilot valve setting. This allows the light spring to hold the spool in a wide open position.

When the motor is stopped, the fluid supply to line 'A' is shut off (an open or float center directional valve is used). The resulting loss of pressure in line 'A' causes the brake valve spool to start to close. Momentum keeps the motor running, which acts as a pump, drawing fluid from the reservoir and increasing the pressure in line 'B' up to the brake valve setting (the internal pilot acting on the small piston holds the spool open). This creates a hydraulic brake on the motor to bring it to a gradual stop.

The brake valve has all the advantages of the overcenter valve arrangement with the added advantage of not requiring a cross port relief to prevent dangerous pressure build up when a high inertia load is to be stopped.

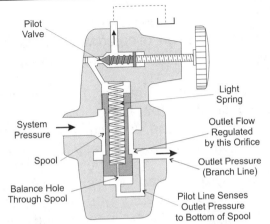

Illustration #178 — Pilot Operated Pressure Reducing Valve

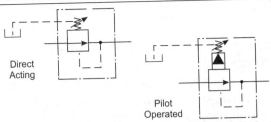

Illustration #179 — Graphic Symbols for Pressure Reducing Valves

When the outlet pressure reaches the pilot valve setting, the pilot valve opens and bleeds fluid from above the main spool area. This limits the pressure above the main spool. Any further increase in outlet pressure results in unbalanced hydraulic forces on the spool. This causes the spool to rise against a light spring which begins to cut off flow to the outlet.

The spool will then regulate the flow to the outlet to maintain the required outlet pressure. If the outlet flow becomes static, the spool will close to a point where flow past the spool is equal to the bleed off flow through the orifice and pilot valve.

Note: If there is an unexpected loading on an actuator in the branch line, the pressure will rise accordingly (the pilot valve will bleed a small amount of fluid, but not enough to act as a safety relief). For this reason, a relief valve should also be installed in the branch line if unexpected loads may occur. Some pressure reducing valves are available that incorporate a built in branch line relief to tank.

Direction Control

Directional valves are used to control the direction of fluid flow in hydraulic lines. Check valves will generally limit the flow in a line to one direction only; whereas, rotary and spool type valves have the ability to select the port to which the flow from a particular line is directed.

Directional valves are usually described by:

- *Type of Internal Element:* Common internal elements are: poppet, ball, rotary spool or sliding spool.

- *Method of Actuation:* These may include one, or a combination, of the following: hydraulic (pilot operated), electric (solenoid), pneumatic and various manual methods.

- *Number of Flow Paths to the Valve:* The number of flow paths to the valve is simply the number of main line connections.

Note: Some descriptions may specify a number of flow paths for a valve. This specification relates to the actual flow paths within the valve.

Check Valves (Non Return Valves)

Simple check valves are similar in construction to some direct acting relief valves. The only difference being is their location in the circuit and the function for which they are being used. Most relief valves will have a much heavier spring and a means of adjusting the spring tension. Check valve graphical symbols are shown in illustration #180.

Note: For illustration #180, Symbol 'A' is used for most simple check valves even when a light spring is present. Symbol 'B' is usually used when the spring pressure is significant, such as when maintaining a pilot pressure (often a 75 psi [517 kPa] spring).

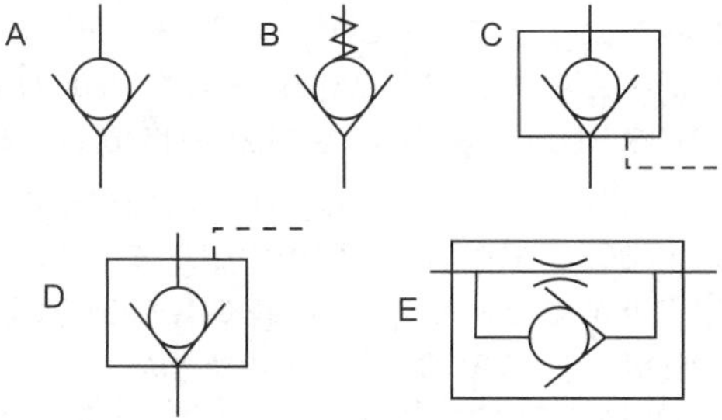

A – Free

B – Spring seated

C – Pilot pressure can hold the valve open

D – Pilot pressure can hold the valve closed

E – With restriction

Illustration #180 — Graphic Symbols for Check Valve

Simple Check Valves

The simple check valve is a directional valve, in that it allows flow in one direction but prevents flow in the other direction (see illustration #181). Light spring pressure (usually approximately 5 psi [34 kPa] unless a more significant spring load is required for pressure control purposes) holds the valve closed when the pressure is equal on both sides of the poppet.

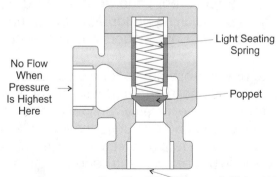

Illustration #181 — Simple Check Valve

The relative pressures on either side of the valve will determine when the valve opens and closes. A higher pressure on the spring side of the poppet increases the closing force and prevents fluid flow. A higher pressure on the seat side of the poppet opens the valve and allows free flow.

Restriction Check Valves

The restriction type check valve is similar to the simple check valve, except that there is an orifice through the poppet. When the higher pressure is on the spring side of the poppet, the poppet is seated, and the orifice will allow a controlled flow rate through the poppet. The flow rate will depend on the size of the orifice and the pressure difference across the poppet.

When the higher pressure is on the seat side of the poppet, the valve opens in the normal manner and allows free flow in the opposite direction.

Pilot-to-Open Check Valves

The pilot-to-open check valve can operate as a normal check valve, in that it will allow free flow in one direction and prevent flow in the opposite direction. When pilot pressure is applied to the pilot port, the pilot piston will unseat the main poppet and allow flow in either direction.

If the pressure behind the main poppet is high, there may not be sufficient force from the pilot piston to open the main poppet. In this case, the main poppet may be provided with a decompression poppet (refer to illustration #182). When pilot pressure is applied to the pilot port, the pilot piston will first unseat the decompression poppet, to relieve the pressure behind the main poppet and then open the main poppet.

Pilot-to-open check valves are commonly used in various load holding situations in cylinder circuits.

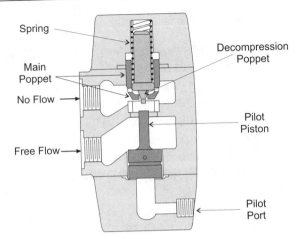

Illustration #182— Pilot-to-Open Check Valve with Decompression Poppet

Pilot-to-Close Check Valves

The pilot-to-close check valve is equipped with a pilot piston that will hold the main poppet in a closed position when pilot pressure is applied (refer to illustration #183).

With no pilot pressure, the valve will operate as a simple check valve.

The pilot-to-close check valve may be used in accumulator circuits if the system is to be automatically drained of pressure when the pump is shut down.

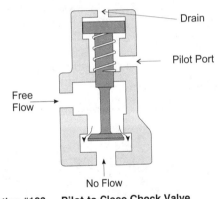

Illustration #183 — Pilot-to-Close Check Valve

Sliding Spool Type Directional Valves

A sliding spool type valve (refer to illustration #184) contains a housing to which a number of ports are connected. The actual number of ports (main piping connections) will determine if the valve is a two-way, three-way, four-way, etc. The inside of the housing is bored to connect to the ports. This internal bore contains a cylindrical rod, called a spool.

The spool is machined with lands and undercuts so that various ports will be blocked or connected, depending on the axial position of the spool. The lands will usually have a number of grooves machined around the periphery (balancing grooves). These grooves allow pressure to equalize around the diameter and aids in keeping the spool concentric to the bore.

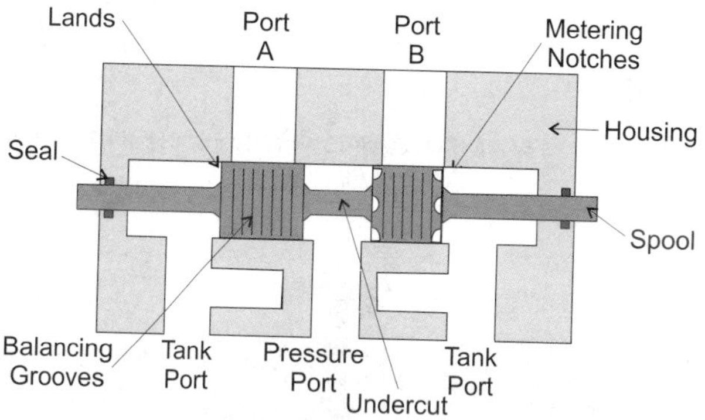

Illustration #184— Basic Sliding Spool Valve

The spool may also have notches machined into the edges (metering notches), which are designed to allow for a smoother or more gradual transition from one position to another as the spool is shifted.

Elastomer type seals are used where the spool leaves the housing. Sealing between the high and low pressure ports is achieved by the close fit between the spool lands and the housing bore.

Illustration #184 shows a basic four-way sliding spool valve. For comparison purposes, one land is shown with metering notches, one without.

When the spool is moved to the left, port 'A' will be open to the pressure port and port 'B' will be open to the tank port. If the spool is moved to the right, it will be port 'B' that is open to the pressure port, and port 'A' that is open to the tank.

Graphic Symbol Representation

Graphic symbols that represent directional valves will show the actual flow paths through the valve for each of the various positions of the spool. The method of actuating the spool and a positioning device, if present, will also be represented.

The spool in the valve shown in illustration #185 has three distinct positions. It is referred to as a three-position valve; therefore, the graphic symbol has three squares or envelopes to represent these positions. Ports 'A' and 'B' are used for connecting to an actuator, 'P' is the pressure port, and 'T' is the tank or reservoir connection.

When the spool is shifted to the left, the fluid from port 'A' is returned to the reservoir through port 'T' and port 'B' is supplied with pressurized fluid from port 'P'.

When the spool is centered, all the ports are blocked off and there is no flow. This is referred to as a closed center. Shifting the spool to the right reverses the flow, with 'B' going to tank and 'A' connected to pressure. A hand operated valve of this type is usually spring centered or detented (refer to "Initial Spool Position" below).

Note: When the graphic symbol of a multi-position valve is used in a schematic diagram, the circuit lines are connected to only one of the valve positions (envelopes). It is usual to use the position that the valve would be in when the method of actuation is de-energized or not actuated. For example, if the valve is spring centered, the circuit lines would be connected to the center position. If there is no specific centering device, a three position valve is usually shown in the center position. Two position valves may be shown in either position.

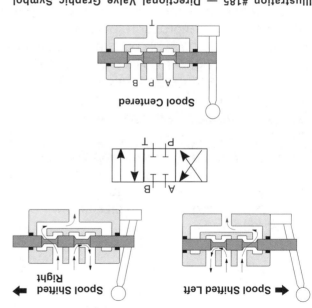

Spool Centered

Spool Shifted Right ◀

Spool Shifted Left ▶

Illustration #185 — Directional Valve Graphic Symbol Representation

Two and Three Position Spool Valves

Two-position valves are designed to operate with the spool in either one extreme position or the other, with no means of holding the center position. This type would be used when a center or neutral position is not required, such as when a cylinder is continually reciprocated. The functional diagram and graphic symbol for a two-position three way valve is shown in illustration #186. A three-way valve such as this, would be used to operate a single acting cylinder. In the position shown, pressure is directed to the 'A' port, which would raise the cylinder. When the button is depressed, the 'A' port is opened to the reservoir and the cylinder would lower, either by gravity or spring pressure.

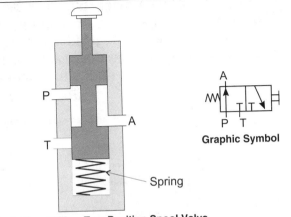

Graphic Symbol

Illustration #186 — Two Position Spool Valve

Three-position valves provide greater flexibility when designing circuits, due to the various center conditions that are available.

Center Conditions

There are a number of standard center conditions available from most manufacturers. Four of the most common centers are described below.

Closed Center

Illustration #185 shows a closed center three-position spool valve. When the valve is in the center position all four ports are blocked off preventing any movement of fluid to or from the actuator ports (A and B). Pump flow is available for other operations.

Open Center

The open center three-position spool valve is shown in illustration #187.

This type is often used with hydraulic motors. When the spool is moved to the center position the motor can coast to a stop with a minimum of shock (high inertia systems would require the use of a brake valve, as shown in illustration #177).

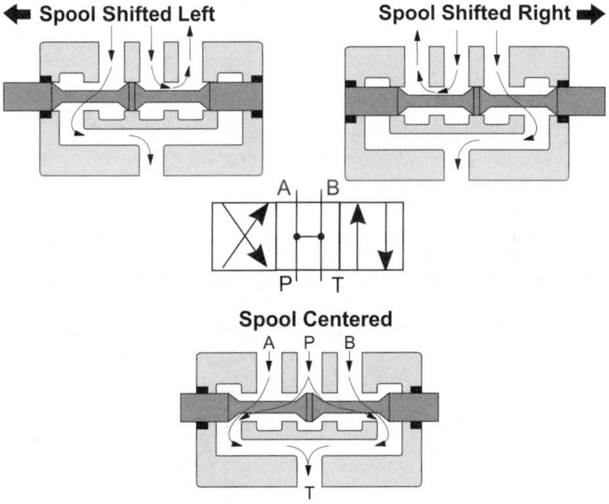

Tandem Center

The tandem center spool shown in illustration #188 will stop actuator motion when it is in the center position, but at the same time allow the pump output to be returned to the reservoir at almost zero pressure.

Illustration #187 — Open Center Spool

Spool Centered

◄ Spool Shifted Right

Spool Shifted Left ►

This "unloads" the pump and reduces power input and heat generation.

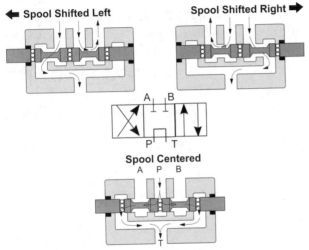

Illustration #188 — Tandem Center Spool

Float Center

The center position of this spool blocks off the pump flow so that it can be used elsewhere (as with the closed center spool).

The actuator ports (A and B) are open to the tank port (refer to illustration #189) and if connected to a cylinder will allow the cylinder to float. This is often required on such equipment as snow ploughs or grader blades, where the blade must float up and down to follow undulating contours.

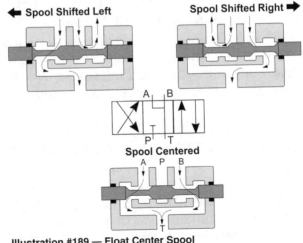

Illustration #189 — Float Center Spool

Other Center Conditions

To provide maximum flexibility for circuit designers, other centers and spool configurations are available. Graphic symbols for a selection of other centers are shown in illustration #190.

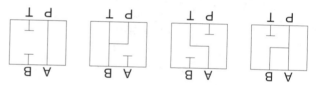

Illustration #190 — Other Center Conditions

Initial Spool Position

The initial spool position refers to the position the spool assumes when there are no actuating forces acting on the spool.

Spools positioned by springs will return to their initial position when actuating forces are removed. Spools held by detent will maintain their position until the actuator moves them to another position.

Spring Centered (refer to illustration #191)

Many three-position spools are designed to return to the center position when the actuating force is released. This is accomplished simply by locating two springs, each with equal tension, one at each end of the spool. When the spool is moved, one spring pressure increases while the other spring relaxes. Removing the actuator force causes the springs to move the spool back to the center position.

Illustration #191 shows the valve spool moved to the right, to place it in the actuating position P to A and B to T.

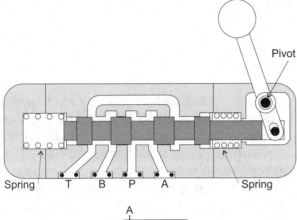

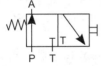

Graphic Symbol

Illustration #191 — Spool Positioning - Spring Centered

Spring Offset (refer to illustration #192)

This method is common with two-position valves. A single spring holds the spool in one extreme position. The actuator overcomes the spring force to move the spool to the other extreme position. Removing the actuator force permits the spring to move the spool back to its original position.

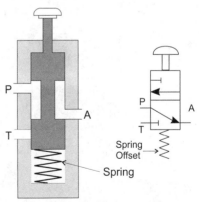

Illustration #192 — Spool Positioning - Spring Offset

Detent Positioning (refer to illustration #193)

A spool may be held in a particular position by the use of a detent. The detent consists of a spring loaded ball or plunger, positioned to engage into a groove or slot in the spool. A two position valve will have two grooves, while a three position will have three.

When the spool is moved the spring allows the plunger to be pushed out of the slot and then re-engage the next slot when it lines up. When a spool is located by a detent it does not have a position to which it will return when the actuating forces are removed, but will maintain the last set position until moved by the actuator to another position.

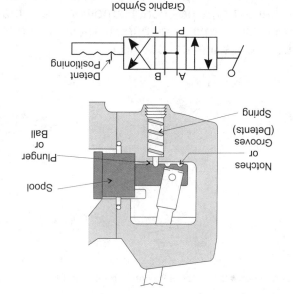

Graphic Symbol

Illustration #193 — Spool Positioning - Detent

Methods of Direct Actuation

The spools of many valves, especially the smaller ones, are moved by the direct application of a force to the ends of the spool. This force may be applied using one of the following methods: manual, mechanical, electrical, hydraulic and pneumatic.

Illustration #194 shows the graphic symbols for the various direct acting methods.

Manual Actuation (refer to Illustration #191 and #192)

The hand lever is probably the most common manual type. It can be used with two, three, or four position valves. Positioning can be achieved by spring centering, spring offset, or by detents. Push button and foot operation are also used, usually with two position spring offset valves.

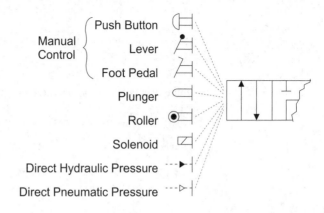

Illustration #194 — Direct Acting Valve Actuation Graphic Symbols

Mechanical Actuation (refer to illustration #195)

Cams attached to a moving machine part, or to the piston rod of a cylinder, are common methods of actuating a directional valve spool. Two position spring offset directional valves are most suitable, but three position valves can be used in some situations. For correct operation and prevention of damage to the valve, correct installation is essential. Over travel may damage the valve and under travel may prevent the valve from operating.

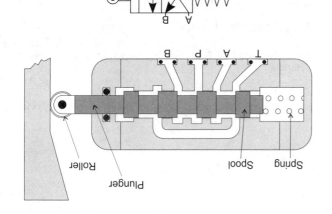

Graphic Symbol

Illustration #195 — Mechanical Actuation

Electrical Actuation

Electrical actuation of a conventional spool type directional valve is accomplished by the use of "on/off" solenoids. A solenoid consists of a frame, a wire coil and an armature. The wire coil is wound inside the frame. The armature is located inside the wire coil. In the non-energized state, the armature is only partially entered into the coil (refer to illustration #196A). Energizing the coil creates a magnetic field, which draws the armature into the coil (refer to illustration #196B). The force from the armature is transferred to the spool by a pushpin, or rod, causing the spool to move to a new position. Solenoids are often provided with a manual override that allows the armature to be manually actuated.

This feature can be invaluable when troubleshooting, or in the event of a control circuit power failure.

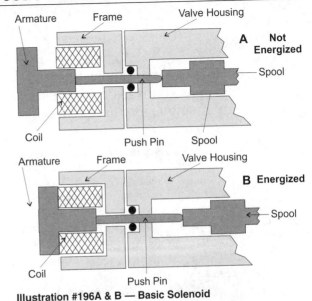

Illustration #196A & B — Basic Solenoid

A three position valve, or a two position valve with detents, will normally have a solenoid at each end of the spool. A two position spring offset valve will have only one solenoid.

Types of Solenoids

The two basic designs of solenoids are:

- *Air gap solenoids* operate with the coil and armature surrounded by air. This requires a dynamic seal on the pushpin that separates the spool side of the valve from the electrical coil and armature (refer to illustration #197). Over time, the dynamic seal may be prone to leakage.

- *Wet armature solenoids* operate with the armature and coil exposed to hydraulic fluid (refer to illustration #198). Sealing is much simpler, and as there is no requirement for a push pin seal, only two static seals are required. These are the seals between the solenoid housing and the valve housing, and the manual override pin seal (this only becomes dynamic when the manual override is used).

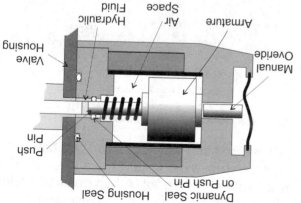

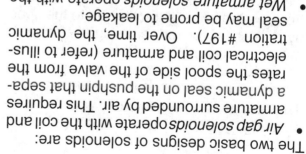

Illustration #197 — Air Gap Solenoid

Valve Housing
Hydraulic Fluid
Air Space
Armature
Manual Override
Push Pin
Housing Seal
Dynamic Seal on Push Pin

The wet armature is quieter in operation, operates cooler (due to the circulation of oil), and usually has a longer life than the air gap design.

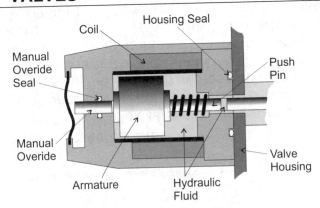

Illustration #198 — Wet Armature Solenoid

AC and DC Power Supply

Solenoids can be designed to operate on either AC or DC power.

- *The AC solenoid* draws a high current (inrush current) when power is initially applied (before the armature is pulled into the coil) and a lower current (holding current) when the armature has fully moved into the coil.

The low current draw, when fully actuated, allows the solenoid to be held in the energized condition with no problems. High cycling rates, a sticking spool, or an armature that holds the solenoid where the current draw is high, will burn the coil out.

- *The DC solenoid* has a constant current draw regardless of the armature position. It is designed so that high cycling rates and a continuous current draw in any position will not cause burn out problems.

Pneumatic Actuation

The pneumatic actuated spool valve uses a piston at the end of the spool to shift the spool when air pressure is applied behind the piston. The piston acts to transfer the force from the pressurized air and also to seal the air chamber from the hydraulic fluid.

A three-position spring centered valve will have a piston at each end of the spool (refer to illustration #199).

Two Stage Actuation - Pilot Operated Valves

The large directional valves required to handle high flow rates require greater forces to move the spool than is available from most direct actuation methods. At flow rates above approximately 25 gpm [114 litres per min], pilot operated valves are used.

Pilot operated directional valves consist of a pilot valve (master valve) mounted above the main valve (slave valve).

Control of the pilot valve is usually by solenoid, although pneumatic, manual or mechanical methods may also be used.

Illustration #200 is an example of a typical pilot operated, spring centered, four-way directional valve.

The pilot valve, which is also spring centered, is solenoid controlled. Pilot pressure is internally supplied from the main pressure port ("P").

Hydraulic Actuation

Hydraulic actuation is similar to the pneumatic principle, except that, instead of acting on a piston, the actuating oil pressure acts directly on the end of the spool. Usually, a second pilot valve controls the pressurized actuating fluid (refer to "Two Stage Actuation").

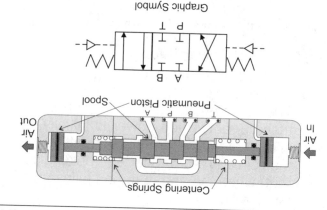

Illustration #199 — Pneumatic Actuation

Graphic Symbol

When the left solenoid is energized (moving the pilot spool to the right), pilot pressure is directed to the right side of the slave valve spool, moving it to the left. This will direct the main oil flows as follows: port 'P' connects to port 'A' and port 'B' connects to port 'T'.

De-energizing the left solenoid will allow the pilot spool to move to the center position (spring centered). This will drain the pressure on the right side of the main spool through the pilot spool passages to tank (port 'T'), allowing the main spool, which is also spring centered, to move to the center position.

Energizing the right solenoid will reverse the process.

Pilot Pressure

Pilot operated directional valves require a minimum pilot pressure (65 to 75 psi [448 to 517 kPa]) to move the main spool.

If pilot pressure is lost, the main valve will not move when the pilot valve is actuated.

It is common for pilot pressure to be supplied from the pressure port 'P', as shown in illustration #200.

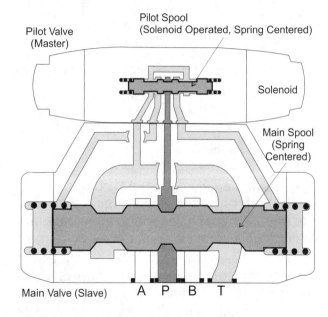

Illustration #200 — Typical Pilot Operated Valve

The closed center main valve spool ensures adequate pilot pressure when in the center position (refer to illustration #201).

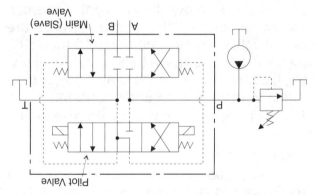

Illustration #201 — Maintain Pilot Pressure - Closed Center Main Spool

When a spool configuration such as tandem or open center is used, the pump flow is directed to the reservoir when the main valve is in the center position. This depressurizes the system.

Activating the pilot valve will have no effect on the main valve unless some device is used to ensure that minimum pressure is available.

Illustration #202 shows a circuit with a minimum pressure check valve located in the return line. This maintains the minimum pressure required for pilot valve operation.

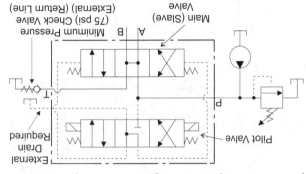

Illustration #202 — Maintain Pilot Pressure - Return Line Minimum Pressure Check Valve

Note: With this arrangement, the pilot valve must be externally drained.

Some directional valves have a minimum pressure check valve built into the 'P' port (sometimes referred to as a "P port sequence"), as shown in illustration #203. With this arrangement, the pilot can be internally drained.

If a circuit is designed to unload the pump as in illustration #204, an external check valve will be required in the line between the pump and the directional valve. The pilot pressure is then supplied externally. The pilot valve can be internally drained.

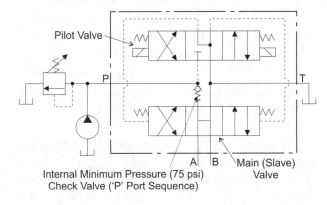

Illustrations #203 — Maintain Pilot Pressure - Internal Minimum Pressure Check Valve

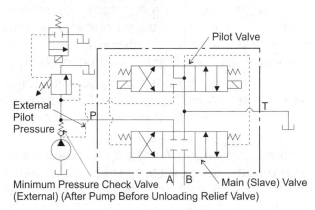

Illustration #204 — Maintain Pilot Pressure - Pump Discharge Minimum Pressure Check Valve

Controlling Main Spool Shifting Speed

If the shifting speed of the slave spool is excessive, hydraulic shock or "water hammer" may occur. High pressure fluid rapidly changes velocity or direction when the slave spool is shifted. This problem becomes more acute with large valves and high flow rates. Metering notches on the lands of the spool may help, but in some situations some method of controlling the slave spool shifting speed is required.

The main spool of a pilot operated directional valve operates as a linear actuator or cylinder.

The speed of an actuator is fixed by the flow rate to or from the actuator and the displacement (refer to Section Six for more on actuators). The shifting speed of the main spool can therefore be reduced by decreasing the flow rate to the ends of the spool.

One method of achieving this is to place an orifice (non adjustable) in the pressure port of the pilot valve. This will meter the flow between the pilot valve and the ends of the main spool. Selecting the correct size orifice may be somewhat trial and error and a few tries may be necessary before satisfactory valve operation is achieved.

The second method is to place adjustable flow control valves in the lines between the pilot valve and the slave spool ends.

The flow control valves, as shown in illustration #205, are mounted in a sandwich plate that is installed between the pilot valve and the slave valve. The flow control valves are usually oriented in a meter out direction and provide separate speed control for each direction.

Limiting Slave Spool Stroke

It may be required that the maximum flow from the valve be reduced. This can be achieved by installing end caps that are equipped with screw thread adjusters as shown in illustration #205.

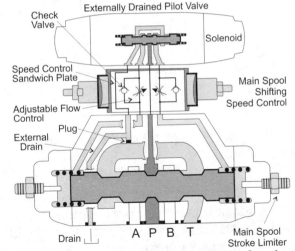

Illustration #205 — Limiting Slave Spool Shifting Speed

Rotary Type Directional Valves

The rotary type directional valve consists of a stationary body and a central rotor. The body contains the connection ports. Flow passages are machined into the rotor. A handle or lever is attached to the rotor for actuation purposes. Actuation is usually accomplished by manual or mechanical means. The rotor will connect or block the various ports, depending on the angular position of the rotor. The rotor center position is usually located by detent.

Illustration #206 shows how the body ports and rotor passages interconnect on a three-position, four-way, closed center rotary valve. The graphic symbol (also shown in illustration #206) for the rotary type directional valve is the same as for the spool type directional valve. Total angular movement of the rotor is usually limited to 90°.

Flow Control

Non-Pressure Compensated Flow Control

Non-pressure compensated flow control can be achieved by installing a simple device, such as a needle valve or a fixed orifice, to restrict fluid flow through a hydraulic line (refer to Section One for more information on flow through an orifice). The fixed orifice (refer to illustration #207A for graphic symbol) is used where adjustment of flow is not required (some situations may require changing orifice plates until the correct flow rate is achieved).

A typical example is found in some pilot operated directional valves, where the shifting speed of the main spool is reduced by placing a fixed orifice in the pressure port of the pilot valve.

This type of valve is usually used in low flow applications and is often seen as the pilot valve controlling a high flow spool type directional valve

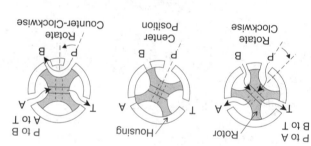

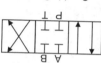

Graphic Symbol

Illustration #206 — Rotary Type Directional Valve

A needle valve (refer to illustration #207B for graphic symbol) provides an adjustable method of controlling flow and may be used for actuator speed control where accuracy is not critical and the load induced pressures remain relatively constant.

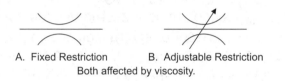

A. Fixed Restriction   B. Adjustable Restriction
Both affected by viscosity.

Illustration #207A & B — Graphic Symbol (Non-Compensated Flow Control)

Pressure Compensated Flow Control

Assuming no change in viscosity, the flow through a needle valve will only remain constant if the pressure difference across the valve remains constant.

Usually, due to changing loads and system demands, pressures on one or both sides of a flow control valve can change.

This will consequently change the flow through the valve (refer to Section One for more information on flow through an orifice). To overcome this problem, a pressure compensated flow control valve may be used. There are two types that are available. One is the bypass type and the second is the restrictor type.

Restrictor Type, Pressure Compensated Flow Control Valve

The restrictor type pressure compensated flow control valve, shown in illustration #208, is a two-way valve that consists of an adjustable orifice connected in series to a normally open hydrostat. The hydrostat is essentially a spool type direct acting pressure reducing valve.

When the restrictor type flow control valve is operating, the hydrostat, which senses the pressures on both sides of the adjustable orifice, restricts the amount of fluid entering the upstream side of the orifice. This arrangement maintains a constant pressure difference (set by the spring) across the adjustable orifice, which in turn maintains a constant flow rate for a particular setting.

If the adjustable orifice is opened wider, the constant pressure difference causes an increase in flow. If the adjustable orifice is closed off the flow rate is reduced.

An increase in pressure on the outlet side of the adjustable orifice will cause the hydrostat control orifice to open wider, increasing the pressure on the inlet side to maintain the pressure difference.

An increase in pressure at the inlet would cause the hydrostat to move in the opposite direction, restricting flow and therefore maintaining the pressure difference.

A reverse flow check valve may be included in the valve design.

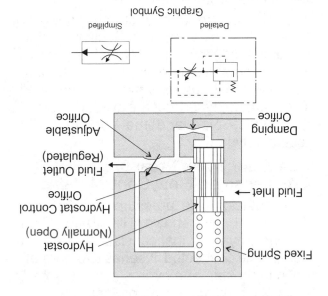

Graphic Symbol

Detailed   Simplified

Illustration #208 — Restrictor Type Pressure Compensated Flow Control Valve

Damping Orifice

Fluid Inlet

Fixed Spring

Adjustable Orifice

Fluid Outlet (Regulated)

Hydrostat Control Orifice

Hydrostat (Normally Open)

Bypass Type, Pressure Compensated Flow Control Valve

The bypass type flow control valve is a three-way valve that operates in a similar manner to the restrictor type, in that a hydrostat maintains a constant pressure difference across an adjustable orifice.

The bypass type uses a totally different method of maintaining the constant pressure difference across the adjustable orifice. The restrictor type simply limits the amount of flow to the adjustable orifice by blocking the inlet, whereas the bypass type directs the excess fluid to a tank port.

Referring to illustration #209, the normally closed hydrostat, which senses the pressure on both sides of the adjustable orifice, is in parallel with the adjustable orifice. Fluid from the inlet enters the chamber between the adjustable orifice and the hydrostat.

Inlet pressure opens the hydrostat sufficiently to allow fluid in excess of that required through the adjustable orifice to flow to the tank port. If the adjustable orifice is opened wider, the constant pressure difference causes an increase in flow. If the adjustable orifice is closed off, the flow rate reduced.

An increase in pressure on the outlet side of the adjustable orifice causes the hydrostat control orifice to reduce in size, thereby increasing the pressure on the inlet side of the adjustable orifice to maintain the pressure difference.

An increase in pressure at the fluid inlet causes the hydrostat control orifice to open. This allows more flow to the tank port to maintain the pressure difference.

A pilot relief valve (not shown) may also be included to give the bypass type flow control valve a second function, which is that of relief valve. The pilot relief valve limits the fluid pressure on the spring side of the hydrostat.

Temperature Compensated Flow Control

The viscosity of oil changes as the temperature changes. The viscosity decreases as the temperature becomes higher. The amount of viscosity change as the temperature changes is referred to as Viscosity Index (VI), and is not the same for all oils (for more information on viscosity and VI, refer to Section Two).

The amount of fluid flowing through an orifice is dependent on the pressure drop across the orifice and the viscosity of the fluid. The decrease in viscosity associated with an increase in fluid temperature increases the flow rate through an orifice for a specific pressure drop.

Any pressure on the inlet side of the adjustable orifice, greater than the pilot relief valve setting plus the spring pressure, will open the hydrostat and direct fluid flow to the reservoir.

Note: Before using a bypass type flow control valve to replace the relief valve, it must be verified that the pilot relief valve option is included.

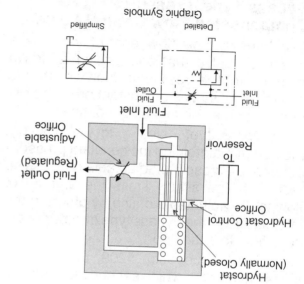

Illustration #209 — Bypass Type Pressure Compensated Flow Control Valve

There are two methods used to reduce the effect of temperature on flow rate. One method uses a sharp edge orifice, and the other a metallic rod.

Sharp Edged Orifice

The shape of the orifice has a direct bearing on its sensitivity to any change in viscosity. Because viscosity is a measure of the internal friction of a fluid, the amount of fluid flowing for a specific pressure drop through a long orifice, such as a capillary tube, depends on the viscosity. This is due to the friction between the fluid molecules and the wall of the capillary tube. A longer tube increases the effects of viscosity. Therefore, if the tube or orifice is shorter, any change in viscosity has less effect on the flow. By making the orifice as short as possible and using what is referred to as a sharp edged orifice, the effects of viscosity change is kept to a minimum.

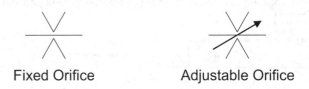

Fixed Orifice   Adjustable Orifice

Illustration #210 — Graphic Symbols for Temperature Compensated Flow Control

The sharp edged orifice can be either a fixed or adjustable orifice, and may be incorporated in the design of pressure compensated valves to provide both pressure and temperature compensation. See illustration #210 for the graphic symbols for non-pressure compensated sharp edged orifice flow control.

Metallic Rod

This method utilizes a metallic rod to change the size of the orifice opening when the temperature changes. In the example shown in illustration #211, a metallic rod is located between the adjusting screw and the spring loaded throttle.

As the temperature increases, the length of the metallic rod also increases and raises the throttle slightly, thereby reducing the metering notch opening. This compensates for the increased flow rate due to the reduction in viscosity from the temperature increase. Due to the wide variety of hydraulic fluids in use, pressure compensated valves using the metallic rod for temperature compensation are designed for an average fluid. This results in its accuracy depending on the type of fluid being used. The metallic rod type of temperature compensation is most commonly used in industrial pressure and temperature compensated flow control valves.

Another temperature compensated design using the thermal expansion of metal utilizes a bi-metallic rod that bends as the temperature changes. This bending is due to the different expansion rates of the two metals the rod is composed of.

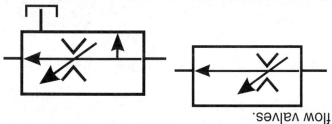

Illustration #211 — Metallic Rod Temperature Compensated Flow Control

The valve design utilizes the bending feature of the bi-metallic rod to vary the metering notch size as the temperature changes. See illustration #212 for the graphic symbols of temperature and pressure compensated flow valves.

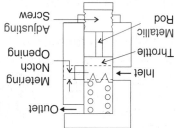

Illustration #212 — Graphic Symbols for Temperature and Pressure Compensated Flow Control

Actuator Speed Control Methods

There are three methods available when using flow control valves to regulate actuator speed. They are:

- Meter-In
  - With restrictor type flow control
  - With bypass type flow control
- Meter-Out
- Bleed-Off

Meter-In
- With Restrictor Type Flow Control

The meter-in circuit controls the speed of an actuator by metering the flow of fluid *to* the actuator. This is accomplished by placing a restrictor type flow control valve in the line supplying fluid to the hydraulic motor or cylinder. Illustration #213 shows a two-way pressure compensated flow control valve controlling the extension speed of a cylinder.

The retraction speed can also be controlled by the meter-in method by placing a restrictor type flow control valve in the supply line to the rod end of the cylinder.

Meter-in speed control is most suitable where the load offers a continual resistance to the actuator (refer to illustration #213A). If the load attempts to move faster than the supply fluid, a high vacuum will be produced in the supply end of the cylinder as the load extends the cylinder faster than the oil supply (see illustration #213B).

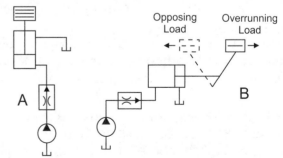

Illustration #213 — Meter-In, Resistive and Variable Load

When a restrictor type flow control valve is used in a meter-in circuit, excess oil from the pump is being passed over the relief valve at the relief valve pressure.

When the speed of the actuator is low, a high proportion of the pump output is passed over the relief valve, and most of the hydraulic power is being converted to heat (refer to Section One for more on heat generation). As the actuator speed is increased, the amount of heat generation is reduced because more fluid is used to do useful work and less fluid goes over the relief valve.

To conclude, a meter-in restrictor type flow control circuit:

- Will not control an overrunning load.
- Will not be effected by variations in pump internal leakage with regards to speed control.

Changes in the amount of internal leakage at the pump will not effect the speed control as long as the pump can supply an adequate quantity of fluid to the flow control valve.

Changes in the amount of internal leakage at the actuator will directly affect the actuator speed.

Illustration #214 shows that when there is no internal leakage at either the motor or pump, 4 gpm (15.1 litres) flows over the relief valve and the motor operates at a 6 gpm (22.7 litres). Any leakage at the pump will reduce the amount of fluid passing over the relief valve, and will not effect the motor speed. The flow control valve will continue to supply 6 gpm (22.7 litres) to the motor. Internal leakage at the motor will cause the motor to slow down, because the fluid from the motor is not being used to produce rotation.

- Cannot compensate for variations in actuator leakage.
- Is most inefficient when actuator speed is slow (high heat generation) but becomes more efficient as actuator speed is increased.

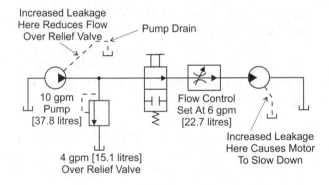

Illustration #214 — Meter-In, Affects of Leakage

Meter-In
- With Bypass Type Flow Control

This method of flow control uses a bypass type (three-way) pressure compensated flow control valve situated in a meter-in position in the circuit (refer to illustration #215). This circuit provides the accuracy of the restrictor type meter-in circuit with the efficiency of the bleed-off circuit. Unfortunately it retains two of the main disadvantages. There is no control of an overrunning load and it can only be used in single use circuits, since the excess fluid is directed back to tank from the flow control valve.

Note: The gain in efficiency depends on the pressure generated by the load. If the load requires a pressure close to the relief valve setting, the efficiency gain will be small.

To conclude, a meter-in, with bypass type flow control valve circuit:

- Will not control an overrunning load.
- Will not be effected by variations in pump internal leakage with regards to speed control.
- Will be effected by variations in actuator leakage with regards to speed control.
- Will more accurately control a cylinder circuit than a motor circuit (assuming little or no cross port leakage from the cylinder).
- Provides a more efficient system than either the restrictor type meter-in or meter-out circuits, especially with light actuator loads and a slow speed setting.
- Can only be used in a single use circuit as there is no excess fluid from the pump that can be used for other operations.

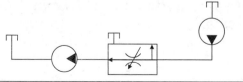

Illustration #215 — Meter-in with Bypass Type Flow Control Valve

Meter-Out

The meter-out circuit controls the speed of an actuator by metering the flow of fluid that is coming out of the actuator discharge. This is accomplished by placing a restrictor type flow control valve in the line carrying the fluid from the hydraulic motor or cylinder. Illustration #216 indicates that by restricting the flow that is discharged from the actuator, the speed will be controlled regardless of the direction of load, therefore the meter-out circuits can be used to control overrunning loads.

When used with cylinders having relatively large diameter piston rods, there is a possibility of obtaining pressures that are much higher than the relief valve setting at the rod end of the cylinder (refer to Section Six for more on pressure intensification in cylinders).

As with meter-in circuits, any changes in internal leakage at the actuator will effect the speed regulation, although the amount by which the leakage changes the spool regulation will be somewhat different due to the fact that the inlet to the actuator is always at relief pressure and the outlet pressure fluctuates according to the load. The effects of internal actuator leakage will depend on whether the actuator is a motor or cylinder.

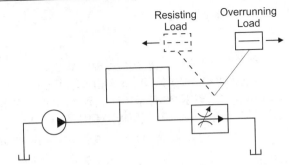

Illustration #216 — Meter-Out Flow Control

Note: Motor leakage consists of cross port leakage and case drain leakage. Cross port leakage occurs when fluid bypasses directly from the inlet to outlet without doing any useful work. Cross port leakage occurs in motors and cylinders. Case drain leakage occurs in certain motors only and is the result of fluid escaping past the clearances in the motor to the casing. Case drain leakage is directed back to the reservoir via a separate drain line.

To conclude, a meter-out flow control circuit:

- Will control an overrunning load.
- Will not be effected by variations in pump internal leakage with regards to speed control.
- Will be effected by variations in actuator leakage with regards to speed control.
- Is most inefficient when actuator speed is slow (high heat generation) but becomes more efficient as actuator speed is increased.
- Can create much higher (pressure intensification) than the relief valve setting when used with high ratio cylinders.

Bleed-Off

The bleed-off circuit controls the speed of an actuator by placing a restrictor type flow control valve in parallel with the actuator (refer to illustration #217). Allowing more, or less flow through the flow control valve, will control the amount of flow to the actuator.

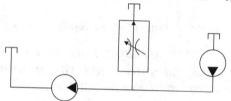

Illustration #217 — Bleed-Off Flow Control

The total pump output is divided between the flow control valve and the actuator. The main advantage to this type of flow control is that the system pressure is determined by the load.

Fluid will not pass through the main relief valve unless the load on the actuator causes the pressure to reach the relief valve setting.

The excess fluid is directed to the reservoir through the flow control valve at load induced pressure, instead of over the relief valve at maximum system pressure, as it is with the restrictor type meter-in and meter-out circuits. Therefore the bleed-off circuit is a much more efficient circuit, especially when the load induced pressures are low.

As with the meter-in circuit, because there is no control of the discharge fluid from the actuator, the bleed-off system will not control an overrunning load.

To conclude, a bleed-off flow control circuit:

- Will not control an overrunning load.
- Will be effected by variations in both pump and actuator internal leakage with regards to speed control.
- Will not provide the same speed control accuracy as restrictor type meter-in or meter-out systems.
- Provides a more efficient system than either the restrictor type meter-in or meter-out circuits, especially with light actuator loads and a slow speed setting.
- Can only be used in a single use circuit as there is no excess fluid from the pump that can be used for other operations.

SECTION SEVEN QUESTIONS

Basic Control Valves

1. List the three basic hydraulic control valve functions:

   Answer: *Pressure, Direction & Flow control*

2. A relief valve is a "normally open" valve.

   ❑ true   ☑ false

3. Explain the relief valve term "cracking pressure":

   Answer: *when it first starts bleeding fluid*

4. Explain the relief valve term "full flow pressure":

   Answer: *pressure required to pass total amount of flow*

5. Explain the relief valve term "pressure override":

   Answer: *difference between "crack" + "full flow"*

6. The pilot operated relief valve must be supplied with a separate pilot line to be able to operate.

   ☑ true   ❑ false

7. When the pressure equalizes on both sides of the balanced piston of a balanced piston relief valve, the spring will then hold the valve open.

   ☑ true   ❑ false

8. If it is required that the full pump output is to be returned to the reservoir under little or no pressure by venting the relief valve, the most suitable type of relief valve would be:

   ☑ pilot operated
   ☑ direct acting

9. The pumps, used in a two pump system that provides an initial high volume of low pressure fluid and then as pressure rises a low volume of high pressure fluid, would be:

   ❑ a single variable volume pump
   ❑ two low volume high pressure pumps
   ❑ two high volume low pressure pumps
   ☑ one low volume high pressure and one high volume low pressure pump

10. *Some accumulator circuits use an unloading relief valve to control pressures in the circuit. The unloading relief valve would most likely be a:*

- ☑ direct acting relief
- ☐ normal pilot operated relief valve
- ☐ special pilot operated relief with built-in isolating check valve and unloading piston
- ☐ direct acting relief valve operating in conjunction with a pressure reducing valve

11. *When the maximum system pressure has been reached in an accumulator circuit that is controlled by an unloading relief valve, the unloading relief valve will:*

- ☑ direct the full pump output to tank at full system pressure
- ☐ direct approximately 75% of the pump output to tank at very low pressure
- ☐ shut the pump off
- ☐ direct the full pump output to tank at very low pressure

12. *A single sequence valve can be used to control the sequence of operation of up to 4 cylinders.*

☑ true   ☐ false

---

13. *If a sequence valve is used to control the sequence of extension of two cylinders, what device is incorporated in the sequence valve to allow the cylinders to retract?*

Answer: *Return flow check valve*

14. *A counterbalance valve may be required when the load on an actuator exerts a continual force that tends to move the actuator faster than the designed hydraulic speed. When would an overcenter valve arrangement be required?*

Answer: *When there is a continual force* *As a cylinder*

15. *What type of valve arrangement is shown in the illustration?*

Answer: *quick outlet controlly* *a cylinder*

16. *What type of valve arrangement is shown in the illustration?*

Answer: *Directacting spool valve*

17. What type of valve arrangement is shown in the illustration?

Answer: Direct acting spool used as a brake valve

18. A pressure reducing valve is a "normally open" valve.
   ☑ true   ❏ false

19. Pressure reducing valves can be either pilot operated or direct acting.
   ☑ true   ❏ false

20. List three features that are used to describe directional control valves:

   Answer: _____
   _____

21. Although a check valve is usually classified as a type of direction control valve, it is sometimes also used for pressure control purposes.
   ❏ true   ❏ false

22. Some "pilot-to-open" check valves used in high pressure situations may be provided with a special feature to relieve the pressure behind the main poppet before the main poppet opens. What is this feature?

   Answer: _____
   _____

23. What is the purpose of the grooves that are machined around periphery of the lands of spool type directional valve spools?

   Answer: _____
   _____

24. A valve that is represented by the graphic symbol shown could be used to operate a double acting cylinder.
   ❏ true   ❏ false

25. *The symbol shown would be used to represent a:*

    ❏ three position, four way, open center directional valve

    ❏ three position, four way, tandem center directional valve

    ❏ three position, four way, float center directional valve

    ❏ three position, four way, closed center directional valve

26. *The symbol shown would be used to represent a:*

    ❏ three position, four way, open center directional valve

    ❏ three position, four way, tandem center directional valve

    ❏ three position, four way, float center directional valve

    ❏ three position, four way, closed center directional valve

27. *The symbol shown would be used to represent a:*

    ❏ three position, four way, open center directional valve

    ❏ three position, four way, tandem center directional valve

    ❏ three position, four way, float center directional valve

    ❏ three position, four way, closed center directional valve

28. *The symbol shown would be used to represent a:*

    ❏ three position, four way, open center directional valve

    ❏ three position, four way, tandem center directional valve

    ❏ three position, four way, float center directional valve

    ❏ three position, four way, closed center directional valve

29. *Directional valve spools that use detents will always return to the center position when the actuating forces are removed.*

    ❏ true   ❏ false

30. Two position directional valves are usually spring centered.

    ❏ true   ❏ false

31. When the solenoid on a directional valve is energized the force from the solenoid:

    ❏ pushes on the spool
    ❏ pulls the spool

32. A three position solenoid operated directional valve will normally have:

    ❏ a solenoid at each end of the spool
    ❏ a solenoid at one end of the spool and a spring at the other

33. A potential problem with the air gap solenoid is that leakage at the dynamic seal on the push pin may eventually occur.

    ❏ true   ❏ false

34. A potential problem with the wet armature solenoid is that leakage at the dynamic seal on the push pin may eventually occur.

    ❏ true   ❏ false

35. A pneumatically actuated three position spring centered directional valve will usually have:

    ❏ a single acting pneumatic piston at one end of the spool
    ❏ a single acting pneumatic piston at each end of the spool
    ❏ a double acting pneumatic piston at one end of the spool
    ❏ a double acting pneumatic piston at each end of the spool

36. A two stage or pilot operated directional valve would be required when:

    ❏ flow rates become high
    ❏ pressures become high

37. The most common method of controlling the pilot valve of a pilot operated directional valve is by solenoid.

    ❏ true   ❏ false

38. Pilot operated directional valves require a minimum pilot pressure of approximately:

    ❏ 2 to 5 psi
    ❏ 8 to 12 psi
    ❏ 65 to 75 psi
    ❏ 300 to 400 psi

39. *A two stage directional valve with an open or tandem center main spool will not have the required pilot pressure to operate the main valve unless a minimum pressure check valve is used.*

❏ true   ❏ false

40. *If a minimum pressure check valve is used in the return line the pilot valve of a pilot operated directional valve must:*

❏ be internally drained
❏ be externally drained
❏ have no drain

41. *When adjustable orifices are used to control the main spool shifting speed of a pilot operated directional valve, they are oriented to meter the flow of fluid returning from the end of the main spool (meter out).*

❏ true   ❏ false

42. *A needle valve is a typical example of a pressure compensated flow control valve.*

❏ true   ❏ false

43. *The restrictor type pressure compensated flow control valve is three way valve that directs the excess flow to the reservoir.*

❏ true   ❏ false

44. *The bypass type pressure compensated flow control valve is a three way valve that directs the excess flow to the reservoir.*

❏ true   ❏ false

45. *All pressure compensated flow control valves are also temperature compensated.*

❏ true   ❏ false

46. *An increase in fluid viscosity would decrease the amount of fluid flowing through a fixed orifice as long as the pressure difference remained the same.*

❏ true   ❏ false

47. *What are the three flow control valve arrangements used when designing circuits to regulate actuator speed?*

Answer: _____

_____

48. *A restrictor type flow control valve is used in a meter-in circuit to control the speed of a rotary actuator. What affect would a small reduction in pump output (due to internal leakage) have on the actuator speed?*

❏ the actuator would slow down by an amount corresponding to the amount of leakage
❏ no affect as long as the pump output is higher than that required by the actuator

49. A meter-in restrictor type flow control arrangement is not suitable for overrunning actuator loads.
   ❏ true   ❏ false

50. A restrictor type flow control valve is used in a meter-in circuit to control the speed of a rotary actuator. What affect would any internal leakage at the actuator have on the actuator speed?
   ❏ the actuator would slow down by an amount corresponding to the amount of leakage
   ❏ no affect as long as the pump output is higher than that required by the actuator

51. The most efficient flow control system when actuator speeds and loads are low is:
   ❏ meter-in circuit using a two-way or restrictor type flow control
   ❏ meter-in circuit using a three-way or bypass type flow control

52. The type of flow control valve that would be used when using a meter-out flow control arrangement would be a:
   ❏ three-way or bypass type
   ❏ two-way or restrictor type

53. Which flow control arrangement would be most suitable to control an overrunning load?
   ❏ meter-in using a restrictor type flow control valve
   ❏ meter-in using a bypass type flow control valve
   ❏ meter-out
   ❏ bleed off

54. Any pump internal leakage will have a major affect on the speed of an actuator when a meter-out flow control arrangement is used.
   ❏ true   ❏ false

55. A bleed-off flow control arrangement uses a restrictor type flow control valve teed in to the inlet line to the actuator.
   ❏ true   ❏ false

56. The bleed-off arrangement of flow control is suitable for multiple circuits, as the excess fluid can be directed to other branches of the circuit.
   ❏ true   ❏ false

SECTION EIGHT

CARTRIDGE VALVES

Introduction

The requirement of greater hydraulic system efficiency had led to increased use of manifold blocks and cartridge valves and less use of conventional valves and components.

A manifold block contains a number of inter-connecting passageways. These passageways are accessed by the cartridge valves that are installed in cavities machined into the manifold blocks. The cavity dimensions for each valve size is controlled by the specification DIN 24342.

A section through a typical cavity compatible with a two-way slip-in cartridge valve is shown in illustration #218.

The use of manifold blocks reduces the number of pipes, hoses and fittings that connect individual components, while at the same time, giving greater flexibility for circuit design and also providing a considerable saving in space.

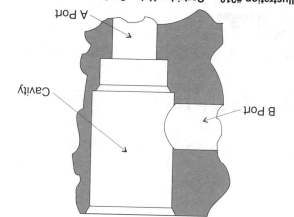

Illustration #218 — Cartridge Valve Cavity

A Port

Cavity

B Port

Although cartridge valves are commonly used in manifold blocks, they can also be used as individual valve assemblies. The majority of cartridge valves are two-way valves with either a poppet or spool controlling the flow between the two main passages. Some designs are three or four way spool type valves. Cartridge valves can provide all the necessary functions (flow, direction and pressure control) required of hydraulic valves.

Cartridge Valve Sizes

Cartridge valves are available in a number of different sizes depending on the expected flow rate. Typical sizes are 16, 25, 40, 50 and 63 mm. This size refers to the diameter of the main ports ('A' and 'B' in the case of two-way valves). Refer to information from the manufacturer regarding maximum flow rates and pressures.

Slip-In Type Cartridge Valves

The majority of cartridge valves are the slip-in type. This type is held in place using a bolted cover that also seals the cavity and provides pilot passages to control the opening and closing of the valve. Although the slip-in type may be a spool valve, the majority are poppet type pilot operated check valves that are arranged to operate either independently or as part of a group to provide directional, pressure and flow control functions. These valves are also referred to as logic valves or logic elements.

Basic Operation

Illustration #219 shows the construction of a typical slip-in, poppet type cartridge valve that consists of a sleeve, poppet valve and spring.

The sleeve fits inside a two-way manifold cavity. The poppet valve, which makes contact on the sleeve seat, will allow or prevent fluid movement between the 'A' and 'B' ports depending on whether the valve is open or closed. Illustration #218 shows a section through a typical two-way manifold cavity.

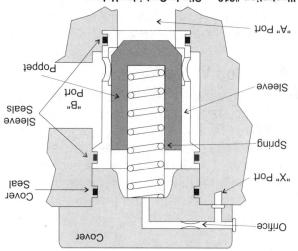

Illustration #219 — Slip-In Cartridge Valve

A spring provides an initial closing force on the poppet valve. Static seals prevent fluid from migrating between areas of differing pressures at the cover and between the sleeve and the housing.

The cartridge valve cover, which is bolted to the manifold, holds the complete insert assembly (sleeve, poppet and spring) in place. The cover shown in illustration #219 is the basic cover. An orifice is fitted in the connecting passage between the spring chamber and the 'X' port to control the flow rate of the fluid to and from the spring chamber and therefore control the opening and closing speed of the poppet. Many other covers are available, containing features that allow flexibility of circuit design and cartridge use.

The poppet will be in the open or closed position depending on the various pressures existing at ports 'A', 'B' and in the spring chamber.

There are two separate designs with regard to the sleeve and poppet that will effect the net opening or closing force on the poppet. The design differences, which determine if the poppet is balanced or unbalanced, are shown in illustration #220 and illustration #221.

Balanced Poppet

In illustration #220, the poppet is straight sided and seals on a tapered seat machined into the sleeve. The area on the spring or pilot side of the poppet (A_P) is the same as the area exposed to port 'A' (A_A).

$$A_P = A_A$$

This is referred to as a balanced poppet. The closing force will be the sum of the spring force and the hydraulic force acting on area A_P. The opening force will be the hydraulic force acting on area A_A. If the hydraulic pressure is equal on both sides of the poppet, the valve will be held closed by the spring pressure.

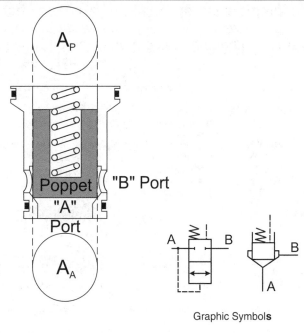

Graphic Symbols

Illustration #220 — Balanced Poppet

The poppet in illustration #221 has a chamfered end that seats on a sharp edged seat. The area exposed to port 'A' (A_A) is less than the area on the spring or pilot side of the poppet (A_P). Due to the chamfer, the pressure in port 'B', which acts on annulus area (A_B) will increase the opening force on the unbalanced poppet. This is referred to as an unbalanced poppet.

$$A_P = A_A + A_B$$

The closing force will be the sum of the spring force and the hydraulic force acting on area A_P. The opening force will be the sum of the hydraulic force acting on both areas A_A and A_B. The opening and closing of the poppet is achieved by managing the pressures acting on the three areas A_P, A_B and A_A.

Note: *Two types of symbols that may be used to represent poppet type cartridge valves are shown in illustration #220 and illustration #221.*

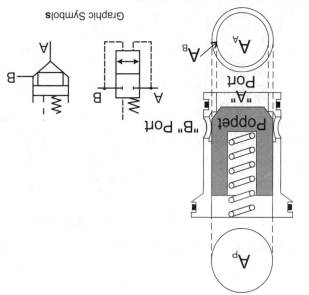

Graphic Symbols

Illustration #221 — Unbalanced Poppet

Area Ratios

The ratio between the spring chamber area (A_P) and the area of the poppet exposed to the 'A' port (A_A) is referred to as the cartridge valve area ratio.

The difference between the areas A_P and A_A will be the area of the poppet exposed to port B (A_B). Three typical area ratios for poppet cartridge valves are shown below, including the calculations for the opening and closing forces when specific pressures are present at ports A, B and on the spring side of the poppet.

Note: For the metric SI calculations, areas are converted from mm^2 to m^2 ($x\ 10^{-6}$) and pressures are converted from kPa to pascals (Pa) ($x\ 10^3$). 10^{-6} multiplied by 10^3 equals 10^{-3}.

1. *1:1 Area Ratio:*

This is a balanced poppet, shown in illustration #220, where:

A_P is equal to A_A and $A_B = 0$.

The opening and closing forces on the valve shown in illustration #222 are as follows:

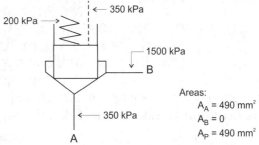

Areas:
$A_A = 490\ mm^2$
$A_B = 0$
$A_P = 490\ mm^2$

Illustration #222 — 1:1 Area Ratio Opening/Closing Forces (Metric SI)

Opening force Fo is equal to:
$(A_A \times P_A) + (A_B \times P_B)$
$Fo = ((490 \times 350) + (0 \times 1500)) \times 10^{-3}$
$Fo = 171.5\ N$

Closing force Fc is equal to:
$A_P \times$ (spring pressure + hydraulic pressure)
$Fc = A_P \times (P_S + P_P)$
$Fc = 490 \times (200 + 350) \times 10^{-3}$
$Fc = 269.5\ N$

This valve will be closed.

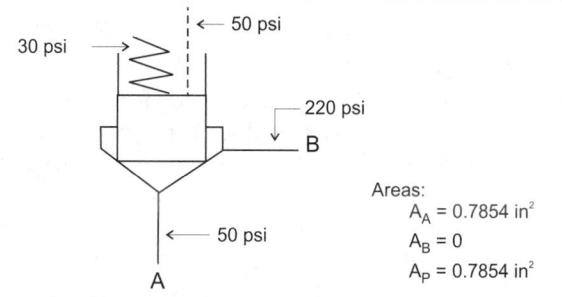

Illustration #223 — 1:1 Area Ratio Opening/Closing Forces (In-lb-gal)

The opening and closing forces on the valve shown in illustration #223 are as follows:

Opening force Fo is equal to:

$(A_A \times P_A) + (A_B \times P_B)$

$Fo = (0.7854 \times 50) + (0 \times 220)$

$Fo = 39.27$ lbs

Closing force Fc is equal to:

A_P x (spring pressure + hydraulic pressure)

$Fc = A_P \times (P_S + P_P)$

$Fc = 0.7854 \times (30 + 50)$

$Fc = 62.83$ lbs

This valve will be closed.

2. *1:1.1 Area Ratio:*

This is an unbalanced poppet, shown in illustration #221, where:

A_P divided by A_A equals 1.1.

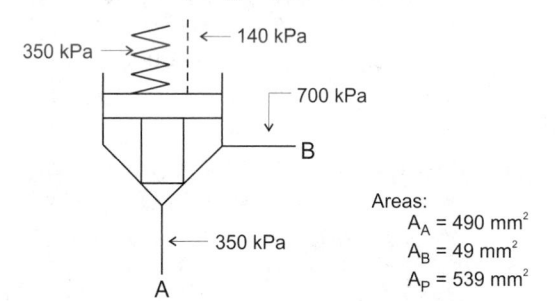

Illustration #224 — 1:1.1 Area Ratio Opening/Closing Forces (Metric SI)

The opening and closing forces on the valve shown in illustration #224 are as follows:

Opening force Fo is equal to:

$(A_A \times P_A) + (A_B \times P_B)$

$Fo = ((490 \times 350) + (49 \times 700)) \times 10^{-3}$

$Fo = 205.8$ N

Closing force Fc is equal to:

A_P x (spring pressure + hydraulic pressure)

$Fc = A_P \times (P_S + P_P)$

$Fc = 539 \times (350 + 140) \times 10^{-3}$

$Fc = 264.11$ N

This valve will be closed.

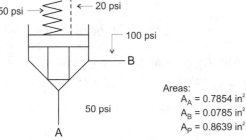

Areas:
$A_A = 0.7854$ in^2
$A_B = 0.0785$ in^2
$A_P = 0.8639$ in^2

Illustration #225 — 1:1.1 Area Ratio Opening/Closing Forces (In-lb-gal)

The opening and closing forces on the valve shown in illustration #225 are as follows:

Opening force Fo is equal to:

$(A_A \times P_A) + (A_B \times P_B)$

$Fo = (0.7854 \times 50) + (0.0785 \times 100)$

$Fo = 47.12$ lbs

Closing force Fc is equal to:

A_P x (spring pressure + hydraulic pressure)

$Fc = A_P \times (P_S + P_P)$

$Fc = 0.8639 \times (50 + 20)$

$Fc = 60.47$ lbs

This valve will be closed.

3. *1:2 Area Ratio:*

This is an unbalanced poppet, shown in illustration #221, where:

A_P divided by A_A equals 2.

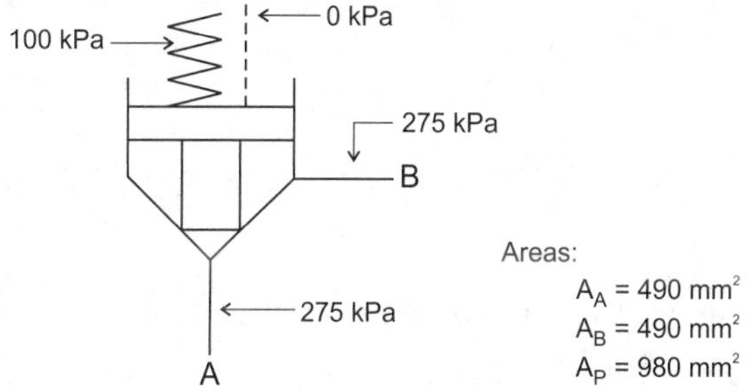

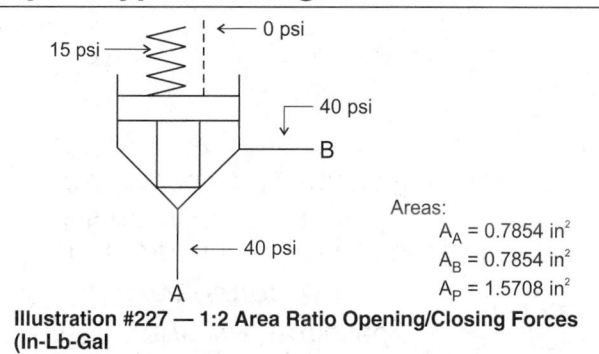

Illustration #226 — 1:2 Area Ratio Opening/Closing Forces (Metric SI)

Illustration #227 — 1:2 Area Ratio Opening/Closing Forces (In-Lb-Gal

The opening and closing forces on the valve shown in illustration #226 are as follows:

Opening force Fo is equal to:

$(A_A \times P_A) + (A_B \times P_B)$

$Fo = ((490 \times 275) + (490 \times 275)) \times 10^{-3}$

$Fo = 269.5$ N

Closing force Fc is equal to:

A_P x (spring pressure + hydraulic pressure)

$Fc = A_P \times (P_S + P_P)$

$Fc = 980 \times (0 + 100) \times 10^{-3}$

$Fc = 98$ N

This valve will be open.

The opening and closing forces on the valve shown in illustration #227 are as follows.

Opening force Fo is equal to:

$(A_A \times P_A) + (A_B \times P_B)$

$Fo = (0.7854 \times 40) + (0.7854 \times 40)$

$Fo = 62.83$ lbs

Closing force Fc is equal to:

A_P x (spring pressure + hydraulic pressure)

$Fc = A_P \times (P_S + P_P)$

$Fc = 1.5708 \times (15 + 0)$

$Fc = 23.56$ lbs

This valve will be open.

Examples of Slip-In Cartridge Valve Use

The following are some of the more common uses of slip-in type cartridge valves:

- Check Valve
- Four-Way Directional Control
- Relief Valve
- Pressure Reducing
- Non-Compensated Flow Control

Check Valve: One of the simplest directional control functions is the check valve. The 1:2 ratio cartridge valve in illustration #228 is acting as a check valve to prevent the cylinder from lowering. Spring load plus the pressure from port 'B' acting on area A_P is holding the valve closed. The pressure required in port 'A' to open the valve will be equal to the pressure in port 'B' plus the pressure to overcome the spring load.

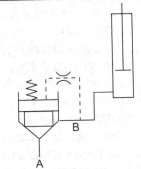

Illustration #228 — Cartridge Check Valve

Four-Way Directional Control: Illustration #229 shows four unbalanced cartridge valves arranged to provide control of a double acting cylinder. Ports 'A' and 'B' on the cylinder will be either pressurized, vented to tank or blocked off depending on the condition (piloted or vented) of each of the pilot lines to the cartridge valves.

Twelve combinations of pilot line states, either piloted (P) or vented (V) are shown in

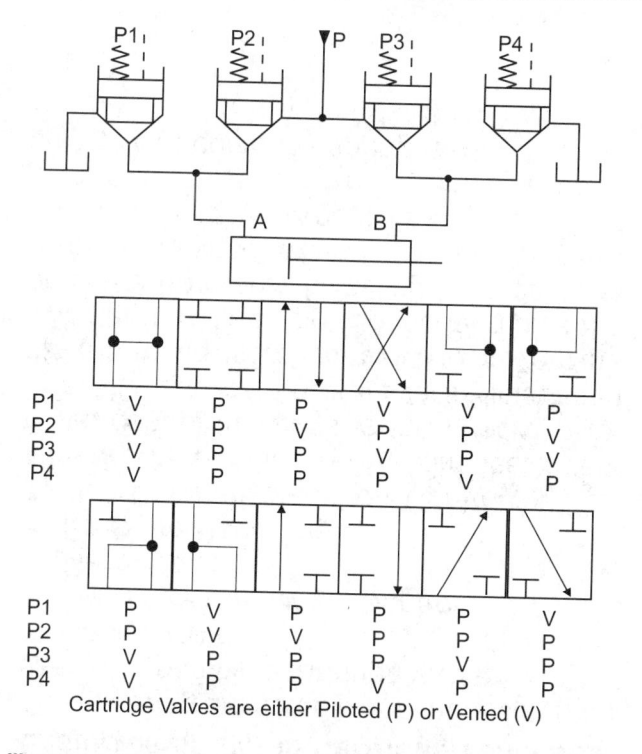

Cartridge Valves are either Piloted (P) or Vented (V)

Illustration #229— Using Cartridge Valves for Directional Control

illustration #229 along with the equivalent spool valve conditions.

Illustration #230 shows that by using a solenoid operated pilot valve to control four cartridge valves, a three-position four way spool valve can be simulated. The pilot pressure is taken from the system pressure line. When the pilot spool is in the center position, pilot pressure is directed to all four cartridge valves. This essentially closes all four cartridge valves.

Note: In illustration #230, check valves are shown in the spool equivalent condition when the pilot valve is centered and all the cartridge valves have pilot pressure applied. This is because an external load on the cylinder could generate a pressure high enough to open either cartridge valve P2 (load pushing on the cylinder rod) or P3 (load pulling on the cylinder rod). The pressure required from the cylinder for this to occur would be system pressure plus spring pressure.

When the left solenoid is energized, moving the pilot spool to the right, cartridge valves P1 and P3 are piloted, keeping them closed, and valves P2 and P4 are vented, which allows them to open. Fluid enters port 'A' via valve P2 and fluid from port 'B' passes through valve P4 to tank, which extends the cylinder. Energizing the right solenoid moves the pilot spool to the left, causing valves P2 and P4 to be held closed by pilot pressure and valves P1 and P3 are vented. Fluid enters port 'B' via valve P3 and fluid from port 'A' passes to tank via valve P1, which retracts the cylinder.

Note: If system pressure was lost, the only thing preventing the cylinder from moving is the spring pressure holding the cartridge valves closed. For this reason the circuit shown in illustration #230 could not be used for a vertical cylinder that must support a load when the pump is shut off.

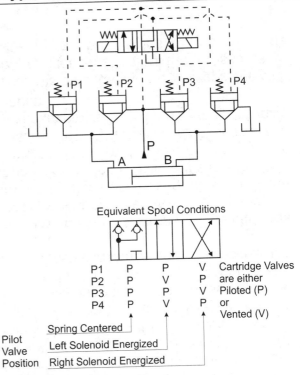

Illustration #230 — Cartridge Valves with Pilot Valve

Typically, the four cartridge valves shown in illustration #230 would be housed in a mani-fold. Internal passages in the manifold and cartridge valve covers would provide the control lines shown. One of the cartridge valve covers would have a special mounting surface to accept the pilot valve.

Relief Valve: Probably the most common pressure control function is the pressure re-lief valve. Illustration #231 shows a balanced (1:1 ratio) cartridge valve that is controlled by a pilot valve to perform as a relief valve. The pilot valve is built into the cartridge valve cover.

System pressure at port 'A' is acting on the underside of the poppet (area A_A) and is pro-viding the opening force. This same pressure is ported to the spring side of the poppet (area A_P) and in conjunction with the spring force provides the closing force.

As long as the pilot valve is closed, the hy-draulic opening and closing forces are equal due to the equal areas A_A and A_P. The spring force will keep the cartridge poppet closed. If pressure in port 'A' rises sufficiently, the pilot poppet will open to limit the pressure on the spring side of the cartridge poppet (area A_P). If the pressure in port 'A' continues to rise, the pressure on area A_A will now become greater than the pressure on area A_P. The cartridge poppet will open when the difference in hy-draulic forces becomes greater than the spring closing force. This will allow the fluid from port 'A' to flow to the tank. The system pressure (in port 'A') will be maintained at this maximum pressure as long as the pilot valve is open.

When the pressure in port 'A' drops, the pilot poppet closes allowing the pressures to equalize on both sides of the cartridge poppet.

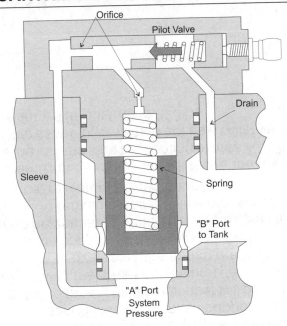

Illustration #231 — Pilot Operated Relief Valve

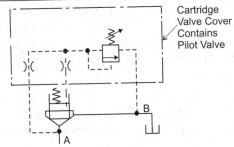

Illustration #231s — (Graphic Symbol) Pilot Operated Relief Valve

The cartridge poppet, which now has equal hydraulic forces on both sides will close due to the spring force.

If the relief valve shown in illustration #231 is required to also perform as an unloading valve, the pilot valve can be vented by mounting a two position solenoid operated directional valve on the appropriate cartridge relief valve covers.

Illustration #232 shows a schematic diagram of the pilot operated relief valve from illustration #231 with the addition of a venting valve. When the solenoid is de-energized, the area on the spring side of the main poppet (A_p) is vented to tank. The main poppet will be open whenever the pressure in port 'A' is high enough to overcome the spring pressure on the main poppet. All the fluid from port 'A' will then be vented to tank. This would allow the pump to remain running at low pressure and hence, minimum power input.

Energizing the solenoid will move the spool to the left and stop the venting of area A_p. The valve assembly will then act as a relief valve as shown in illustration #231.

Pressure Reducing: Pressure reduction can be achieved by the use of spool type cartridge valves. Illustration #233 shows a balanced, normally open, spool type cartridge valve arranged to limit the pressure to port 'A'. A pilot valve mounted in the cover senses and limits the pressure on the cover side of the spool (area A_p).

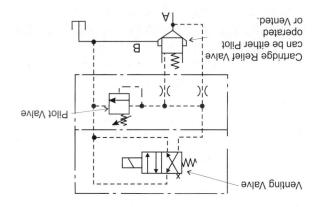

Illustration #232 — Venting the Relief Valve

Pilot Valve

Venting Valve

Cartridge Relief Valve can be either Pilot operated or Vented.

A

B

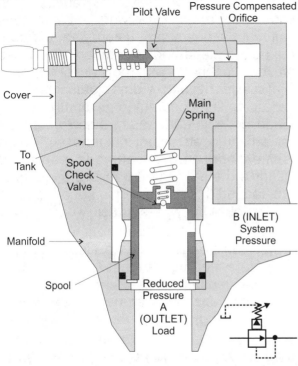

Illustration #233 — Spool Type Pressure Reducing Cartridge Valve

Pilot Valve

Pressure Compensated Orifice

Cover

To Tank

Spool Check Valve

Main Spring

Manifold

Spool

Reduced Pressure A (OUTLET) Load

B (INLET) System Pressure

Graphic Symbol

If the pressures on both sides of the spool are equal, the main spring force will hold the spool in the open position, allowing fluid to flow from the inlet (port 'B') to the outlet (port 'A'). When the load and system pressure rise above the pilot valve setting, the pilot valve opens and limits the pressure on the cover side of the spool (area A_P). The spool will start to move towards the spring when the pressure in port 'A' increases enough to overcome the combined spring and hydraulic pressure on the cover side of the spool. This will restrict flow from port 'B' to maintain the reduced pressure at port 'A'. The pressure compensated orifice in the pilot line from port 'B' to the pilot valve reduces the pilot valve pressure override by maintaining a constant the flow through the pilot circuit when the pilot valve is open. The check valve built into the spool allows any load generated pressure surges at port 'A' to be relieved by the pilot valve instead of quickly closing the spool.

Note: The spool check valve is not intended to act as a relief valve for the load side of the circuit.

Non-Compensated Flow Control: Flow control valves can be either pressure compensated or non-pressure compensated. A simple, non-pressure compensated cartridge flow control valve, or throttling valve is shown in illustration #234.

This valve, which has a 'V' type notch machined into the unbalanced (1:2) poppet, operates in a similar manner to the previously described unbalanced cartridge valves. When the opening forces become greater than the closing forces the valve will open. The maximum lift of the poppet is controlled by the adjustable stop. When the valve is fully open (up to the stop), the amount of fluid that passes the poppet will be dependent on the area of the 'V' notch that is above the valve seat and the pressure difference across ports 'A' and 'B'.

Adjusting the position of the stop will increase or decrease the flow rate, as will changes to the pressure difference across the 'V' notch.

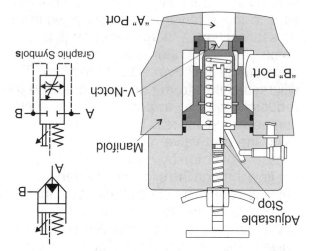

Illustration #234 — Non-Pressure Compensated Restrictor Flow Control

"A" Port

"B" Port

V-Notch

Manifold

Stop

Adjustable Stop

Graphic Symbols

A

B

This valve will control fluid flow in either direction and has an advantage over a simple needle valve in that it can be quickly closed at any time by the application of pilot pressure to the spring side of the poppet.

Pressure compensated flow control valves can be either:

- By-Pass Type Flow Control
- Restrictor Type Flow Control

By-Pass Type Pressure Compensated Flow Control: The by-pass flow control shown in illustration #235 uses a standard throttling valve as described in illustration #234 to supply fluid to the load. A balanced poppet type cartridge valve acts as a pressure compensator to keep the pressure difference across the 'A' and 'B' ports of the throttling valve constant.

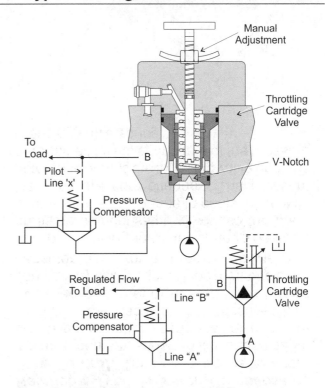

Illustration #235 — Pressure Compensated By-pass Flow Control

The compensator allows excess fluid to flow to tank when the load line pressure (line 'A') exceeds the supply line pressure (line 'B') by an amount set by the compensator spring. If the pressure generated by the load (sensed by pilot line 'x') increases, it will take a corresponding increase in pressure in the supply line for the excess fluid to flow through the compensator to the tank. Thus the same pressure difference across the throttling valve will be maintained.

When load pressure decreases, the pressure compensator will open wider, reducing the pressure in the supply line so that the same pressure difference across the 'V' notch will be maintained. Adjustment of the flow to the load is accomplished by the manual adjustment of the throttling valve. This changes the size of the throttling orifice ('V' notch). The pressure difference across ports 'A' and 'B' remains the same.

Restrictor Type Pressure Compensated Flow Control: The restrictor type flow control arrangement, shown in illustration #236, also uses a throttling cartridge valve to supply fluid to the load line. The pressure difference across the orifice is maintained constant by using a spool type pressure compensator to control the pressure to line 'A'.

The load sensing line to the spring side of the pressure compensator will cause the pressure in line 'A' to change in conjunction with load line pressure changes. The pressure difference across the throttling valve orifice is determined by the spring rate of the pressure reducing valve spring.

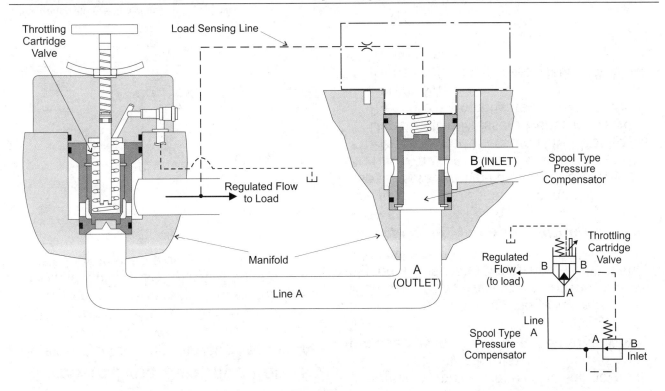

Illustration #236 — Pressure Compensated Restrictor Flow Control

Screw-in Type Cartridge Valves

Screw-in type cartridge valves differ from the slip-in type in three ways.

1. The screw-in type cartridge valve can only be attached to the appropriate threaded manifold cavity. See illustration #237 for screw-in type examples.

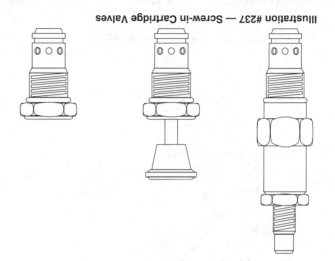

Illustration #237 — Screw-in Cartridge Valves

2. Screw-in type cartridge valves do not usually require any pilot function such as that provided with the slip-in cartridge valve covers.

3. The screw-in type cartridge valve is more likely to be a spool type valve and may be designed for use with 3-way and 4-way manifold cavities.

Examples of Screw-in Cartridge Valve Use:

The following are some of the more common uses of screw-in type cartridge valves:

- Two-Way Directional Control
- Pilot Operated Pressure Relief Control
- Direct Acting Pressure Reducing Valve
- Pressure Compensated By-Pass Flow Control Valve
- Pressure Compensated Restrictor Flow Control Valve

Two-way Directional Control: The cartridge valve shown in illustration #238 is a normally closed, 2-way spool valve. A spring holds the balanced spool in the closed position. Energizing the solenoid causes the armature to move against the closing spring, pulling the spool up to uncover the 'B' port, allowing fluid to flow between the two ports.

The hole through the center of the spool and armature allows fluid pressure to equalize on both sides of the spool. De-energizing the solenoid will cause the spring to close the valve.

Pilot Operated Pressure Relief Valve: The screw-in pilot operated relief valve shown in illustration #239 uses a balanced main spool that is held in the closed position by light spring pressure. An orifice through the spool center balances the pressure on both sides of the spool. A pilot valve limits the pressure on the spring side of the spool.

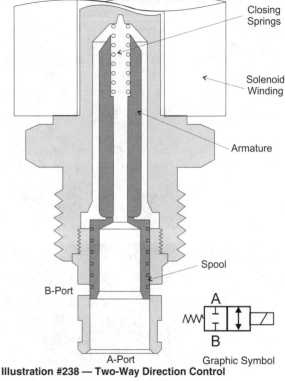

Closing Springs

Solenoid Winding

Armature

Spool

B-Port

A-Port

A
B

Graphic Symbol

Illustration #238 — Two-Way Direction Control

When system pressure reaches the pilot valve setting, the pilot valve opens and limits the pressure on the spring side of the spool. Fluid flowing past the pilot valve is drained to tank. A further rise in system pressure creates unbalanced hydraulic forces on the spool, causing the spool to move up and open the pressure port to tank. If the system pressure falls below the pilot valve setting, the pilot valve closes allowing the pressures to again equalize on both sides of the spool and the light spring pressure pushes the spool down to close off the tank port.

Direct Acting Pressure Reducing Valve: The direct acting, normally open, three-way spool type valve shown in illustration #240 is primarily used as a pressure reducing valve, but will also act as a pressure relief valve for the reduced pressure circuit.

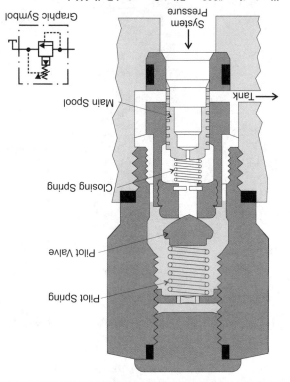

System Pressure

Graphic Symbol

Main Spool

Tank →

Closing Spring

Pilot Valve

Pilot Spring

Illustration #239 — Pilot Operated Relief Valve

When the pressure in the reduced pressure line is below the main spring setting, there is an unrestricted flow from the system to the reduced pressure port. As the reduced pressure approaches the spring setting, hydraulic force pushes the spool against the spring and begins to close off the system pressure port. If pressure in the reduced pressure port becomes high enough the system pressure port will be completely closed.

Further pressure increases in the reduced pressure line will cause the spool to move even higher, allowing fluid from the reduced pressure port to be drained to tank, preventing any further rise in the reduced pressure port.

When pressure in the reduced pressure port drops, the spool moves down and again allows fluid from the system pressure port to the reduced pressure port.

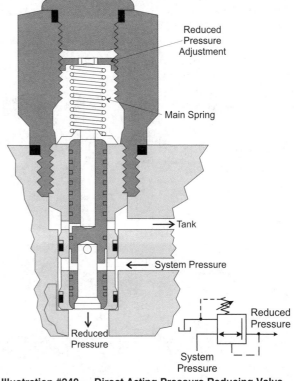

Reduced Pressure Adjustment

Main Spring

Tank

System Pressure

Reduced Pressure

Reduced Pressure

System Pressure

Illustration #240 — Direct Acting Pressure Reducing Valve

Pressure Compensated By-pass Flow Control Valve: Illustration #241 shows a three-way screw-in cartridge valve that uses a balanced spool to control the flow rate to the "regulated flow" port. Excess fluid is drained to tank. This simple valve uses a fixed orifice and is therefore not readily adjustable.

The pressure difference across the fixed orifice (set by the spring force) causes the spool to move up against the opposing spring force. This uncovers enough of the tank port to maintain the pressure difference across the orifice by allowing the excess fluid to flow to tank.

If the pressure in the regulated flow line increases, the resulting increase in pressure inside and above the spool will cause the spool to move down, restricting the flow to tank so as to maintain the same pressure difference across the spool.

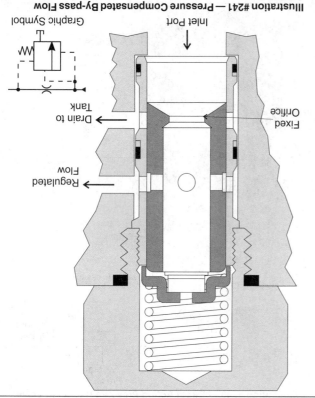

Inlet Port

Fixed Orifice

Drain to Tank

Regulated Flow

Graphic Symbol

Illustration #241 — Pressure Compensated By-pass Flow Control Valve

Changing the spring tension or the size of the fixed orifice would change the regulated flow rate.

Pressure Compensated Restrictor Flow Control Valve: The restrictor type flow control valve shown in illustration #242 operates in a similar manner to the previously described valve, i.e. a constant pressure difference, set by the spool spring, is maintained across the fixed orifice. The method of maintaining the pressure difference is by restricting the flow to the regulated flow port rather than allowing the excess fluid to flow to tank.

The higher pressure on the inlet side of the spool causes the spool to move up, adjusting the regulated flow opening, to maintain the predetermined pressure difference across the fixed orifice.

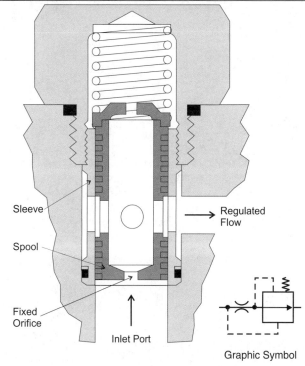

Sleeve
Spool
Fixed Orifice
Inlet Port
Regulated Flow
Graphic Symbol

Illustration #242 — Pressure Compensated Restrictor Flow Control Valve

SECTION EIGHT QUESTIONS

Cartridge Valves

1. *What are three reasons for using manifold blocks?*

   Answer: _____

   _____

2. *What other piece of equipment are cartridge valves usually used in conjunction with?*

   Answer: _____

   _____

3. *The majority of cartridge valves are:*
   - ❏ 2-way poppet or spool valves
   - ❏ 3-way spool valves
   - ❏ 4-way spool valves

4. *The majority of cartridge valves are the:*
   - ❏ slip-in style
   - ❏ screw-in style

5. *What is used to retain the slip-in style cartridge valve in the cavity?*

   Answer: _____

   _____

6. *The slip-in cartridge valve shown in the illustration is a/an:*
   - ❏ balanced design
   - ❏ unbalanced design

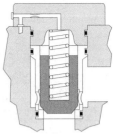

7. *A balanced slip-in cartridge valve is subject to the pressures shown in the illustration. Calculate the opening and closing forces and specify if the valve will be open or closed.*

   Answer:

   _____

   _____

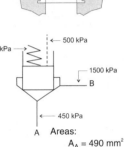

240 kPa →
← 500 kPa
↓ 1500 kPa
B
← 450 kPa
A   Areas:
$A_A = 490$ mm^2
$A_B = 0$
$A_P = 490$ mm^2

8. A balanced slip-in cartridge valve is subject to the pressures shown in the illustration. Calculate the opening and closing forces and specify if the valve will be open or closed.

Answer: _____

_____

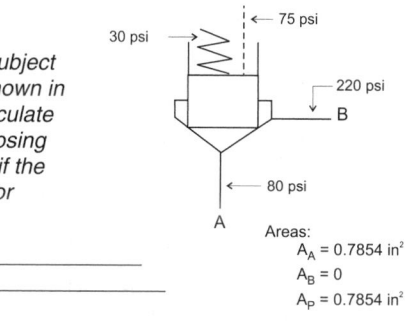

75 psi
30 psi
220 psi
B
80 psi
A

Areas:
$A_A = 0.7854$ in^2
$A_B = 0$
$A_P = 0.7854$ in^2

10. A 1:2 ratio slip-in cartridge valve is subject to the pressures shown in the illustration. Calculate the opening and closing forces and specify if the valve will be open or closed.

Answer:

_____

_____

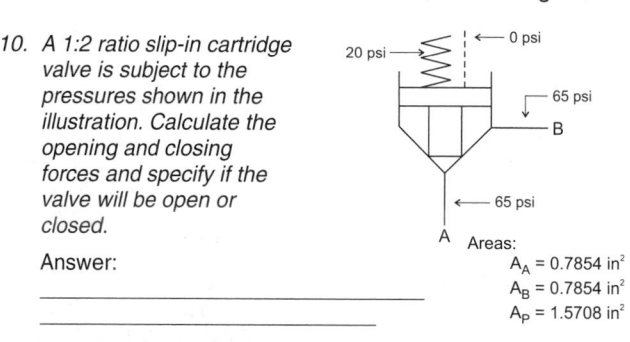

0 psi
20 psi
65 psi
B
65 psi
A

Areas:
$A_A = 0.7854$ in^2
$A_B = 0.7854$ in^2
$A_P = 1.5708$ in^2

9. A 1:2 ratio slip-in cartridge valve is subject to the pressures shown in the illustration. Calculate the opening and closing forces and specify if the valve will be open or closed.

Answer:

_____

_____

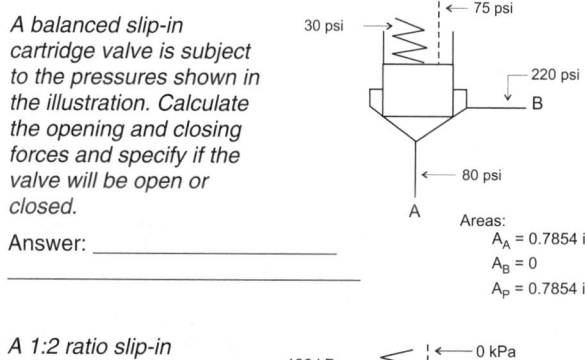

0 kPa
180 kPa
350 kPa
B
350 kPa
A

Areas:
$A_A = 490$ mm^2
$A_B = 490$ mm^2
$A_P = 980$ mm^2

11. The illustration shows a 1:2 ratio cartridge valve acting as a check valve. If the pressure in line 'B' is 850 psi, and the spring force is equal to 15 psi, what pressure is required in line 'A' to open the valve?

❏ 15 psi
❏ 425 psi
❏ 850 psi
❏ 865 psi

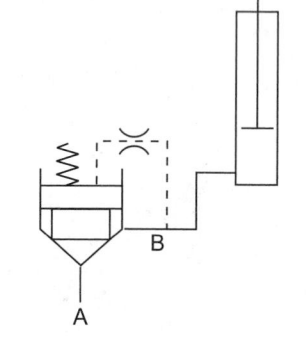

B

A

12. How many unbalance cartridge valves would be used to provide 4-way directional control?

- ❏ 1
- ❏ 2
- ❏ 3
- ❏ 4

13. In the illustration shown, when the left solenoid is energized (moving the pilot valve to the right), the state of the four cartridge valves would be:

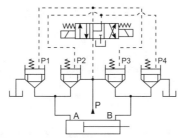

- ❏ P1 and P3 piloted, P2 and P4 vented
- ❏ P1 and P2 piloted, P3 and P4 vented
- ❏ P3 and P4 piloted, P1 and P2 vented
- ❏ P1 and P4 piloted, P2 and P3 vented

14. The illustration shows a cartridge valve being used as a relief valve. If line 'A' is to be relieved to tank at 2000 psi, the maximum pressure in the pilot line to the cartridge valve will:

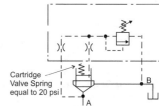

- ❏ be 1980 psi
- ❏ be 2000 psi
- ❏ be 2020 psi
- ❏ depend on the area of the cartridge valve spool

15. The illustration shows a cartridge valve being used as venting relief valve. When the venting valve is in the position shown, at what pressure will the cartridge valve open line 'A' to tank?

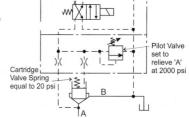

- ❏ 20 psi
- ❏ 1010 psi
- ❏ 2000 psi
- ❏ 2020 psi

16. *When the pressures are equal on both sides of the spool in a spool type pressure reducing cartridge valve, the main spring will hold the spool in the closed position.*

    ❏ true   ❏ false

17. *An unbalanced cartridge valve with 'V' notches machined into the poppet may be used as a non-pressure compensated flow control valve. What advantage would this device have over a simple needle valve?*

    Answer: _____

    _____

18. *The type of pressure compensated flow control shown in the illustration would be a:*

    ❏ by-pass type
    ❏ restrictor type

    Control Flow B
    Line "B"
    Line "A"
    A Inlet

19. *The type of pressure compensated flow control shown in the illustration would be a:*

    ❏ by-pass type
    ❏ restrictor type

    Control B   B
    Flow
    A
    Line
    A
    B
    Inlet

20. *Screw-in type cartridge valves can be used in the same cavities as the slip-in type as long as the appropriate threaded cover is used.*

    ❏ true   ❏ false

21. *Many screw-in type cartridge valves do not require a pilot connection.*

    ❏ true   ❏ false

22. *Many screw-in type cartridge valves use a spool design rather than a poppet.*

    ❏ true   ❏ false

23. *The direct acting pressure reducing valve shown in the illustration will:*

    Reduced Pressure
    System Pressure

    ❏ not provide any pressure relief functions
    ❏ act as a pressure relief valve for both the system and the reduced pressure circuit
    ❏ act as a pressure relief valve for the reduced pressure circuit
    ❏ act as a pressure relief valve for the system

SECTION NINE

PROPORTIONAL AND SERVO VALVES

Introduction

Servo and proportional valves are used when fast and accurate control of hydraulic actuators and functions are required.

Servo valves are infinitely variable direc- tional control valves that provide the highest degree of control accuracy and are usually used in closed loop systems.

Proportional valves can be used for direction, pressure and flow control. The degree of control accuracy falls somewhere in between conventional valves and servo valves. The simpler designed proportional valve is a less costly alternative to the servo valve when ab- solute accuracy is not required. Proportional valves are usually used in open loop systems.

When compared to proportional valves, servo valves:

- Are more accurate
- Have a faster response time

- Are more expensive
- Usually have more complex electronic controls
- Are much more intolerant to fluid contamination

Closed Loop System

A closed loop system shown in illustration #243 has a feed back arrangement from the actuator output that compares an output sig- nal to the input signal. If the output signal de- viates from that set by the input, adjustments are made to correct the deviation.

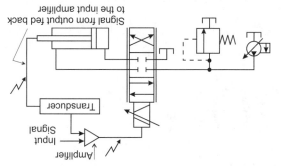

Amplifier

Input Signal

Transducer

Signal from output fed back to the input amplifier

Illustration #243 — Closed Loop Example

Open Loop System

An open loop system, as shown in illustration #244, has no feed back from the actuator output to the input signal; therefore, any inaccuracies in the output will not be corrected unless external changes are made to the input.

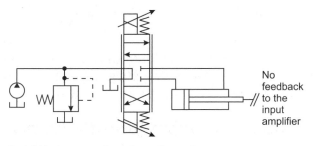

No feedback to the input amplifier

Illustration #244 — Open Loop Example

Proportional Valves

Proportional valves can be used as directional, pressure or flow control valves. A proportional valve is so named, because it uses a special type of solenoid called a proportional solenoid.

Conventional valve solenoids are essentially on/off devices that move from one extreme position to the other.

Proportional valves are designed to either provide a specific force relative to the magnitude of the input signal (force controlled solenoid) or move a specified amount relative to the input signal (stroke controlled solenoid).

Force Controlled Solenoids

Proportional Force Controlled Solenoid:

The wet pin DC solenoid, shown in illustration #245, is similar in appearance to the conventional DC solenoid described in Section Seven.

When current is applied to a conventional solenoid, the force output changes significantly as the armature moves through its working stroke. The force applied is dependent on the amount of current supplied and the position of the armature.

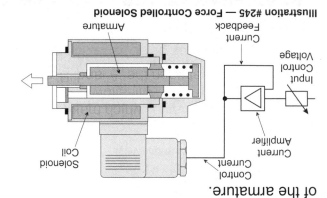

Illustration #245 — Force Controlled Solenoid

When a specific current is applied to a proportional force controlled solenoid, the force output is relatively constant throughout the working stroke. If the current input is increased, there is a corresponding increase in the force output. It can be seen from illustration #246 that for the duration of the working stroke, the force output is dependent only on the amount of current supplied and is independent of the armature position.

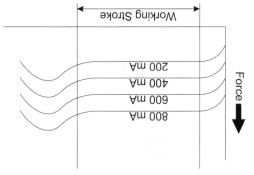

Illustration #246 — Proportional Solenoid Force Characteristics

Stroke Controlled Solenoids

Stroke Controlled Proportional Solenoid:
The stroke controlled solenoid shown in illustration #247 is similar to the force controlled solenoid, but has a built in position sensor that allows accurate control on the actual position of the armature. The sensor, which is attached to the end of the solenoid, is usually referred to as a LVDT (linear variable differential transformer). The LVDT is an electrical device that measures the actual position of the armature and sends a signal back to the amplifier. The amplifier compares this feedback signal with the input signal. If they do not match, a corrected signal is sent to the solenoid coils to correct the error.

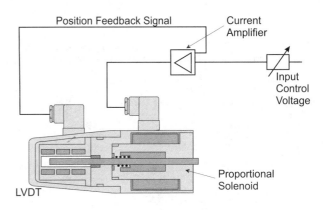

Illustration #247 — Stroke Controlled Solenoid

Note: The fact that the solenoid has feedback does not necessarily make it a closed loop system. A closed loop system requires feedback from the actuator output. The solenoid just described has feedback from the armature position, not the actuator output.

Prop. Pressure Control Valves

Pressure Relief Valves

Direct acting proportional relief valves operate in a similar manner to conventional direct acting relief valves; except that, instead of using a manually adjustable spring to control the pressure at which the valve opens, an electronically adjustable proportional solenoid is used. The direct acting proportional relief valve is also used as the pilot stage for two stage proportional pressure relief and pressure reducing valves.

There are a number of different styles and designs available. The poppet type, which is fairly common, is discussed below.

The poppet type relief valve shown in illustration #248 uses a force controlled solenoid armature, acting directly on the poppet valve to hold it in a closed position.

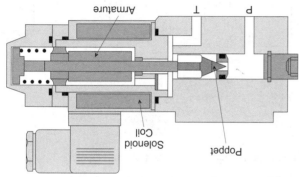

Armature

Solenoid Coil

Poppet

Illustration #248 — Direct Acting Relief Valve, Poppet with Force Controlled Solenoid

When the opening force from fluid pressure acting on the poppet becomes greater than the closing force from the armature, the poppet will open, allowing fluid to flow to the tank.

The relief pressure can be remotely adjusted during operation by varying the input signal to the solenoid.

The example shown in illustration #249 is a spring-loaded poppet relief valve. The spring tension is determined by the position of the armature of the stroke-controlled solenoid. LVDT feedback provides accurate positioning of the armature and hence accurate control of the spring tension on the poppet valve.

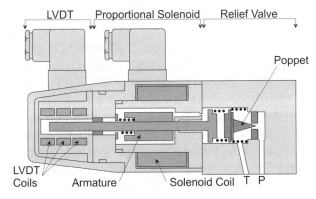

Illustration #249 — Direct Acting Relief Valve, Poppet with Stroke Controlled Solenoid

As with the previous example, the relief pressure can be remotely adjusted during operation by varying the input signal to the solenoid.

Because of the limited force available from proportional solenoids, the poppet area exposed to pressure must be small if a moderate to high pressure range is required. For example, if the maximum force exerted by the solenoid was 14 pounds [62.3 N], a poppet seat of 0.06 inches [1.524 mm] diameter would provide a cracking pressure of 5000 psi [34.474 MPa]. A larger seat reduces the pressure range of the valve.

Such small diameter flow paths only allow low flow rates, usually less than 1 gpm [3.785 liters/min.]. Direct acting proportional relief valves can therefore only be used in low flow situations.

When higher flow rates are required of a pro-portional relief valve, a pilot operated (two-stage) relief valve is used. Pilot operated pro-portional relief valves operate in a similar manner to conventional manually adjusted pilot operated relief valves (see Section Seven for more information on conventional relief valves). The main difference is that the pilot stage is a proportional relief, rather than a manually adjusted spring relief. The pilot operated relief valve shown in illustration #250 consists of a poppet type main stage and a proportional pilot stage similar to the example shown in illustration #248.

Referring to illustration #250, the basic oper-ation of a pilot operated relief valve is as follows:

- System pressure is ported through an ori-fice to the pilot valve and the spring side of the main poppet valve by an interconnect-ing passage.
- This equalizes the pressure above and below the main poppet.
- When the system pressure is less than the proportional solenoid setting the main poppet spring (light pressure) holds the main poppet on its seat.
- When system pressure reaches the pro-portional solenoid setting, the pilot valve unseats, limiting the pressure above the main poppet (flow through the intercon-necting passage is limited by the orifice). The pilot fluid flow is externally drained di-rectly to the tank rather than internally to the main return line. This prevents any possible back-pressure from causing er-ratic operation.

- Any further rise in system pressure will unbalance the forces acting on the main poppet, causing it to unseat and allow system fluid to flow to the reservoir.
- When system pressure falls the pilot valve closes, allowing the pressure to equalize on both sides of the main poppet. The main poppet spring will then close the main poppet.

This type of valve can also be provided with a standard spring-loaded maximum pressure relief in the pilot stage, acting as a safety backup in case of unexpected high solenoid forces.

A loss of power to the solenoid will allow system pressure to flow to the tank at very low pressure.

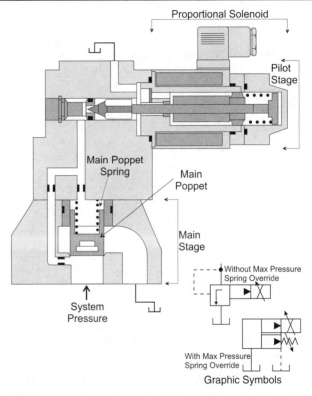

Illustration #250 — Pilot Operated Proportional Relief Valve

Pressure Reducing Valves

Proportional pressure reducing valves may be direct acting or pilot operated. As with pilot operated relief valves, the major difference between proportional pilot operated reducing valves and their conventional counterpart is the use of a proportional pilot relief valve, instead of the spring loaded relief valve for the pilot circuit (see Section Seven for more information on conventional pressure reducing valves).

The 3-way direct acting proportional reducing valve shown in illustration #251 uses a force controlled proportional solenoid to regulate the pressure at port 'A'.

When the solenoid is not energized, the spring force holds the valve spool to the left, blocking off port 'P' and opening port 'A' to tank.

Energizing the solenoid creates a force on the spool that is proportional to the input signal, thus pushing the spool to the right and allowing fluid to flow from 'P' to 'A', via the pressure orifice.

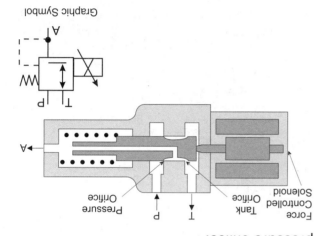

Graphic Symbol

Illustration #251 — Direct Acting Proportional Pressure
Reducing Valve

Pressure Orifice

P

T

Tank Orifice

Force Controlled Solenoid

A

When the pressure in port 'A' rises sufficiently, it will overcome the force from the solenoid and move the spool back toward the left reducing the size of the pressure orifice and increasing the size of the tank orifice. If the pressure at 'A' falls, due to leakage or movement of an actuator, the force from the solenoid moves the spool to the right, reducing the tank orifice and increasing the pressure orifice, therefore maintaining the pressure set by the solenoid.

As long as the supply pressure at 'P' is greater than the output pressure at 'A', there will be flow to the tank.

Because back-pressure in the tank line would change the pressure setting, this valve must be externally drained to the tank rather than through a return line.

Proportional Directional Control Valves

Proportional directional control valves control not only the direction, but also the fluid flow rate to, and/or from an actuator. In appearance, the valve itself looks similar to a conventional spool type directional control valve. The two main differences are that proportional valves use proportional solenoids instead of on/off solenoids, as well as a spool that is designed to allow for accurate metering of the fluid flow in relation to its axial position within the valve body. This type of valve can be direct acting when low flow rates are required, or pilot operated for higher flow situations. Both may be with or without spool position feedback.

Proportional Direction Valve Spools

The spools used in proportional directional valves are similar to those used in conventional valves, except that the proportional valve has metering notches machined into the spool lands.

These metering notches are designed to meter fluid proportional to the amount of spool movement.

Proportional valve spools must be designed and matched to the intended application. Spools are available with various center conditions and flow path flow rates.

Illustration #252 shows a closed center spool that has eight metering notches (four on each side) machined into each of the two lands. This will provide equal metering for all flow paths, when the spool is moved in either direction from the center position.

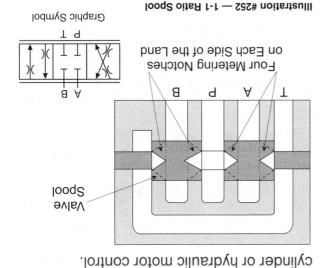

Four Metering Notches on Each Side of the Land

Valve Spool

Illustration #252 — 1-1 Ratio Spool

Graphic Symbol

When the spool is moved to the right:

P→B; flow = Q and A→T; flow = Q

When the spool is moved to the left:

P→A; flow = Q and B→T; flow = Q

This type of spool would be used for 1-1 ratio cylinder or hydraulic motor control.

Illustration #253 is a similar spool, except that the land on the left has only four metering notches (two on each side), the land on the right has eight (four on each side).

When the spool is moved to the right:
P → B; flow = Q and A → T; flow = Q/2

When the spool is moved to the left:
P → A; flow = Q/2 and B → T; flow = Q

Note: 'P → B' indicates that the 'P' port is open to the 'B' port and that the flow direction is from 'P' to 'B'. 'A → T' indicates that the 'A' port is open to 'T' allowing flow to the tank. 'Q' is the symbol used for the quantity of flow when an amount in gallons or litres/min. is not specified.

This type of spool would be used for a 2 - 1 ratio cylinder. The 'A' port would be connected to the rod end.

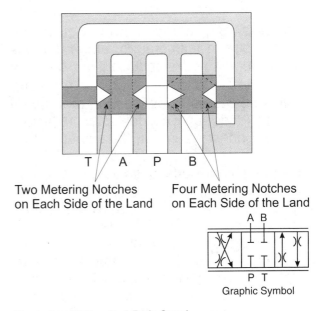

Two Metering Notches on Each Side of the Land   Four Metering Notches on Each Side of the Land

Graphic Symbol

Illustration #253 — 2 - 1 Ratio Spool

The spool shown in illustration #254 provides a restricted flow from the 'A' and 'B' ports to the tank when in the center position. When used to control cylinders, the restricted flow center allows leakage from the pressure port 'P' to the cylinder ports 'A' and 'B' to be directed to tank. This prevents cylinder drift and pressure intensification.

There are other directional valve spools available that are designed to suit the requirements of various industrial and mobile applications.

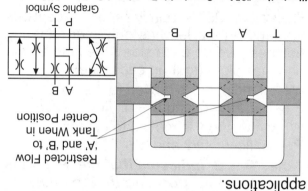

Restricted Flow
'A' and 'B' to
Tank When in
Center Position

Graphic Symbol

Illustration #254 — Spool with Restricted Center

Direct Acting - No Feedback

The direct acting proportional directional valve — no feedback, shown in illustration #255, is spring centered and has a force controlled solenoid at each end of the spool. When the solenoid on the left is energized, it will exert a force on the spool proportional to the input signal, moving the spool to the right against the centering spring. Fluid will flow via the spool metering notches from ports 'P' to 'B' and 'A' to 'T'. The fluid flow rate will depend on the amount of spool movement and the pressure difference across the open ports. Increasing the current supply will increase the force applied to the spool, moving it further to the right and increasing the flow rate.

Shutting off the input signal will allow the spool to return to the center position. Energizing the right spool will reverse the process.

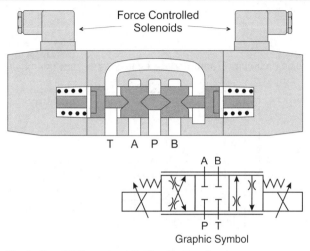

Illustration #255 — Direct Acting No Feedback

Direct Acting - With Feedback

The directing acting proportional directional valve - with feedback, shown in illustration #256, provides greater spool position accuracy than the no feedback type previously described.

This is due to the use of stroke controlled, rather than force controlled solenoids.

A LVDT position sensor attached to the armature of one of the solenoids ensures that the armature position, and thus the spool position, corresponds to the input signal command.

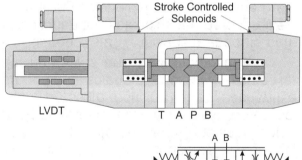

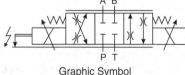

Graphic Symbol

Illustration #256 — Direct Acting With Feedback

To maintain a flow rate consistent to the input signal, a hydrostat may be installed in the inlet line to the directional valve (see illustration #257). The hydrostat will provide a constant pressure difference between the pressure port 'P' and ports 'A' or 'B' (whichever is higher) to ensure a more consistent flow rate for a particular spool position.

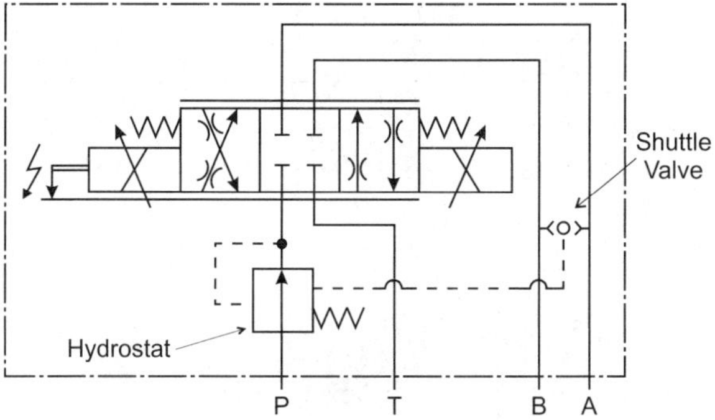

Illustration #257 — Symbol for Proportional Directional Valve with Hydrostat

Pilot Operated - No Feedback

When high flow rates are required, a pilot operated (two stage) proportional directional valve is used.

The valve shown in illustration #258 consists of a spring centered main stage spool and a pilot valve, that is essentially two 3-way direct acting pressure reducing valves, each with a proportional solenoid (refer to 'Pressure Reducing Valves' and illustration #250).

In illustration #257, the main spool is centered when the solenoids are de-energized. Energizing solenoid #1 will cause the pressure in line 1 to rise proportional to the input signal to the solenoid, causing the main spool to move to the right against the spring force.

The distance the main spool moves is dependent on the pressure supplied to the end of the spool, which is determined by the input signal to the proportional solenoid.

De-energizing solenoid #1 will allow the fluid on the left side of the spool to drain to tank, and center the spool. Energizing solenoid #2 will, through the same process, move the main spool to the right.

The fluid output from the main valve will be dependent on the pressure drop across the valve and the control signal to the solenoid.

The pilot pressure may be internally or externally ported. Manufacturers will specify the minimum and maximum pilot pressure. If system pressures are high, internally piloted valves will require a pressure reducing valve to limit the pilot pressure. There will also be a minimum required pilot pressure to ensure that full movement of the main spool is possible.

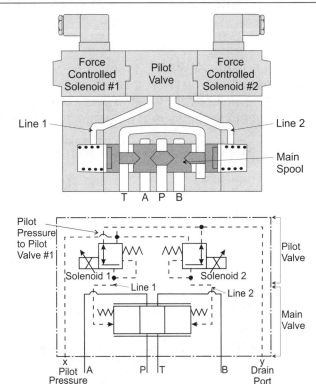

Illustration #258 — Pilot Operated Proportional Directional Valve with Detailed Symbol

Proportional Flow Control Valves

As stated earlier in this section, proportional directional valves control not only direction, but also flow. Flow through a single line can be controlled using one pair of ports of a four port, two-position, proportional directional valve.

This type of flow control, or throttling valve can use either force or stroke controlled solenoids.

When only low flow rates are to be controlled, the valve would be connected as shown in illustration #259A. With the solenoid de-energized, all ports are blocked off. Energizing the solenoid connects ports 'P' and 'B'. Ports 'A' and 'T' are blocked. The flow rate will be controlled by the solenoid input signal.

When higher flow rates are required, the same valve can be connected as shown in illustration #259B, where 'P' is connected to 'A' and 'T' is connected to 'B'.

When the solenoid is energized, the fluid entering the valve will flow through ports 'P' and 'A' to ports 'B' and 'T'. The combined flow from these two ports is the controlled flow.

Illustration #259A, B — Flow Control Using Four Port Proportional Directional Valve

A. Low Flow Rates

Inlet

Proportional Solenoid

P
T
A
B

Controlled Flow Out

B. Higher Flow Rates

Inlet

Proportional Solenoid

Controlled Flow Out

If greater control over the spool position is required, a stroke controlled solenoid may be used. To ensure that a consistent flow rate is achieved, a pressure compensator, or hydrostat, can be installed in the supply line to the throttle valve. See illustration #260.

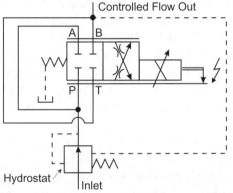

Illustration #260 — Pressure Compensated Flow Control

Servo Valves

A servo valve is a directional valve that has infinitely variable positioning capability to control the fluid direction and flow rate. When used with feedback sensing devices from the actuator or process, the position, velocity and acceleration of the actuator can be accurately controlled.

The method of feedback can be either mechanical (mechanical-hydraulic servo valve) or electrical (electro-hydraulic servo valve). The mechanical-hydraulic servo valve, which is sometimes referred to as a follow valve or booster, has been in use for many years. The electro-hydraulic servo valve, which is a more recent arrival to hydraulic systems, provides the highest degree of hydraulic control.

Mechanical Servo Valves

Illustration #261 shows a diagrammatic view of a mechanical-hydraulic servo that can be used as a force amplifier and positioning device. If a small input force is applied to the valve spool to move it a specific distance to the right, inlet fluid will pass through port 'A' to the left side of the cylinder. Fluid will be exhausted through port 'B' to the tank, as the piston moves to the right. The feedback link will push the moveable valve housing to the right and eventually block off ports 'A' and 'B' again. Each time the valve spool is moved, the piston output will move a corresponding amount. The amount of output movement, compared to the input movement, will depend on the feedback linkage dimensions. The magnitude of force available at the output shaft is dependent on the cylinder diameter and fluid pressure.

Note: Probably the most common use of this type of servomechanism is for power steering units used on mobile equipment.

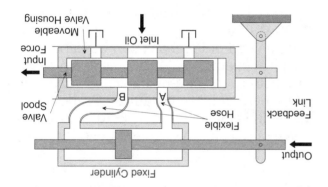

Illustration #261 — Mechanical Servo Valve

Electro-Hydraulic Servo Valves

An electro-hydraulic servo valve uses a torque motor to directly, or indirectly, position a directional valve spool to control the speed or position of an actuator.

A block diagram of the electronic control is shown in illustration #262.

The operation of this is as follows:

- A command signal from a device such as a potentiometer is sent to the amplifier.
- The amplified signal is sent to the servo valve torque motor.
- The torque motor moves the servo valve spool a distance relative to the torque motor signal, causing the actuator to move the load at a required speed, or to a specific position.
- A feedback transducer attached to the load sends an electrical signal back to the comparator, where the feedback signal is compared to the input command signal.
- A difference between the two signals results in an error signal being sent to the amplifier. The resulting correction signal to the torque motor repositions or changes the speed of the actuator.
- When the difference between feedback signal and the input command signal is zero, the error signal becomes zero and no further changes are made to the position of the servo valve spool until the input command signal is changed.

Pilot Operated Servo Valves

The two stage, or pilot operated servo valve shown in illustration #263, uses a small directly operated spool type servo to control the main spool.

A mechanical link between the main spool and the pilot sleeve provides a mechanism for resetting the pilot valve after the main spool has moved.

The axial location of the main spool is controlled by hydraulic pressure.

The area of the left end of the main spool is double the area of the right end. The right end of the main spool has constant pressure acting on it at all times, which is equal to the pilot pressure.

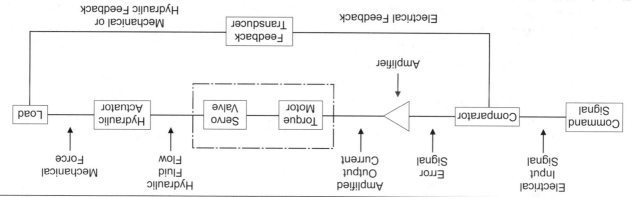

Illustration #262 — Block Diagram of an Electro-hydraulic Servo System

The pressure at the left end will vary depending on the position of the pilot valve. The pilot pressure is held constant by the use of a pressure reducing valve.

When the pilot valve is in the neutral position in illustration #263, the pilot line from the left end of the main spool is blocked off. Due to the 2:1 area ratio of the main spool, the pressure at the left end of the main spool is one half of the control pressure. Assuming there is no leakage, the main spool will maintain this position.

When the torque motor moves the pilot spool right, the pilot line from the left end of the main spool is exposed to the drain.

The resulting pressure drop on the left side of the main spool (control pressure is acting on the right side) causes it to move left. If the main spool was initially in the center position, moving the main spool left would open port 'A' to system pressure and port 'B' to tank.

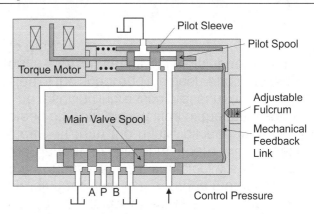

Illustration #263 — Pilot Operated Servo Valve

Movement of the main spool to the left allows the spring loaded pilot sleeve to follow the pilot spool to the right, resetting the pilot valve to the neutral position again. The main spool will remain in this position until an error correction is made or the input command signal is changed.

Flapper Nozzle Servo Valves

The flapper nozzle servo valve in illustration #264 uses hydraulic pressure to control the position of the main servo valve spool. Pilot pressure is directed through two orifices to both ends of the main spool. Any pressure difference across the main spool ends will cause the spool to move. Each end has a bleed off nozzle to a flapper valve. When the flapper valve is centered there is equal bleed off and pressure at each end of the main spool. If a signal to the torque motor causes the armature to twist anti-clockwise, moving the flapper to the right, there will be less bleed off from the right side and increased bleed off from the left side of the main spool. The resulting increased pressure on the right side of the spool and the decreased pressure on the left will cause the main spool to move to the left.

When the torque motor moves the pilot spool left, control pressure is ported to the left side of the main spool, increasing the pressure. Because the left spool end is double the area of the right, the main spool is moved to the right.

If the main spool were initially in the center position, moving the spool to the right would open port 'B' to system pressure and port 'A' to tank. Movement of the main spool to the right causes the feedback linkage to push the pilot sleeve to the left, resetting the pilot valve to the neutral position. Again, the main spool will remain in this position unless an error correction is made, or the input command signal is changed.

As the spool moves to the left, the feedback spring exerts a torque in a clockwise direction on the armature, which will eventually overcome the torque produced by the torque motor, centering the flapper valve. The main spool will then remain in this position until the signal to the torque motor is changed.

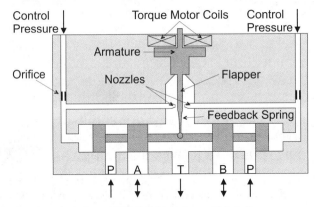

Illustration #264 — Flapper Nozzle Servo Valve

Jet Pipe Servo Valves

The jet pipe servo valve in illustration #265 is similar to the flapper valve type, in that the main spool is positioned by adjusting the pressure difference on the spool ends. A continuous jet of oil is directed at tubes connected to each end of the main spool. When the jet is centered on the two tubes, the resulting pressure at each end of the spool is equal.

The torque motor can deflect the jet left or right (the amount dependent on the input signal). If the jet is deflected right, pressure increases on the right side of the main spool and decreases on the left, causing the spool to move to the left.

As the spool moves to the left, the feedback spring exerts a torque in a clockwise direction on the armature that will eventually overcome the torque applied by the torque motor, centering the jet nozzle.

Pressure will then equalize at each end of the main spool and it will remain in this position until the signal to the torque motor is changed.

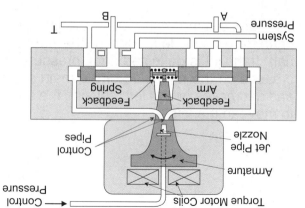

Illustration #265 — Jet Pipe Servo Valve

SECTION NINE QUESTIONS

Proportional and Servo Valves

1. Compared to proportional valves, servo valves are which of the following?
   - ❏ more accurate
   - ❏ have a faster response time
   - ❏ bare more intolerant to fluid contamination
   - ❏ all of the above

2. A closed loop system has a feed back arrangement from the actuator output that compares the output and input signal.
   - ❏ true ❏ false

3. In an open loop system, inaccuracies in the output signal are automatically corrected.
   - ❏ true ❏ false

4. Proportional valve solenoids are basic on/off solenoids.
   - ❏ true ❏ false

5. What happens to the force output with a conventional solenoid as the armature goes through its working stroke?

   Answer: _____
   _____

6. What happens to the force output with a proportional force solenoid as the armature goes through its working stroke?

   Answer: _____
   _____

7. A LVDT (linear variable differential transformer) is found where?
   - ❏ conventional solenoid
   - ❏ force controlled solenoid
   - ❏ stroke controlled solenoid

8. A direct acting proportional relief valve is used as the pilot stage for proportional pilot operated pressure reducing valves.
   - ❏ true ❏ false

9. Direct acting proportional relief valves are used only in:
   - ❏ low flow applications
   - ❏ high flow applications

10. *Why is the pilot fluid flow externally drained directly to tank in a pilot operated relief valve?*

Answer: _____

_____

11. *What can be used as a safety backup protecting against unexpected high solenoid forces in a pilot operated relief valve?*

Answer: _____

_____

12. *Proportional pressure reducing valves can be direct acting or pilot operated.*
   ☐ true　　　　☐ false

13. *A proportional pilot operated reducing valve uses a spring loaded relief valve for the pilot circuit.*
   ☐ true　　　　☐ false

14. *A proportional directional control valve will control the fluid flow rate, however it cannot control the flow direction to/from the actuator.*
   ☐ true　　　　☐ false

15. *A proportional directional control valve is which of the following?*
   ☐ direct acting for low flow rates
   ☐ pilot operated for high flow rates
   ☐ may be with or without spool position feedback
   ☐ all of the above

16. *Metering notches are machined into the spools of proportional directional valves for which of the following purposes?*
   ☐ meter fluid proportional to the amount of spool movement
   ☐ prevent the spool from binding
   ☐ equalize the pressure around the spool
   ☐ prevent leakage between the high and low pressure ports

17. *Proportional valve spools are so adaptable that any spool will work for any center condition or flow path flow rate.*
   ☐ true　　　　☐ false

18. *The spool of a spring centered direct acting proportional directional valve – no feedback, with a solenoid on each end, will move which way when the left solenoid is energized?*
   ☐ right
   ☐ left
   ☐ could go in either direction depending on the signal

19. Referring to number 18, what happens when input signal is cut off?
    ❏ spool remains stationary
    ❏ spool moves to center

20. A direct acting proportional directional valve – with feedback is what, compared to the type referenced in number 18?
    ❏ slower
    ❏ faster
    ❏ more accurate
    ❏ less accurate

21. What can be added to the inlet line of a proportional directional valve to maintain a more consistent flow rate?

    Answer: _____
    _____

22. If system pressure is high, what may be required with an internally piloted, pilot operated proportional directional valve?

    Answer: _____
    _____

23. A proportional flow control valve can use either force or stroke controlled solenoids.
    ❏ true   ❏ false

24. A four port two-position proportional directional valve can be used as a flow control valve.
    ❏ true   ❏ false

25. A hydrostat, or pressure compensator, cannot be used with a proportional flow control valve.
    ❏ true   ❏ false

26. A servo valve will accurately control the velocity and speed of an actuator but not the position.
    ❏ true   ❏ false

27. A feedback sensing device from the actuator cannot be used with a servo valve.
    ❏ true   ❏ false

28. An electro-hydraulic servo valve is not as accurate as a mechanical-hydraulic servo valve.
    ❏ true   ❏ false

29. What is probably the most common use of a mechanical servo valve?

Answer: _____

_____

30. List three types of electro-hydraulic servo valves:

Answer: _____

_____

31. What is used to control the axial location of the main spool in a pilot operated (two stage) servo valve?

Answer: _____

_____

32. Moving the flapper to the left (clockwise) on a flapper nozzle servo valve would cause the main spool to move to the right.

❏ true   ❏ false

33. The jet pipe servo valve main spool has no feed back, therefore the jet pipe must be centered by the torque motor.

❏ true   ❏ false

SECTION TEN

TEN

TROUBLESHOOTING

Introduction

Due to inexperience and/or a lack of knowledge of the system, a hit and miss approach is often taken when trying to correct hydraulic system problems. This usually takes the form of randomly changing out components that may appear to be involved with the problem. This hit and miss method may eventually be successful if it is a component that is causing the problem, but often success is only achieved by unnecessarily changing out a number of components. This approach will not be successful when the hydraulic problem is caused by other factors; such as actuator loads changing due to process changes or the breakdown of associated equipment, restrictions in piping or filters, or unauthorized tampering with valves or component settings.

A list of the various problems that could occur in hydraulic systems would be endless. It is for this reason that a systematic approach must be taken when troubleshooting.

No matter what method is used to troubleshoot a problem, an intimate knowledge of the system, which includes the layout of components and the process itself, goes a long way towards finding the solution.

Problems developing in a system are often accompanied by an increase in temperature, noise, or fluid contamination. As these three indicators are often detected by sight, touch, or hearing, operating and maintenance personnel should be encouraged to report any noticed changes, as these are the early warning signs of impending trouble.

Excessive friction causes the temperature of components such as pumps and actuators to become higher than normal. A misaligned coupling or a breakdown of the lubrication system may be one of the causes. High-pressure fluid bypassing to a lower pressure also causes heat to be generated. This may be due to excessive clearances in a pump, valve, or actuator, or may be due to the fact that a relief valve is cracked partially open.

Some systems may have a temperature gage at the reservoir, but a small increase in temperature of the fluid may be thought of as a normal fluctuation due to operational changes. It will take an observant operator or technician to notice that a particular component or part of the system is operating at a higher temperature than usual.

Often increases in component temperature will be accompanied by an increase in the level of noise. Again, observant personnel are usually required to detect the changes in noise level. Changes in pump suction conditions can cause cavitation, which will cause high noise levels at the pump.

Any changes in the level of solid contamination will only be found if the system fluid is regularly sampled and tested. This is more likely to be carried out on large, expensive, or critical systems. Contamination due to water or air in the fluid can change the colour and consistency of the fluid, which may be noticed by operations and/or maintenance people.

General Knowledge

Hydraulic Symbols and Schematics

The ability to interpret schematic drawings of the hydraulic equipment being worked on is essential. The technician should be familiar with the equipment schematic circuits before problems occur. Attending manufacturer's or company training sessions or seminars is probably the ideal way of gaining this knowledge, but if these are not available self study is the next best method.

The hydraulic symbols used in this book are based on the ISO 1264 standard. Other symbols such as those published by the American National Standards Institute (ANSI) may be used on the schematic drawings supplied by the equipment manufacturer. Fortunately most of the symbols used by the various organizations are the same or quite similar, but the troubleshooter must be familiar with the type of symbol being used.

Note: Always have hydraulic schematics on hand when troubleshooting a circuit.

Function of the Components

Knowledge of the hydraulic schematic is a start, but it is important that the function of each of the individual components is known along with its relationship to the other components. Without this knowledge it is virtually impossible to use logic to pinpoint a problem.

Component Identification and Location

Being able to identify and then physically locate components is required when the time comes to test or change out any of the components. The mechanical installation drawings may be required for this purpose, along with the schematic diagrams.

Electrical Circuit Analysis

Electrical controls are the most common method for controlling fluid power systems. The simplest system may only involve a power supply and a switch to control a solenoid operated directional valve, whereas more sophisticated control systems may employ programmable controllers using microprocessors to provide a high level of control of conventional, servo, and proportioning valves. An understanding of the electrical controls and circuitry for the particular system being worked on will be required when troubleshooting.

Safety

When maintenance work is to be carried out on any machine, safety must be a prime consideration. Shutting down and dismantling machinery can affect not only those directly involved in the shutdown, but also other people in the general area, or those working on related equipment.

The various valves and components assembled on a power pack may be controlling rotary and/or linear actuators not in the general vicinity. It is therefore extremely important when working on larger complex systems that the technician be familiar with the plant layout and in particular the location of all the hydraulic components.

Many plants will have standard shutdown procedures that must be followed.

General Shut Down Procedure

Rope off Affected Areas

Often guards may have to be removed to check various components, and in the course of testing, unexpected machinery movement may be necessary. These areas should be roped off and warning signs posted. Personnel in the vicinity should also be told what is happening.

Lower all Loads

All loads should be secured so they are not being supported by the hydraulic system. This usually involves either lowering the load or blocking it up securely so that it will not move.

Shut Down the Pump

Turn the pump off using the local switch located close to the pump.

Isolate the Power Supply

Isolate the power supply at the main panel, then lockout and tag. Illustration #266 shows a typical lockout and tag situation.

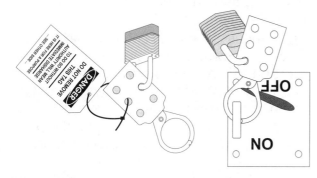

Illustration #266 — Typical Lockout and Tag

Test

Go back to the local switch and attempt to start the pump. If it does not start, it has been isolated at the correct main panel. Lockout and tag the pump at this local switch if possible.

Depressurize Accumulators

Accumulators should have valves designed into the piping system to allow for controlled release of hydraulic pressure. Be aware that gas charged and spring loaded accumulators could still have unreleased energy in the form of compressed gas or spring pressure present after the hydraulic pressure has been discharged.

Depressurize Piping System

Operate manual and electrical directional control valves a number of times to release hydraulic pressure within the system. Check that all pressure gages are reading zero. This step may have to be carried out before the power supply is turned off at the main panel.

Dismantling Equipment

When opening up the system:

- Have plastic or metal containers available to hold fluid leakage.
- Have a supply of cleanup rags, cotton waste, or floor-dry, for soaking up fluid that lands on the floor.
- Have some means of sealing off open lines and fittings such as a selection of plastic plugs or sheet plastic and tape.
- Always assume there is pressure within the system when loosening off pipe and hose fittings.
- If threaded joints are to be disconnected, only loosen off partially until you are sure that there is no pressure in the line and all the fluid has been drained. When all the fluid has been drained, completely disconnect.

- If disconnecting a flanged joint, slightly loosen off the side away from you and then crack the bolts closest to you. The object is to have a wider opening on the side away from you. This will reduce the likelihood of being sprayed with hydraulic fluid if there is still pressure in the system.

- Be aware that accumulators may still contain potential energy in the form of compressed gas or springs, even after they have been drained of hydraulic pressure.

- If a load has been blocked up with the cylinder, there will be a considerable quantity of hydraulic fluid left in the cylinder.

Checking the System

Most operators and maintenance personnel are continually making checks as they are working with or around a machine or hydraulic system. They become familiar with the noise, heat and vibrations produced by the system. The observant operator will usually notice any substantial changes and report them to the appropriate people, however, detecting many faults requires the use of instruments such as pressure gages and flow meters.

When checking a system to determine the cause of a malfunction the technician is confronted with the questions:

- What to check?
- Where to check?
- What to check with?

Note: When installing temporary equipment such as pressure gages and flow meters, care must be taken to prevent any contamination from entering the system.

Hydraulic test units are available that combine a number of test instruments in a single unit. The instruments contained in the test unit should be matched to the system with regards to pressures and flow. The test unit shown in illustration #267 contains pressure gages for checking high and low pressures, and also vacuums. The flow meter must be capable of producing accurate readings of the expected flow rates to be tested. Temperature gages should be calibrated in both degrees Fahrenheit and Celsius.

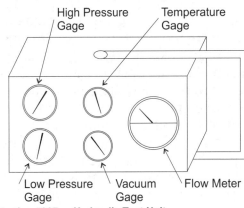

Illustration #267 — Hydraulic Test Unit

Checking Pressure

Checking pressures in various parts of the system can be compared to an electrician checking the voltage in an electrical circuit. Pressures are usually checked using a pressure gage; other methods are manometers and pressure transducers. The pressure transducer can be used in conjunction with a recorder for providing a continual readout and will provide the most accurate pressure readings. Most hydraulic circuits will have at least one pressure gage permanently installed (usually for setting the system pressure). Larger systems may have other pressure gages located at strategic points throughout the system. For troubleshooting purposes it is usually necessary to check the pressures in various parts of the circuit where there may be no permanent pressure gages.

Therefore the technician should have a variety of pressure gages on hand along with enough suitable fittings and valves for installing the gages.

Some well-designed systems may be provided with test points at various locations to simplify the installation of test pressure and flow gages. Due to the widely varying pressures around the circuit a single pressure gage will not suffice. A 5000 psi (34 474 kPa) pressure gage used for checking a pump discharge pressure of 3000 psig (20 684 kPa) is not suitable to accurately check the pressure in a return line that is close to 0 psig. The pressure gage selected should have a scale that is approximately double the expected reading. This will provide the most accurate readings at half scale and also provide a reasonable reserve in cases where the pressure unexpectedly high. Subjecting a pressure gage to go beyond its intended limit will permanently damage the gage.

Pressure gages permanently installed should be provided with an isolation valve and vent that will isolate the pressure gage from the system when it is not required (refer to illustration #268C). When a pressure reading is required, the isolating valve is opened and the reading taken. The valve is then closed and the pressure drained from the pressure gage. Pressure gages that are permanently installed with no isolation valve (refer to illustration #268A) are continually subject to all the pressure variations and shocks in the system. This will cause them to lose their accuracy more quickly than an isolated pressure gage. The simple needle valve shown in illustration #268C will allow the gage to be isolated from the system, but the gage will continually read the last pressure checked.

System test points provide a simple way to attach and remove a pressure gage.

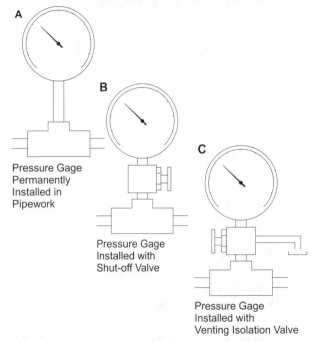

Pressure Gage Permanently Installed in Pipework

Pressure Gage Installed with Shut-off Valve

Pressure Gage Installed with Venting Isolation Valve

Illustration #268A, B & C — Pressure Gage Installation

Checking the System

A test point may consist of an installed tee and isolation valve (refer to illustration #269A) or some type of quick release snap connector (refer to illustration #269B).

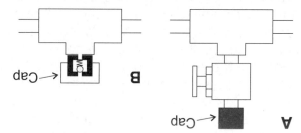

Illustration #269A & B — System Test Points

When pressures are checked, sometimes two pressure figures are compared to obtain a pressure difference as shown in Illustration #270, where the pressure difference across a filter is being measured.

This is similar to checking the voltage in an electrical circuit, where the voltmeter is connected across two points and the voltmeter directly reads the voltage difference. A single pressure reading is often taken such as when setting the system pressure. In this case we are then comparing the pressure reading on the pressure gage with atmospheric pressure (0 psig).

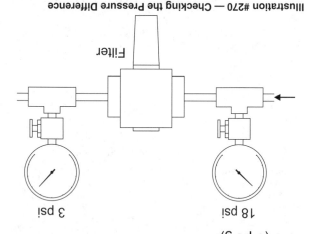

Illustration #270 — Checking the Pressure Difference

Checking Flow

Checking for flow in most circuits will invariably involve dismantling some piping or hoses in order to connect a flow meter, as flow meters are not normally permanently connected into a system.

Flow can be checked either by installing a flow meter, or in the case where a low flow rate is encountered, by directing the flow into a graduated container and using a stopwatch to measure time for a specified amount of fluid to flow into the container.

The simplest flow meter is the float type (refer to illustration #271) and consists of a graduated sight glass and flow indicator. Flow through the meter must be in the direction indicated. Flow causes the indicator to move up the sight glass and the flow rate is read directly off the graduated scale.

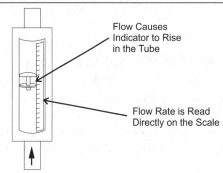

Flow Causes Indicator to Rise in the Tube

Flow Rate is Read Directly on the Scale

Illustration #271 — Float Type Flow Meter

A second type that provides a more accurate electronic readout is the turbine type (refer to illustration #272). As with the float type, the hydraulic lines must be connected so as to provide the correct direction of flow.

Note: Do not connect a flow meter between the pump and the system relief valve or between the relief valve and the tank. A positive displacement pump must have a direct connection to the relief valve and the relief valve must have an unrestricted flow to the tank.

Illustration #272 — Turbine Type Flow Meter

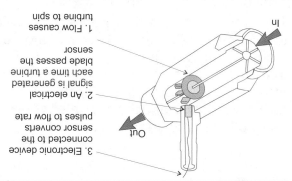

In

1. Flow causes turbine to spin

2. An electrical signal is generated each time a turbine blade passes the sensor

Out

3. Electronic device connected to the sensor converts pulses to flow rate

Illustration #273A shows a flow meter installed to check the flow of fluid to the system when the pump is subject to operating pressures. When used in this location the flow meter must be able to withstand operating pressures. Any flow over the relief valve will affect the flow meter reading; therefore, if the flow meter is being used to measure pump output, the return line from the relief valve to the reservoir should be checked to ensure that flow over the relief valve is not affecting the measurement.

Illustration #273B shows another method of connecting a flow meter to check the pump output. In this situation the flow is diverted from the system, through the flow meter and then back to the reservoir. As shown, the pump is not loaded and the unloaded flow from the pump is checked.

Illustration #273A & B — Flow Meter Installation - Checking Pump Output

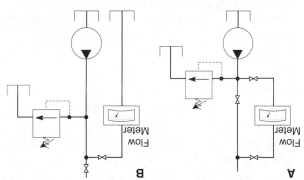

A

Flow Meter

B

Flow Meter

If a throttling valve is placed in the line between the flow meter and the reservoir, the pump output can be checked with the pump operating from no load to relief valve setting. As with the previous example, flow from the relief valve should be checked to ensure that this does not affect the flow meter readings.

The condition of a pump is often checked by measuring the flow through the case drain line from the pump to the reservoir (refer to Illustration #274). Although a flow meter may be used for this purpose, a measuring jar and stopwatch is usually more suitable due to low flow rates. This test is even more useful if the result of the same test, carried out when the pump was first installed, is available for comparison purposes.

If pump output is found to be adequate, the actual flow available to an actuator can be checked by connecting the flow meter across the inlet and discharge line at the actuator as shown in Illustration #275.

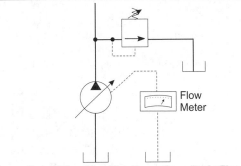

Illustration #274— Checking Pump Case Drain Flow

When the two isolation valves are closed the total flow will be through the flow meter at low pressure. A more meaningful test would be to place a throttling valve in the line between the flow meter and the reservoir. By throttling the flow the test can be carried out at operating pressure.

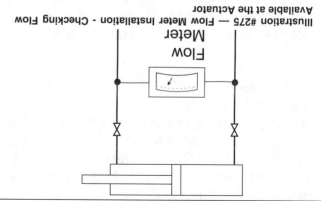

Illustration #275 — Flow Meter Installation - Checking Flow Available at the Actuator

Checking Fluid Condition

Having samples of the hydraulic fluid tested by a laboratory is the normal way to check solid and liquid contamination. Some fluid or filter suppliers may provide this service as will various oil testing laboratory services available in most cities. If high quality hydraulic fluid is not being used, there may be excessive foaming in the reservoir and emulsification may occur if water is present.

Systematic Troubleshooting

There is a difference between maintenance and troubleshooting. Maintenance is the repair or replacement of damaged or worn parts such as changing the piston rod seals on a cylinder or replacing a leaking hose. The troubleshooter looks for the cause of a problem, after this is determined, some form of maintenance will usually be required to correct the problem.

A hydraulic system is made up of four main parts (see illustration #276). They are:

- Energy input
- Fluid control system
- Energy output
- Load

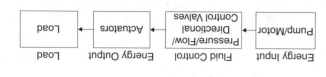

Illustration #276 — Parts of a Hydraulic System

When troubleshooting, all four parts have to be considered. For example, if a hydraulic motor fails to rotate when it is switched on, any one of the four parts could be the cause. For example:

- *Load:* The load may have jammed.
- *Energy output:* The actuator may be by-passing the fluid to the reservoir.
- *Fluid control system:* The directional control valve solenoid may be burned out.
- *Energy input:* The pump/drive motor shaft coupling may have sheared.

Step 1.

When a hydraulic system fails or malfunctions, the first measurable indications are at the energy output or actuator part of the system. The troubleshooter must understand the correct functions of the machine to be able to determine if the actuator has any of the following operational faults:

- No movement
- Movement is too fast
- Movement is too slow
- Movement is erratic
- Incorrect amount of thrust or torque
- Control or directional problems such as:
  a. Incorrect sequence of events
  b. Movement in the wrong direction

If possible it should be determined if the operational fault is being caused by problems concerning pressure, flow, or direction

Step 2

Find out if the problem has suddenly occurred, or is it a problem that started some time ago and is gradually getting worse.

The sudden occurrence of a problem often indicates that something may be broken or jammed, or a wrong adjustment (see step 3) was made.

A problem that gradually gets worse over time may point to the wearing of components or the build up of dirt and silt.

Step 3

Check to see if any of the following has oc-curred recently:

- Adjustments to any of the components, such as setting pressures or flow rates
- Maintenance work carried out, such as the replacement or repair of components, filters, hoses etc.
- Modifications to the system
- Any changes made to the load

Step 4

Make a list of all the possible components that may be the cause or a part of the cause of the malfunction. A complete schematic di-agram of the hydraulic circuit will be required and the function of each of the system com-ponents must be identified. Any previous knowledge and understanding of the system will be of great help when making this list. Put the list in priority order with any compo-nent that is mentioned above in step 3.

Step 5

Complete a preliminary check of all the listed components for excessive or unusual noise, heat and vibration by listening and feeling. At the same time visually check for any obvious abnormalities including external fluid leakage.

Step 6

If step 5 fails to provide a starting point, then further investigation will have to be carried out using instrumentation, such as flow me-ters and pressure gages. A component should not be changed out or dismantled un-til a particular test has proven that it is at fault.

Step 7

Any component found to have a problem when completing either steps 5 or 6 can be repaired or changed out. This decision will depend on the type of fault and component and the availability of spare parts.

Troubleshooting Tables

The following tables are arranged as follows:

Tables #24, #25 and #26 deal with primary malfunctions with regards to the actuator and load. Possible causes for these malfunctions are listed along with a suggested possible solution for each cause. Some of these possible solutions will refer to tables #27 and #28. Table #27 provides lists of the possible causes for various pressure problems. Table #28 is similar but deals with various problems associated with flow.

Tables #29 and #30 list the common causes for excessive system heat and noise along with suggested possible solutions.

Primary Malfunctions

- No movement - see table #24
- Movement too slow - see table #25
- Movement too fast - see table #25
- Movement is erratic - see table #25
- Thrust or torque too high - see table #26
- Thrust or torque too low - see table #26

NO MOVEMENT	
Check pressure at actuator (see note a)	
Correct Pressure	**Low/No Pressure**
Actuator is jammed, seized or broken Possible Solution: b)	Fluid is bypassing relief valve Possible Solution: see table #27
Load is jammed or seized Possible Solution: c)	Fluid is bypassing through the actuator Possible Solution: b)
Load is too high Possible Solution: d)	No flow from the pump Possible Solution: see table #28
Counter balance valve defective or misadjusted Possible Solution: b) or e)	

a) When there is no movement at the actuator there will normally be no flow (If there is flow it will be due to the fluid bypassing through the actuator)
b) Repair or replace
c) Locate problem and repair
d) Determine the cause of the excess load and reduce if possible (it may be necessary to increase the pressure or install a larger actuator if nothing can be done about the load)
e) Adjust to correct setting

Table #24 — No Movement

SPEED TOO HIGH	SPEED TOO LOW	ERRATIC MOVEMENT
Flow rate is too high Possible Solution: see table #28	Flow rate is too low Possible Solution: see table #28	Erratic pressure Possible Solution: see table #27
Over-riding load Possible Solution: a) or b)	Load or mechanism is binding or requires lubrication Possible Solution: c)	Load is binding or requires lubrication Possible Solution: c)
Cylinder bypassing on extension (meter-out) Possible Solution: d)	Load is too high Possible Solution: e)	Load is erratic Possible Solution: e) or f)
	Worn/damaged cylinder or motor Possible Solution: d)	Worn/damaged cylinder or motor Possible Solution: d)
	Sticking valve Possible Solution: d)	Sticking valve Possible Solution: d)
	Accumulator not charging Possible Solution: h)	Erratic control signal Possible Solution: g)
a) Correct counter-balance valve problems b) Install counter-balance valve c) Repair or lubricate d) Repair or replace e) Correct load f) Install a counterbalance, over-center or brake valve g) Repair electrical controls h) Repair accumulator		

Table #25 — Faulty Movement

FORCE/TORQUE TOO HIGH	FORCE/TORQUE TOO LOW
Pressures are too high Possible Solution: see table #27	Pressures are too low Possible Solution: see table #27
Replacement actuator is the wrong size Possible Solution: a)	Replacement actuator is the wrong size Possible Solution: a)
	Actuator is worn or damaged. Possible Solution: b)
a) Replace with correct actuator b) Repair or replace actuator.	

Table #26 — Torque or Force Problem

INCORRECT PRESSURE		
PRESSURE TOO LOW	**PRESSURE TOO HIGH**	**ERRATIC PRESSURE**
No flow or low flow rate Possible Solution: see table #28	Pressure reducing valve/relief valve/pump compensator set too high Possible Solution: b)	Air in fluid: Possible Solution d)
No load or low load on actuator Possible Solution: a)	Pressure reducing valve/relief valve/pump compensator defective Possible Solution: c)	Worn relief valve Possible Solution: c)
Pressure reducing valve/relief valve/pump compensator set too low Possible Solution: b)	Variable volume mechanism on compensated pump defective: Possible Solution: c)	Defective accumulator Possible Solution: c)
Pressure reducing valve/relief valve/pump compensator defective Possible Solution: c)		Solid contamination in fluid causing erratic valve and pump operation Possible Solution: c) and e)
Variable volume mechanism on compensated pump defective Possible Solution: c)		Worn pump motor or cylinder Possible Solution: c)
Worn/damaged pump or actuator Possible Solution: c)		

a) Check load on actuator
b) Adjust to the correct pressure
c) Repair or replace
d) Tighten possible leaking connections on pump suction; make sure that fluid level in reservoir is correct; check actuator seals where there are overrunning loads
e) Check and replace filters

Table #27 — Incorrect Pressure

INCORRECT FLOW		
NO FLOW	**FLOW TOO LOW**	**FLOW TOO HIGH**
Entire flow over relief valve Possible Solution: a)	Flow control valve setting is too low Possible Solution: g)	Flow control valve setting too high Possible Solution: g)
Directional control valve set in wrong position or not operating Possible Solution: b)	Variable displacement pump set too low Possible Solution: g)	Variable displacement pump set too high Possible Solution: g)
Limit switches or sequence valve defective or misadjusted Possible Solution: f) or g)	RPM of driver too low Possible Solution: h) if fixed speed Possible Solution: g) if variable speed	RPM of driver too high Possible Solution: h) if fixed speed Possible Solution: g) if variable speed
Pump not receiving fluid Possible Solution: c)	Volume of replacement pump too low Possible Solution: h)	Volume of replacement pump too high Possible Solution: h)
Pump drive motor not driving the pump Possible Solution: d)	Pressure setting of relief or unloading valve set too low Possible Solution: a)	Defective mechanism on variable displacement pump Possible Solution: f)
Pump drive motor turning in wrong direction Possible Solution: e)	Partially open valve bypassing fluid Possible Solution: b) or f)	
Damaged or worn pump Possible Solution: f)	Fluid viscosity is too high Possible Solution: i)	
Improperly assembled pump Possible Solution: f)	Pilot pressure insufficient for directional valves Possible Solution: g)	
Partially open valve bypassing fluid Possible Solution: b) or f)	Damaged or worn pump Possible Solution: f)	

Table #28 — Incorrect Flow Rate (see next page for possible solutions)

Table #28 — Incorrect Flow Rate con't.

Possible Solutions:

a) Adjust to relieve at the correct pressure

b) Check and repair if necessary:
• Position of manually operated valve
• Electrical circuits on solenoid operated valves
• Pilot circuitry on pilot operated valves including pilot pressures
• That the valve spool is not seized or jammed

c) Check and correct any or all of the following:
• Dirty or plugged inlet filters or piping
• Reservoir fluid level
• Plugged reservoir breather vent
• Faulty supercharge pump

d) Check for and replace if necessary:
• Faulty drive motor
• Broken or sheared coupling

e) Change rotation

f) Repair or replace

g) Adjust to correct setting

h) Replace with correct unit

i) Fluid may be too cold (consider heaters, or changing to a fluid with a higher viscosity index)

Excessive Heat

Ideally, minimum and maximum petroleum based fluid temperatures should be kept between 120°F (49°C) and 130°F (54°C) with an absolute maximum of around 150°F (66°C). Systems may operate out of this range but will eventually pay the price of reduced oil and component life.

Heat is generated in hydraulic systems by friction, and pressure drops with no associated work being done.

Increased mechanical friction occurs in components such as pumps, motors and cylinders when loads and pressures are high and rubbing takes place. When this occurs the offending component will have the highest temperature rise, the wear rate will increase and there will be a corresponding increase in noise.

EXCESSIVE HEAT			
Pump Heated	**Motor Heated**	**Relief Valve Heated**	**Fluid Heated**
Fluid heated Possible Solution: see "fluid" column	Fluid heated Possible Solution: see "fluid heated" column	Fluid heated Possible Solution: see "fluid heated" column	Fluid level is low Possible Solution: d)
System pressure too high Possible Solution: see table #27	System pressure too high Possible Solution: see table #27	Relief valve setting too low Possible Solution: c)	System pressure too high Possible Solution: see table #27
Excessive load Possible Solution: a)	Excessive load Possible Solution: a)	Excessive load Possible Solution: a)	Excessive load Possible Solution: a)
Worn or damaged pump Possible Solution: b)	Worn or damaged motor Possible Solution: b		Worn or damaged pump or motor Possible Solution: b
Cavitation Possible Solution: see table #30			Fluid is contaminated Possible Solution: e)
Air in the fluid Possible Solution: see table #30			Fluid viscosity is incorrect Possible Solution: f)

Table #29 — Excessive Heat (see next page for possible solutions)

Pressure reductions with no work being done, such as when oil is passed over the pressure relief valve, will cause a local increase in temperature at the point of pressure reduction. Internal leakage in a pump as it produces high pressures will also cause local heating.

Table #29 — Excessive Heat con't.

Possible Solutions:

a) Check that the work load is not in excess of the design amount; check and correct any mechanical binding or jamming.

b) Overhaul or replace

c) Using a pressure gage adjust to the correct pressure

d) Fill to correct level

e) Replace filter elements; check for sources of contamination and correct

f) Change fluid to give the correct viscosity at the operating temperature range

g) Check cooler for correct hydraulic and cooling fluid or air flow, clean if required including any filters, check and repair any faulty control valves

The amount that the overall oil temperature is increased will depend on the pressure drop and the volume of fluid involved.

The normal operating temperature of a system is determined when the heat generated is equal to the heat being dissipated. A change in system temperature occurs when this balance is disturbed.

When temperatures become too high, hydraulic fluid will oxidize and breakdown at a higher rate. There is also a reduction in lubricity and viscosity. The reduction in lubricity and viscosity will allow more metal to metal contact of moving parts, which increases the amount of friction and wear, increasing the amount of heat generated and adding contamination to the fluid. The reduction in viscosity will increase the internal leakage rates, again causing an increase in the amount of heat generated.

For troubleshooting purposes some method of checking the temperature in various parts of the circuit may be required.

This may be in the form of a thermocouple that can be attached to the fluid line or an infrared thermometer that can be used to check the temperature of any component or line with no contact with the part being checked. Many systems have a temperature gage permanently installed at the reservoir.

If a thermometer is not available, the temperature of a dry surface can be checked by careful use of the hand or fingers.

Most people can tolerate touching a hot surface that is up to 130°F (54°C) for a few seconds without discomfort. This method can be used to quickly check the reservoir temperature.

Note: Some components such as pumps usually run hotter than the general reservoir temperature and should therefore be approached with caution. This method should not be used for checking the temperature of oil by putting the fingers directly in the oil or on a surface if it is wet with fluid.

Excessive Noise

Noise and vibration are closely associated. Changes in noise level are difficult to detect by ear, especially when there may be other noisy machines in the vicinity. For this reason a meter should be used if an accurate noise measurement is required. After trouble has developed, just checking the noise level will not indicate whether or not there is a problem. However if the noise level was previously checked, or if another similar component is operating close by so that a comparison can be made, then it may be possible to determine if a component is noisier than it should be.

An increase in noise level of the hydraulic system, or from an individual component such as a pump or motor usually indicates a problem. Cavitation, aeration, worn parts, metal to metal contact, fluid bypassing from high to low pressures, turbulence, etc., all cause vibrations that produce noise.

EXCESSIVE NOISE		
Pump	**Motor**	**Relieve Valve**
Cavitation Possible Solution: a)	Coupling misaligned Possible Solution: c)	Worn poppet or seat Possible Solution: d)
Air in fluid Possible Solution: b)	Motor worn or damaged Possible Solution: d)	Setting too close to working pressure of system Possible Solution: e)
	Coupling misaligned Possible Solution: c)	
	Pump worn or damaged Possible Solution: d)	

a) See "Cavitation" below
b) Remove all sources of air entry into the fluid (pump suction and shaft seals, make sure return lines to the reservoir are below the surface)
c) Realign
d) Repair or replace
e) Set to correct pressure

Table #30 — Excessive Noise

Cavitation

The condition of the pump inlet can have a major effect on pump performance. The majority of pumps rely on atmospheric pressure as the energy source to push fluid into the pump. The combination of viscosity and velocity of the fluid as it flows through the suction piping, fittings, and strainers to the pump, cause a reduction in pressure at the pump inlet. Some systems also locate the pump above the surface of the fluid in the reservoir, which will cause an even greater pressure drop as pressure energy is used to raise the fluid up to the pump. The allowable inlet vacuum will depend on the type of fluid (petroleum based, HWCF or synthetic fire resistant fluids), and the temperature of the fluid.

Cavitation is caused when low-pressure liquid that contains vapor bubbles is changed to high pressure.

This change in pressure occurs in pumps as the fluid moves from the suction into the pumping chambers of the pump. The vapor in the liquid is produced when:

- The pressure of the liquid is below the vapor pressure and boiling takes place.
- Dissolved air in the fluid comes out of solution when the fluid is subject to low pressures.
- Air enters the inlet due to leaks at threaded or gasketed joints.
- Air enters the suction due to a vortex (whirlpool) occurring when the surface of the fluid is too close to the suction opening (this occurs more readily when the fluid viscosity is high, such as on cold start ups).

Possible solutions for cavitation are:

- Clean any inlet strainers or filters.
- Reduce the velocity of fluid in the suction line (larger diameter line or slow the flow rate).
- Reduce the number of fittings in the suction line (consider using tubing with bends rather than pipe and fittings).
- Consider using fluid heaters if cavitation occurs on cold starts.
- Consider using coolers if the operating fluid temperature is high (hot fluid will have a higher vapor pressure).
- Make sure that all suction piping is airtight.
- Make sure the reservoir breather is clean.

- Entrained air may also enter the suction line if, due to poor reservoir design, the fluid does not have enough time from when it enters the reservoir, to being drawn into the pump suction, for the entrained air to separate.

Cavitation creates noise in the pump. The sound can range from being barely audible to a loud rattling noise due to the imploding vapor bubbles inside the pump. If allowed to continue for any length of time, cavitation will cause pitting to occur on the effected pump parts. The minute metal particles that are removed from the pump parts by the cavitation process are carried through the system, and until they are picked up by the filtration system, may cause operational problems and cause added wear to other components.

Entrained air will also cause problems elsewhere in the circuit. Actuator motion will be jerky or erratic.

Checking Actuators for Wear

Hydraulic Motor Wear

All hydraulic motors have close fitting clearances to seal between moving and stationary parts. When a motor is new some leakage will occur. The amount will be dependent on the pressure difference across the clearances and the size of the clearances.

Pressure differences are created by the load on the motor shaft; therefore, the maximum leakage will occur when the motor is at full load and consequently, maximum pressure.

As wear occurs, the amount of leakage for a specific load will increase. This will cause the shaft speed to decrease (assuming that the motor is supplied with the same amount of input flow).

If the motor is equipped with a case drain line, the amount of flow through the drain line will increase. On motors that do not have a case drain, the leakage goes back to the discharge.

To check for hydraulic motor wear, it is advisable to make some initial observations when the motor is still in a new condition. For piston motors that have a case drain, observe the amount of flow through the drain line when the motor is operating at a specific pressure (use the operating pressure, if possible). This may be accomplished by either using a flow meter, or by opening the drain line and measuring the time it takes to fill a known container. If there is no case drain line, check the shaft speed at a specific pressure and flow rate.

The motor may then be checked for wear at any time by completing the same test and comparing with the original readings.

Note: Some gear and vane motors may have a drain from the shaft seal area, but the majority of leakage may be occurring due to wear at the vanes and gears, etc. These motors should be checked for wear by checking for a speed reduction.

Hydraulic Cylinders

Piston Seal Leakage

Piston seal leakage can cause a number of symptoms each of which will depend on the circuit design and operating conditions. These symptoms may be:

- Piston drift or creep (slowly lowering under load)
- Pressure intensification at the piston rod end
- Piston speed decrease
- Piston speed increase

For more detailed information refer to Section Six "Cylinder Sealing Problems".

Checking for Piston Seal Leaks

Whether or not the following tests will be possible to accomplish will depend on the cylinder, piping, and load configuration.

Piston seal leaks may occur in both directions across the piston (although not always equally), or in one direction only (when the appropriate pressure difference is applied across the piston). Cast iron rings usually leak in both directions. Cup seals and U-section rings may leak in one direction, if only one of the seals is damaged. The intended application for the cylinder will determine if the leakage across the piston has to be checked in one or both directions.

Cast iron piston rings will leak a small amount due to ring end clearances. This will cause the cylinder to drift under load. Ideally, this type of cylinder would be checked for leakage when new, for comparison purposes.

When testing for piston seal leaks a pressure difference across the piston must be generated.

Method One (Load Method)

This method requires an external load to be exerted on the cylinder and uses piston drift to determine if the seals are leaking.

To be able to complete this test, it must be possible to exert a constant force on the piston rod. Modifications to the piping may also be required.

Often, the first indication that piston seals are leaking is when a load will not maintain a raised position, but slowly lowers back down.

The piston seals in illustration #277A are leaking from the cap end to the rod end. The piston seals in illustration #277B are leaking from the rod end to the cap end.

If attempting to simulate these conditions, note that pressure gages are used to measure the pressure difference across the piston, and that the low pressure side of the piston is open to the reservoir. This allows fluid to flow towards the reservoir in illustration #277A and be drawn from the reservoir in illustration #277B. A shut off valve should be used on the high pressure side to prevent any possible leakage back to the reservoir (do not rely on spool type DCV).

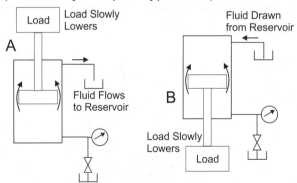

Illustration #277 — Checking for Piston Seal Leakage, Load Method

Accurate measurements for drift can be obtained by using a stopwatch to time the movement over a specified distance. A number of observations should be made at intervals along the stroke.

Method Two (Intensification Method)

Method uses pressure intensification to create the pressure difference across the piston.

This test, which should be carried out with no load on the piston rod, only checks for leakage in one direction (from the rod end to the cap end of the cylinder).

To check on the amount of leakage past the piston seals, a shut off valve (needle or globe) should be piped into the rod end cylinder line (see illustration #278).

Locate the piston at the cap end of the cylinder and close the shut off valve.

When system pressure (2000 psi [13 800 kPa] in this example) is applied to the cap end of the piston, pressure intensification causes 4000 psi [27 600 kPa] to be generated at the rod end of the cylinder. Due to this 2000 psi [13 800 kPa] pressure difference, fluid will migrate from the rod side, to the cap side of the piston, if there is any seal leakage. This will cause the piston rod to slowly extend. The rate of movement will depend on the amount of leakage.

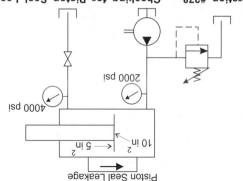

Illustration #278 — Checking for Piston Seal Leakage, Intensification Method

SECTION TEN QUESTIONS

Troubleshooting

1. Randomly changing out components is usually the quickest way of solving any hydraulic system problem.
   ❑ true   ❑ false

2. What factors other than component problems may cause a hydraulic system to malfunction?

   Answer: _____
   _____

3. What three human senses are often used to become aware of a system problem?

   Answer: _____
   _____

4. Problems in a system are often accompanied by which of the following?
   ❑ temperature rise
   ❑ increased noise
   ❑ fluid contamination
   ❑ all of the above

5. What are two causes of temperature rise in a system?

   Answer: _____
   _____

6. The reservoir temperature may fluctuate due to operational changes.
   ❑ true   ❑ false

7. Changes in pump suction can cause cavitation.
   ❑ true   ❑ false

8. Cavitation is always difficult to detect as it is a silent problem.
   ❑ true   ❑ false

9. How is solid contamination of fluid detected?

   Answer: _____
   _____

10. Understanding hydraulic schematics is helpful, but overall, is not necessary when troubleshooting a system.
    ❑ true   ❑ false

11. One plus when using a schematic is the fact that all symbols worldwide are standardized.
    ❑ true   ❑ false

12. When assuming that one component is at fault, it is not necessary to understand the function of other system components.
    ❑ true   ❑ false

13. What two items may be required to locate and identify components when attempting to test or change out a component?

Answer: _____

_____

14. Hydraulic systems are always localized circuits, therefore safety, while always a concern, is not a major factor in equipment repair.

❑ true   ❑ false

15. List several basic steps to follow when repairing a system in a plant:

Answer: _____

_____

16. Why could an accumulator pose a danger even though the system pressure has been released?

Answer: _____

_____

17. When disconnecting a large flanged joint in a piping system, always unloosen which bolts and crack open which side first?

Answer: _____

_____

18. What precaution must be taken to protect the system while installing temporary gages and meters?

Answer: _____

_____

19. When using a gage to check a pressure that is expected to be 1000 psi, which of the following pressure gages would be most suitable?

❑ 10 to 1000 psi
❑ 0 to 1500 psi
❑ 0 to 2000 psi
❑ 0 to 5000 psi

20. What should be installed along with a permanent test pressure gage?

Answer: _____

_____

21. Referring to number 20, what is the reason?

Answer: _____

_____

22. What is the most accurate method to check the pressure difference across a filter?
   - ❏ install a pressure gage on the upstream side and compare with the system pressure
   - ❏ install a pressure gage on the downstream side and compare with the system pressure
   - ❏ install a pressure gage on each side of the filter
   - ❏ check system pressure and compare with previous readings

23. List two locations where a flow meter should not be placed:

   Answer: _____

   _____

24. A turbine flow meter is more accurate than a float type.
   - ❏ true   ❏ false

25. What is the most suitable method of checking the flow from a motor drain line, assuming the flow rate will be very low?
   - ❏ install a float type flow meter in the drain line
   - ❏ install a turbine type flow meter in the drain line
   - ❏ install turbine type flow meters on both the pump inlet and outlet and compare readings
   - ❏ disconnect the drain line and time the flow into a graduated container

26. What are the four main parts of a hydraulic system?

   Answer: _____

   _____

27. If a system fails or malfunctions suddenly, this could be an indication of:

   Answer: _____

   _____

28. If a system slowly malfunctions over time, this could be an indication of:

   Answer: _____

   _____

29. What would be one of the first places to check if there is no movement?

   Answer: _____

   _____

30. An actuator speeds up when the attached load becomes overrunning. What is the possible solution (table #25)?

   Answer: _____

   _____

31. The system pressure is found to be erratic and it is thought that air is getting into the system. Where would you check and correct for possible leaks (table #27)?

Answer: _____

32. The electric motor drive to a hydraulic pump was changed on the previous shift. The motor runs fine but the is no flow from the pump. What is the possible cause (table #28)?

Answer: _____

33. The reservoir fluid temperature is found to be high, on checking the system components it is found that the relief valve is very hot and bypassing fluid most of the time. What is the possible cause (table #29)?

Answer: _____

34. A hydraulic pump is very noisy, list four possible reasons (table #30):

Answer: _____

35. If a hydraulic motor is equipped with a drain line what is the best way of checking for motor wear?

Answer: _____

36. Cast iron piston rings are designed to provide a positive seal with no leakage unless they are worn.

  ☐ true   ☐ false

SECTION ELEVEN

ELEVEN

TABLES AND CONVERSIONS

Metric SI Units — Table #31

Common SI Units	Symbol	Conversion from In-Lb-Gal Units
Acceleration		
centimetre per second squared	cm/s²	1 gal = **1 cm/s²**
metre per second squared	m/s²	1 foot per second squared = **0.3048 m/s²**
kilometre per second squared	km/s²	1 mile per second squared = **1.609 344 km/s²**
Area		
square centimetre	cm²	1 square inch = **6.4516 cm²**
square metre	m²	1 square foot = **929.0304 cm²**
hectare	ha	1 square foot = **0.092 903 04 m²**
square kilometre	km²	1 square yard = **0.836 127 4 m²**
		1 acre = 0.404 685 6 ha
		1 square mile = 2.589 988 km²
Density (Mass per unit volume)		
gram per cubic centimetre	g/cm³	1 pound per cubic inch = 27.679 9 g/cm³
gram per cubic metre	g/m³	1 grain per cubic foot = 2.288 352 g/m³
kilogram per cubic metre	kg/m³	1 grain per gallon = 14.2536 g/m³
		1 pound per cubic foot = 16.018 46 kg/m³
		1 pound per gallon = 99.776 37 kg/m³

Note: **BOLD FACE** type indicates exact conversions

Metric SI Units — Table #31		
Common SI Units	**Symbol**	**Conversion from In-Lb-Gal Units**
Density (Mass per unit length)		
kilogram per metre	kg/m	1 ounce per inch = 1.116 12 kg/m 1 pound per foot = 1.488 16 kg/m 1 pound per inch = 17.857 9 kg/m
Density (Mass per unit area)		
gram per square metre	g/m^2	2000 pounds per acre = 0.224 170 kg/m^2
kilogram per square metre	kg/m^2	1 ounce per square foot = 305.152 g/m^2 1 pound per square foot = 4.882 43 kg/m^2
Density (Mass per unit volume)		
gram per cubic centimetre	g/cm^3	1 pound per cubic foot = 16.018 46 kg/m^3
kilogram per cubic metre	kg/m^3	1 pound per cubic inch = 27.679 90 g/cm^3
tonne per cubic metre	t/m^3	1 ton (short) per cubic yard = 1.186 553 t/m^3 1 ton (long) per cubic yard = 1.328 939 t/m^3

Note: BOLD FACE type indicates exact conversions

Metric SI Units — Table #31

Common SI Units	Symbol	Conversion from In-Lb-Gal Units
Energy		
joule	J	1 erg = 0.1 μJ
kilojoule	kJ	1 foot pound-force = 1.355 818 J
megajoule	MJ	1 calorie (international) = **4.1868 J** 1 Btu (International Table) = 1.055 06 kJ 1 Calorie (dietetic) = 4.1855 kJ 1 horsepower hour = 2.684 52 kJ 1 kilowatt hour = **3.6 MJ**
Flow Rate		
cubic centimetre per second	cm³/s	1 cubic inch per second = 16.387 cm³/s
cubic decimetre per second	dm³/s	1 gallon (US) per minute = 0.063 dm³/s
cubic metre per second	m³/s	1 gallon (Canadian) per minute = 0.075 77 dm³/s
Force		
newton	N	1 dyne = 10 μN
kilonewton	kN	1 poundal = 0.138 255 N
meganewton	MN	1 pound-force = 4.448 222 N 1 kilogram-force = **9.806 65 N**

Metric SI Units — Table #31		
Common SI Units	**Symbol**	**Conversion from In-Lb-Gal Units**
Heat (Flow, Capacity, Conductivity)		
kilojoule per kilogram	kJ/kg	1 Btu per cubic foot = 37.2591 kJ/m^3
kilojoule per kilogram degree Celsius	kJ/(kg •°C)	1 Btu per (cubic foot °F) = 67.0661 kJ/(m^3•°C)
kilojoule per cubic metre	kJ/m^3	1 Btu per hour = 0.293 072 W
kilojoule per cubic metre degree Celsius	kJ/(m^3•°C)	1 Btu per pound = 2.326 kJ/kg
watt	W	1 Btu per (pound °F) = **4.1868** kJ/(kg•°C)
watt per square metre	W/m^2	1 calorie per (gram °C) = **4.1868** J/(g•°C) 1 Btu per (square foot hour) = 3.154 60 W/m^2
watt per metre degree Celsius	W/(m•°C)	1 Btu foot per (sq. ft. hour °F) = 1.730 74 W/(m.•°C)
watt per square metre degree Celsius	W/(m^2•°C)	1 Btu per (sq. ft. hour °F) = 5.678 29 W/(m^2•°C)

Note:
 1) Specific heat and latent heat are now called specific heat capacity and specific latent heat of fusion. 2) 'Kelvin' and 'degree Celsius' are interchangeable wherever they are used to indicate a temperature interval.

Note: BOLD FACE type indicates exact conversions

Metric SI Units — Table #31

Common SI Units	Symbol	Conversion from In-Lb-Gal Units
Light (Illuminance)		
lux	lx	1 foot candle = 10.763 91 lx
kilolux	klx	1 lumen per square foot = 10.763 91 lx
		1 phot = 10 klx
Light (Luminance)		
candela per sq. metre	cd/m²	1 stilb = 1 cd/m²
		1 foot lambert = 3.426 26 cd/m²
		1 candela per sq. foot = 10.763 91 cd/m²
		1 candela per sq. inch = 1550.0 cd/m²
Mass		
milligram	mg	1 ounce (avoirdupois) = **28.349 523 125 g**
gram	g	1 pound (avoirdupois) = **0.453 592 37 kg**
kilogram	kg	1 ton (short, 2000 lb) = 0.907 184 74 t
tonne	t	1 ton (long, 2240 lb) = **1.016 046 908 8 t**

Note: BOLD FACE type indicates exact conversions

Metric SI Units — Table #31		
Common SI Units	**Symbol**	**Conversion from In-Lb-Gal Units**
Power		
watt	W	1 Btu (International Table) per hour = 0.293 072 W
kilowatt	kW	1 foot pound-force per second = 1.355 818 W 1 horsepower (550 ft lbf/s) = 745.6999 W 1 horsepower (electrical) = **746** W
Pressure		
pascal	Pa	1 pound-force per square foot = 47.880 26 Pa
kilopascal	kPa	1 millibar = **100** Pa

megapascal	MPa	1 inch of water (conventional) = 249.089 Pa
		1 inch of mercury, conventional (0°C)
		    = 3.386 39 kPa
		1 pound-force per sq. inch (psi)
		    = 6.894 757 kPa
		1 atmosphere, standard (=760 torr)
		    = **101.325** kPa

Note: BOLD FACE type indicates exact conversions		

Metric SI Units — Table #31		
Common SI Units	**Symbol**	**Conversion from In-Lb-Gal Units**
Temperature		
Degree Celsius	°C	Celsius temperature = (Fahrenheit temperature -32) x 5/9
kelvin	K	Celsius temperature = temperature in kelvins -273.15 Fahrenheit temperature = (**1.8** x Celsius temperature) + **32**
* Time		
second	s	1 min. = **60** s
minute	min.	1 h = **3.6** ks
hour	h	1 d = **86.4** ks
Torque or Moment of Force		
millinewton metre	mN•m	1 ounce-force inch = 7.061 552 mN•m
newton metre	N•m	1 pound-force inch (lbf•in) = 0.112 985 N•m 1 pound-force foot (lbf•ft) = 1.355 818 N•m

Note: BOLD FACE type indicates exact conversions

Metric SI Units — Table #31		
Common SI Units	**Symbol**	**Conversion from In-Lb-Gal Units**
Velocity or Speed		
metre per second	m/s	1 foot per second = **0.3048** m/s 1 foot per minute = **0.00508** m/s
kilometre per hour	km/h	1 mile per hour = **1.609 344** km/h
Viscosity (Dynamic)		
pascal second	Pa•s	1 centipoise (cp) = **0.1** Pa•s 1 poise (p) = **0.1** Pa•s
millipascal second	mPa•s	*1 pound per (foot second) = 1.488 164 Pa•s *1 slug per foot second = 47.880 26 Pa•s
* 1 pound per (foot second) = 1 poundal second per square foot		
Note: BOLD FACE type indicates exact conversions		

Metric SI Units — Table #31

Common SI Units	Symbol	Conversion from In-Lb-Gal Units
Volume		
cubic centimetre	cm³	1 cubic inch = **16.387 064 cm³**
cubic decimetre	dm³	1 cubic foot = 28.316 85 dm³ 1 cubic yard = 0.764 555 m³
cubic metre	m³	1 barrel (oil, 42 US gallons) = 0.158 987 3 m³
millilitre	ml	1 fluid ounce (Canadian) = 28.413 062 5 ml
litre	L	1 fluid ounce (US liquid) = 29.573 53 mL 1 quart (US liquid) = 0.946 353 L 1 quart (Canadian) = **1.136 522 5 L** 1 gallon (US liquid) = 3.785 412 L 1 gallon (Canadian) = **4.546 09 L**
Length		
millimetre	mm	1 inch = **25.4 mm**
centimetre	cm	1 foot = **30.48 cm**
metre	m	1 yard = **0.9144 m**
kilometre	km	1 mile = **1.609 344 km**

Note: BOLD FACE type indicates exact conversions

Fractions and Decimals of an Inch with Millimetre Equivalents — Table #32

Frac-tions	Decimals of an inch	mm
	0.00394	0.1
	0.00787	0.2
	0.01	0.254
	0.01181	0.3
$1/64$	0.015625	0.3969
	0.01575	0.4
	0.01969	0.5
	0.02	0.508
	0.02362	0.6
	0.02756	0.7
	0.03	0.762
$1/32$	0.013125	0.7938
	0.0315	0.8
	0.03543	0.9
	0.03937	1.0
	0.04	1.016

Frac-tions	Decimals of an inch	mm
$3/64$	0.046875	1.1906
	0.05	1.27
	0.06	1.524
$1/16$	0.0625	1.5875
	0.07	1.778
$5/64$	0.078125	1.9844
	0.07874	2.0
	0.08	2.032
	0.09	2.286
$3/32$	0.09375	2.3812
	0.1	2.54
$7/64$	0.109375	2.7781
	0.11	2.794
	0.11811	3.0
	0.12	3.048
$1/8$	0.125	3.175

Frac-tions	Decimals of an inch	mm
	0.13	3.302
	0.14	3.556
$9/64$	0.140625	3.5719
	0.15	3.810
$5/32$	0.15625	3.9688
	0.15748	4.0
	0.16	4.064
	0.17	4.318
$11/64$	0.171875	4.3656
	0.18	4.572
$3/16$	0.1875	4.7625
	0.19	4.826
	0.19685	5.0
$13/64$	0.2	5.08
	0.203125	5.1594
	0.21	5.334

Fractions and Decimals of an Inch with Millimetre Equivalents — Table #32

Fractions of an inch	Decimals of an inch	mm
7/32	0.21875	5.5562
	0.22	5.588
	0.23	5.842
15/64	0.234375	5.9531
	0.23622	6.0
	0.24	6.096
1/4	0.25	6.35
	0.26	6.604
17/64	0.265625	6.7469
	0.27	6.858
	0.27559	7.0
	0.28	7.112
9/32	0.28125	7.1438
	0.29	7.366
19/64	0.296875	7.5406
	0.30	7.62
	0.31	7.874
5/16	0.3125	7.9375
	0.31496	8.0
	0.32	8.128
21/64	0.328125	8.3344
	0.33	8.382
	0.34	8.636
11/32	0.34375	8.7312
	0.35	8.89
	0.35433	9.0
23/64	0.359375	9.1281
	0.36	9.144
	0.37	9.398
3/8	0.375	9.525
	0.38	9.652
	0.39	9.906
25/64	0.390625	9.9219
	0.39370	10.0
	0.40	10.16
13/32	0.40625	10.3188
	0.41	10.414
	0.42	10.668
27/64	0.421875	10.71556
	0.43	10.922
	0.43307	11.0
7/16	0.4375	11.1125
	0.44	11.176
	0.45	11.430
29/64	0.453125	11.5094
	0.46	11.684
15/32	0.46875	11.9062
	0.47	11.938

Fractions and Decimals of an Inch with Millimetre Equivalents — Table #32

Frac-tions	Decimals of an inch	mm	Frac-tions	Decimals of an inch	mm	Frac-tions	Decimals of an inch	mm
	0.47244	12.0		0.59	14.986		0.66929	17.0
	0.48	12.192		0.59055	15.0		0.67	17.018
$31/64$	0.484375	12.3031	$19/32$	0.59375	15.0812	$43/64$	0.671875	17.0656
	0.49	12.446		0.60	15.24		0.68	17.272
$1/2$	0.50	12.7	$39/64$	0.609375	15.4781	$11/16$	0.6875	17.4625
	0.51	12.954		0.61	15.494		0.69	17.526
	0.51181	13.0		0.62	15.748		0.70	17.78
$33/64$	0.515625	13.0969	$5/8$	0.625	15.875	$45/64$	0.703125	17.8594
	0.55	13.970		0.62992	16.0		0.70866	18.0
	0.55118	14.0		0.63	16.002		0.71	18.034
	0.56	14.224		0.64	16.256	$23/32$	0.71875	18.2562
$9/16$	0.5625	14.2875	$41/64$	0.640625	16.2719		0.72	18.288
	0.57	14.478		0.65	16.510		0.73	18.542
$37/64$	0.578125	14.6844	$21/32$	0.65625	16.6688	$47/64$	0.734375	18.6531
	0.58	14.732		0.66	16.764		0.74	18.796

Fractions and Decimals of an Inch with Millimetre Equivalents — Table #32

Frac-tions	Decimals of an inch	mm
	0.74803	19.0
3/4	0.75	19.050
	0.76	19.304
49/64	0.765625	19.4469
	0.77	19.558
	0.78	19.812
25/32	0.78125	19.8438
	0.78740	20.0
	0.79	20.066
51/64	0.796875	20.2406
	0.80	20.320
	0.81	20.574
13/16	0.8125	20.6375
	0.82	20.828
	0.82677	21.0
53/64	0.828125	21.0344

Frac-tions	Decimals of an inch	mm
	0.83	21.082
	0.84	21.336
27/32	0.84375	21.4312
	0.85	21.590
55/64	0.859375	21.8281
	0.86	21.844
	0.86614	22.0
	0.87	22.098
7/8	0.875	22.225
	0.88	22.352
	0.89	22.606
57/64	0.890625	22.6219
	0.90	22.860
	0.90551	23.0
29/32	0.90625	23.0188
	0.91	23.114

Frac-tions	Decimals of an inch	mm
	0.92	23.368
59/64	0.921875	23.4156
	0.93	23.622
15/16	0.9375	23.8125
	0.94	23.876
	0.94488	24.0
	0.95	24.130
61/64	0.953125	24.2094
	0.96	24.384
31/32	0.96875	24.6062
	0.97	24.638
	0.98	24.892
	0.984375	25.0031
	0.99	25.146
1	1.00000	25.400

Si Metric Prefixes — Table #33		
Prefix	**Symbol**	**Factor by which the unit is multiplied**
exa	E	1 000 000 000 000 000 000 10^{18}
peta	P	1 000 000 000 000 000 10^{15}
tera	T	1 000 000 000 000 10^{12}
giga	G	1 000 000 000 10^{9}
mega	M	1 000 000 10^{6}
kilo	k	1 000 10^{3}
hecto	h	100 10^{2}
deca	da	10 10^{1}
		1 10^{0}

SI Metric Prefixes — Table #33		
Prefix	**Symbol**	**Factor by which the unit is multiplied**
deci	d	0.1 10^{-1}
centi	c	0.01 10^{-2}
milli	m	0.001 10^{-3}
micro	μ	0.000 001 10^{-6}
Nano	n	0.000 000 001 10^{-9}
pico	p	0.000 000 000 001 10^{-12}
femto	f	0.000 000 000 000 001 10^{-15}
Atto	a	0.000 000 000 000 000 001 10^{-18}

Use of Equivalent Tables

In using the equivalent tables, units in the left hand column are equivalent to the number under each unit across the top of the table.

Example: In the length equivalent table, 1 yard in the right- hand column is equivalent to 36 inches located under the Inches units column.

When a number of each unit must be converted to another unit, multiply the number of the particular unit times the number found in the table to obtain the needed unit on the top of the table.

Example: 5 yards x 36 inches = 180 inches

Scientific Notation

In the equivalent tables, scientific notation is used to express a number when the amount of zeros needed are excessive (very small or very large in magnitude).

To change a number from scientific notation to ordinary terms simply move the decimal point either left or right as dictated by the exponent.

Positive exponents reflect the number of places the decimal point moves to the right.

Example: 9.53×10^4 to ordinary terms, move the decimal point 4 places to the right and add the needed zeros:

9.53×10^4 [9 5300.] = 95,300

Negative exponent reflects the number of places the decimal point moves to the left.

Example: 9.53×10^{-4} to ordinary terms, move the decimal point 4 places to the left and add the needed zeros:

9.53×10^{-4} [.0009 53)] = .000953

Length Equivalents — Table #34

	Micro-metres	Milli-metres	Centi-metres	Deci-metres	Metres	Inches	Feet	Yards
Micro-metres	1	1×10^{-3}	1×10^{-4}	1×10^{-5}	1×10^{-6}	39.37×10^{-6}	3.2808×10^{-6}	1.0936×10^{-6}
Milli-metres	1000	1	0.1	0.01	0.001	39.37×10^{-3}	3.2808×10^{-3}	1.0936×10^{-3}
Centi-metres	10 000	10	1	0.1	0.01	39.37×10^{-2}	3.2808×10^{-2}	1.0936×10^{-2}
Deci-metres	1×10^5	100	10	1	0.1	3.937	0.3281	0.1094
Metres	1×10^6	1000	100	10	1	39.37	3.2808	1.0936
Inches	25 400	25.4	2.54	0.254	0.0254	1	8.33×10^{-2}	2.778×10^{-2}
Feet	304 800	304.8	30.48	3.048	0.3048	12	1	0.3333
Yards	914 400	914.4	91.44	9.144	0.9144	36	3	1

Area Equivalents — Table #35						
	Square mm	Square cm	Square dm	Square m	Square Inches	Square Feet
Square mm	1	1×10^{-2}	1×10^{-4}	1×10^{-6}	1550×10^{-6}	10.76×10^{-6}
Square cm	100	1	1×10^{-2}	1×10^{-4}	1550×10^{-4}	10.76×10^{-4}
Square dm	1×10^{4}	100	1	0.01	1550×10^{-2}	10.76×10^{-2}
Square m	1×10^{6}	1×10^{4}	100	1	1550	10.76
Square Inches	6.452×10^{2}	6.452	6.452×10^{-2}	6.452×10^{-4}	1	6.944×10^{-3}
Square Feet	9.2903×10^{4}	9.2903×10^{2}	9.29	9.29×10^{-2}	144	1

Volume Equivalents — Table #36								
	Cubic mm	Cubic cm	Cubic dm	Cubic m	Cubic Inches	Cubic Feet	US Gallon	Can. Gallon
Cubic mm	1	1×10^{-3}	1×10^{-6}	1×10^{-9}	61.024×10^{-6}	0.035315×10^{-6}	0.2642×10^{-6}	0.21997×10^{-6}
Cubic cm	1000	1	1×10^{-3}	1×10^{-6}	61.024×10^{-3}	0.035315×10^{-3}	0.2642×10^{-3}	0.21997×10^{-3}
Cubic dm (litres)	1×10^{6}	1000	1	1×10^{-3}	61.024	0.0353	0.2642	0.22
Cubic m	1×10^{9}	1×10^{6}	1000	1	61023.744	35.3147	264.2	219.9694
Cubic Inches	16387.064	1.63871	0.0164	1.638706×10^{-5}	1	5.787×10^{-4}	4.329×10^{-3}	3.606×10^{-3}
Cubic Feet	2.8317×10^{7}	2.8317×10^{4}	2.8317×10	2.8317×10^{-2}	1728	1	7.48055	6.22888
US Gallon	3.785×10^{6}	3.785×10^{3}	3.78541	3.785×10^{-3}	231	0.1337	1	0.833
Can. Gallon	4.5461×10^{6}	4.5461×10^{3}	4.54609	4.5461×10^{-3}	277.4193	0.1605	1.20095	1

Flow Rate Equivalents — Table #37							
	Litres/s	Litres/ minute	Cubic m/hour	US Gal- lons/min.	Can. Gal- lons/min.	Cubic ins/min.	Cubic ft/min.
Litres/s	1	60	2.77778×10^{-7}	15.85	13.20498	3661.44	2.11889
Litres/ minute	0.0167	1	1.66667×10^{-5}	0.2642	0.2201	61.024	0.0353
Cubic m/hour	0.2778	16.66666	1	4.403	3.66615	1017.062	0.5886
US Gal- lons/min.	0.0631	3.78541	0.2271	1	0.833	231	0.1337
Can. Gal- lons/min.	0.0758	4.54609	0.2728	1.20032	1	277.4193	0.1605
Cubic ins/min.	2.7312×10^{-4}	0.0164	9.83226×10^{-4}	4.329×10^{-3}	3.606×10^{-3}	1	5.787×10^{-4}
Cubic ft/min.	0.4719	28.31685	0.0283	7.481	6.22888	1728	1

Pressure Equivalents — Table #38

	kilo-pascal	Bar	Atmo-sphere	Inches of water	Feet of water	Metres of water	Inches Hg	mm Hg	PSI
kilo-pascal	1	0.01	9.869×10^{-3}	4.02157	0.3351	0.1021	0.2953	7.501	0.145
Bar	100	1	0.9869	402.156	33.513	10.21478	29.53	750.1	14.5038
Atmo-sphere	101.325	1.01325	1	407.14	33.93	10.34139	29.92	760	14.696
Inches of water	0.249	2.49×10^{-3}	2.456×10^{-3}	1	8.33×10^{-2}	0.0254	0.0735	1.865	0.0361
Feet of water	2.9839	2.984×10^{-2}	2.947×10^{-2}	12	1	0.3048	0.8819	22.38	0.4332
Metres of water	9.806 65	0.098 0665	0.096 784	39.37	3.28084	1	2.9341	74.5294	1.44116
Inches Hg	3.3864	3.3864×10^{-2}	3.342×10^{-2}	13.61	1.134	0.3457	1	25.4	0.4912
mm Hg	0.1333	1.333×10^{-3}	1.3157×10^{-3}	0.5362	0.0447	0.0136	0.0394	1	0.0193
PSI	6.895	0.0689	0.068	27.7	2.309	0.7036	2.036	51.715	1

Mass Equivalents — Table #39							
	Ounce	Pound	Milligram	Gram	Kilogram	Short Ton	Long Ton	Metric Tonne
Ounce	1	0.0625	28344.67	28.3447	0.02835	3.125×10^{-5}	2.79×10^{-5}	2.835×10^{-5}
Pound	16	1	453257.8	453.2578	0.4536	0.0005	4.464×10^{-4}	4.536×10^{-4}
Milligram	35.28×10^{-6}	2.205×10^{-6}	1	0.001	0.001×10^{-3}	1.102×10^{-9}	9.842×10^{-10}	1×10^{-9}
Gram	35.28×10^{-3}	2.205×10^{-3}	1000	1	0.001	1.102×10^{-6}	9.842×10^{-7}	1×10^{-6}
Kilogram	35.28	2.205	1×10^{6}	1000	1	1.102×10^{-3}	9.842×10^{-4}	0.001
Short Ton	32000	2000	907.2×10^{6}	907.2×10^{3}	907.2	1	0.8929	0.907
Long Ton	35840	2240	1016×10^{6}	1016×10^{3}	1016	1.12	1	1.016
Metric Tonne	35280	2205	1×10^{9}	1×10^{6}	1000	1.103	0.9842	1

Energy Equivalents — Table #40

	BTU	Foot Pounds	Horsepower Hour	Joules	Calorie	Kilowatt Hour
BTU	1	1.285×10^{-3}	3.929×10^{-4}	1055	252	2.93×10^{-4}
Foot Pounds	777.9	1	5.051×10^{-7}	1.356	0.3239	3.766×10^{-7}
Horsepower Hr.	2545	1.98×10^{6}	1	2.685×10^{6}	6.414×10^{5}	0.7457
Joules	9.48×10^{-4}	0.7376	3.725×10^{-7}	1	0.2389	2.778×10^{-7}
Calorie	3.968×10^{-3}	3.087	1.559×10^{-6}	4.186	1	1.163×10^{-6}
Kilowatt Hr.	3413	2.655×10^{6}	1.341	3.6×10^{6}	8.60×10^{5}	1

Power Equivalents — Table #41						
	kW	Joules/ sec (W)	HP (mech.)	HP (elec.)	Foot lbs/min.	Foot lbs/sec	Btu/hour
kW	1	1000	1.341 014	1.340 483	44253.7414	737.56236	3412.113
Joules /sec (W)	0.001	1	1.341×10^{-3}	1.340×10^{-3}	44.25374	0.7376	3.41211
HP (mech.)	0.745 6999	745.6999	1	0.9996	33000	550	2544.4
HP (elec.)	0.746	746	1.0004	1	33013.3	550.222	2545.44
Foot lbs/min.	2.259697×10^{-5}	2.259697×10^{-2}	3.030303×10^{-5}	3.029084×10^{-5}	1	0.1667	0.7855
Foot lbs/sec	$1.355\,818 \times 10^{-3}$	1.355 818	1.818182×10^{-3}	1.81745×10^{-3}	60	1	4.6262
Btu/hour	$0.293\,072 \times 10^{-3}$	0.293 072	3.93016×10^{-4}	3.9286×10^{-4}	12.9696	0.2162	1

Temperature Conversion

To Convert From:	Use the Formula:	To Obtain:
Degrees Celsius	(°C x 9/5) + 32	Degrees Fahrenheit
Degrees Celsius	°C + 273.16	Kelvin
Degrees Fahrenheit	(°F - 32) x 5/9	Degrees Celsius
Degrees Fahrenheit	°F + 459.69	Degrees Rankin

Temperature Scales

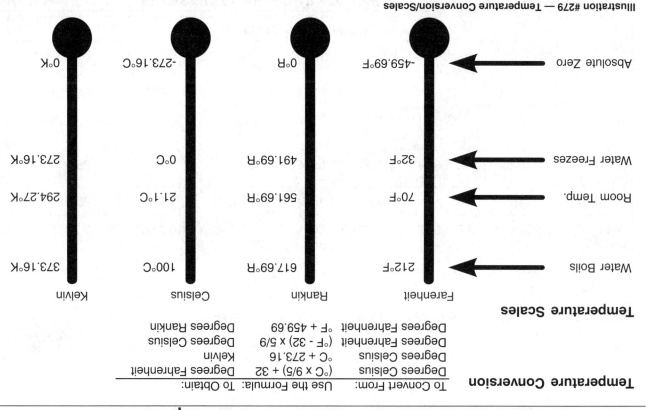

	Fahrenheit	Rankin	Celsius	Kelvin	
Water Boils	212°F	617.69°R	100°C	373.16°K	
Room Temp.	70°F	561.69°R	21.1°C	294.27°K	
Water Freezes	32°F	491.69°R	0°C	273.16°K	
Absolute Zero	-459.69°F	0°R	-273.16°C	0°K	

Illustration #279 — Temperature Conversion/Scales

Standard Twist Drill Sizes — Table #42

Inch	mm	Wire Gage	Decimals of an inch	Inch	mm	Wire Gage	Decimals of an inch	Inch	mm	Wire Gage	Decimals of an inch
		80	0.0135		0.7		0.0276			61	0.0390
		79	0.0145			70	0.0280		1		0.0394
1/64			0.0156			69	0.0293			60	0.0400
	0.4		0.0157		0.75		0.0295			59	0.0410
		78	0.0160			68	0.0310		1.05		0.0413
		77	0.0180	1/32			0.0313			58	0.0420
	0.5		0.0197		0.8		0.0315			57	0.0430
		76	0.0200			67	0.0320		1.1		0.0433
		75	0.0210			66	0.0330		1.15		0.0453
	0.55		0.0217		0.85		0.0335			56	0.0465
		74	0.0225			65	0.0350	3/64			0.0469
	0.6		0.0236		0.9		0.0354		1.2		0.0472
		73	0.0240			64	0.0360		1.25		0.0492
		72	0.0250			63	0.0370		1.3		0.0512
	0.65		0.0256		0.95		0.0374			55	0.0520
		71	0.0260			62	0.0380		1.35		0.0531

Standard Twist Drill Sizes — Table #42

Inch	mm	Wire Gage	Decimals of an inch	Inch	mm	Wire Gage	Decimals of an inch	Inch	mm	Wire Gage	Decimals of an inch
		54	0.0550			49	0.0730		2.3		0.0906
	1.4		0.0551		1.9		0.0748		2.35		0.0925
	1.45		0.0571			48	0.0760			42	0.0935
	1.5		0.0591		1.95		0.0768	3/32			0.0938
		53	0.0595	5/64			0.0781		2.4		0.0945
	1.55		0.0610			47	0.0785			41	0.0960
1/16			0.0625		2		0.0787		2.45		0.0966
	1.6		0.0630		2.05		0.0807			40	0.0980
		52	0.0635			46	0.0810		2.5		0.0984
	1.65		0.0650			45	0.0820			39	0.0995
	1.7		0.0669		2.1		0.0827			38	0.1015
		51	0.0670		2.15		0.0846		2.6		0.1024
	1.75		0.0689			45	0.0860			37	0.1040
		50	0.0700		2.2		0.0866		2.7		0.1063
	1.8		0.0709		2.25		0.0886			36	0.1065
	1.85		0.0728			43	0.0890		2.75		0.1083

Standard Twist Drill Sizes — Table #42

Inch	mm	Wire Gage	Decimals of an inch	Inch	mm	Wire Gage	Decimals of an inch	Inch	mm	Wire Gage	Decimals of an inch
7/64			0.1094			29	0.1360		4		0.1575
		35	0.1100		3.5		0.1378			21	0.1590
	2.8		0.1102			28	0.1405			20	0.1610
		34	0.1110	9/64			0.1406		4.1		0.1614
		33	0.1130		3.6		0.1417		4.2		0.1654
	2.9		0.1142			27	0.1440			19	0.1660
		32	0.1160		3.7		0.1457		4.25		0.1673
	3		0.1181			26	0.1470		4.3		0.1693
		31	0.1200		3.75		0.1476			18	0.1695
	3.1		0.1220			25	0.1495	11/64			0.1719
1/8			0.1250		3.8		0.1496			17	0.1730
	3.2		0.1260			24	0.1520		4.4		0.1732
	3.25		0.1280		3.9		0.1535			16	0.1770
		30	0.1285			23	0.1540		4.5		0.1772
	3.3		0.1299	5/32			0.1563			15	0.1800
	3.4		0.1339			22	0.1570		4.6		0.1811

Standard Twist Drill Sizes — Table #42

Inch	mm	Wire Gage	Decimals of an inch
		14	0.1820
		13	0.1850
	4.7		0.1850
	4.75		0.1870
3/16			0.1875
	4.8		0.1890
		12	0.1890
		11	0.1910
	4.9		0.1929
		10	0.1935
		6	0.1960
		5	0.1969
		8	0.1990
	5.1		0.2008
		7	0.2010
13/64			0.2031

Inch	mm	Wire Gage	Decimals of an inch
		6	0.2040
	5.2		0.2047
		5	0.2055
	5.25		0.2067
	5.3		0.2087
		4	0.2090
	5.4		0.2126
		3	0.2130
	5.5		0.2165
7/32			0.2188
	5.6		0.2205
		2	0.2210
	5.7		0.2244
	5.75		0.2264
		1	0.2280
	5.8		0.2283

Inch	mm	Wire Gage	Decimals of an inch
	5.9		0.2323
		A	0.2340
15/64			0.2344
	6		0.2362
		B	0.2380
	6.1		0.2402
		C	0.2420
	6.2		0.2441
		D	0.2460
	6.25		0.2461
	6.3		0.2480
1/4		E	0.2500
	6.4		0.2520
	6.5		0.2559
		F	0.2570
	6.6		0.2598

Standard Twist Drill Sizes — Table #42

Inch	mm	Wire Gage	Decimals of an inch	Inch	mm	Wire Gage	Decimals of an inch	Inch	mm	Wire Gage	Decimals of an inch
		G	0.2610			L	0.2900			P	0.3230
	6.7		0.2638		7.4		0.2913		8.25		0.3248
17/64			0.2656			M	0.2950		8.3		0.3268
	6.75		0.2657		7.5		0.2953	21/64			0.3281
		H	0.2660	19/64			0.2969		8.4		0.3307
	6.8		0.2677		7.6		0.2992			Q	0.3320
	6.9		0.2717			N	0.3020		8.5		0.3346
		I	0.2720		7.7		0.3031		8.6		0.3386
	7		0.2756		7.75		0.3051			R	0.3390
		J	0.2770		7.8		0.3071		8.7		0.3425
	7.1		0.2795		7.9		0.3110	11/32			0.3438
		K	0.2810	5/16			0.3125		8.75		0.3345
9/32			0.2812		8		0.3150		8.8		0.3465
	7.2		0.2835			O	0.3160			S	0.3480
	7.25		0.2854		8.1		0.3189		8.9		0.3504
	7.3		0.2874		8.2		0.3228		9		0.3543

Standard Twist Drill Sizes — Table #42

Inch	mm	Wire Gage	Decimals of an inch
5/8			0.6250
	15.5		0.6102
39/64			0.6094
19/32			0.5938
	15		0.5906
37/64			0.5781
	14.5		0.5709
9/16			0.5625
	14		0.5512
35/64			0.5469
	13.5		0.5315
17/32			0.5313
33/64			0.5156
	13		0.5118
1/2			0.5000
	12.5		0.4921

Inch	mm	Wire Gage	Decimals of an inch
31/64			0.4844
	12		0.4724
15/32			0.4688
29/64			0.4531
	11.5		0.4528
7/16			0.4375
	11		0.4331
27/64			0.4219
	10.5		0.4134
		Z	0.4130
13/32			0.4063
		Y	0.4040
		X	0.3970
	10		0.3937
25/64			0.3906
	9.9		0.3898

Inch	mm	Wire Gage	Decimals of an inch
		W	0.3860
	9.8		0.3858
	9.75		0.3839
	9.7		0.3819
	9.6		0.3780
		V	0.3770
3/8			0.3750
	9.5		0.3740
	9.4		0.3701
		U	0.3680
	9.3		0.3661
	9.25		0.3642
	9.2		0.3622
23/64			0.3594
	9.1		0.3583
		T	0.3580

Standard Twist Drill Sizes — Table #42

Inch	mm	Wire Gage	Decimals of an inch	Inch	mm	Wire Gage	Decimals of an inch	Inch	mm	Wire Gage	Decimals of an inch
	16		0.6299		19.5		0.7677	$^{29}/_{32}$			0.9063
$^{41}/_{64}$			0.6406	$^{25}/_{32}$			0.7812	$^{59}/_{64}$			0.9219
	16.5		0.6496		20		0.7874		23.5		0.9252
$^{21}/_{32}$			0.6563	$^{51}/_{64}$			0.7969	$^{15}/_{16}$			0.9375
	17		0.6693		20.5		0.8071		24		0.9449
$^{43}/_{64}$			0.6719	$^{13}/_{16}$			0.8125	$^{61}/_{64}$			0.9531
$^{11}/_{16}$			0.6875		21		0.8268		24.5		0.9646
	17.5		0.6890	$^{53}/_{64}$			0.8281	$^{31}/_{32}$			0.9688
$^{45}/_{64}$			0.7031	$^{27}/_{32}$			0.8438		25		0.9843
	18		0.7087		21.5		0.8465	$^{63}/_{64}$			0.9844
$^{23}/_{32}$			0.7188	$^{55}/_{64}$			0.8594	1			1.0000
	18.5		0.7283		22		0.8661		25.5		1.0039
$^{47}/_{64}$			0.7344	$^7/_8$			0.8750	1 $^1/_{64}$			1.0156
	19		0.7480		22.5		0.8858		26		1.0236
$^3/_4$			0.7500	$^{57}/_{64}$			0.8906	1 $^1/_{32}$			1.0313
$^{49}/_{64}$			0.7656		23		0.9055		26.5		1.0433

Standard Twist Drill Sizes — Table #42

inch	mm	Wire Gage	Decimals of an inch
1 3/64			1.0469
1 1/16			1.0625
		27	1.0630
1 5/64			1.0781
	27.5		1.0827
1 3/32			1.0938
		28	1.1024
1 7/64			1.1094
	28.5		1.1220
1 1/8			1.1250
1 9/64			1.1406
		29	1.1417
1 5/32			1.1562
	29.5		1.1614
1 11/64			1.1719

inch	mm	Wire Gage	Decimals of an inch
	30		1.1811
1 3/16			1.1875
	30.5		1.2008
1 13/64			1.2031
1 7/32			1.2188
	31		1.2205
1 15/64			1.2344
	31.5		1.2402
1 1/4			1.2500
		32	1.2598
1 17/64			1.2656
	32.5		1.2795
1 9/32			1.2813
1 19/64			1.2969
		33	1.2992

inch	mm	Wire Gage	Decimals of an inch
1 5/16			1.3125
	33.5		1.3189
1 21/64			1.3281
		34	1.3386
1 11/32			1.3438
	34.5		1.3583
1 23/64			1.3594
1 3/8			1.3750
		35	1.3780
1 25/64			1.3906
	35.5		1.3976
1 13/32			1.4063
		36	1.4173
1 27/64			1.4219
	36.5		1.4370

Tap Drill Sizes (Inches) — Table #43

Tap Size	Pitch	Form	75%
0	80	NF	$3/64$
1	64	NC	53
	72	NF	53
	56	NS	54
2	56	NC	50
	64	NF	50
3	48	NC	47
	56	NF	45
4	40	NC	43
	48	NF	42
	32	NS	45
	36	NS	44
5	40	NC	38
	44	NF	37
6	32	NC	36

Tap Size	Pitch	Form	75%
	40	NF	33
	36	NS	34
8	32	NC	29
	36	NF	29
	40	NS	28
10	24	NC	25
	32	NF	21
	30	NS	22
12	24	NC	16
	28	NF	14
	32	NS	13
14	20	NS	10
	24	NS	7
1/4	20	NC	7
	28	NF	3

Tap Size	Pitch	Form	75%
$5/16$	18	NC	F
	24	NF	I
$3/8$	16	NC	$5/16$
	24	NF	Q
$7/16$	14	NC	U
	20	NF	$25/64$
$1/2$	13	NC	$27/64$
	20	NF	$29/64$
$9/16$	12	NC	$31/64$
	18	NF	$33/64$
$5/8$	11	NC	$17/32$
	18	NF	$37/64$
$11/16$	11	NS	$19/32$
	16	NS	$5/8$
$3/4$	10	NC	$21/32$

Tap Drill Sizes (Inches) — Table #43

Tap Size	Pitch	Form	75%
	16	NF	$11/16$
$7/8$	9	NC	$49/64$
	14	NF	$13/16$
1	8	NC	$7/8$
	12	NF	$59/64$
	14	NS	$15/16$
$1 1/8$	7	NC	$63/64$
	12	NF	$1 3/64$
$1 1/4$	7	NC	$1 7/64$
	12	NF	$1 11/64$
$1 3/8$	6	NC	$1 7/32$
	12	NF	$1 19/64$
$1 1/2$	6	NC	$1 11/32$
	12	NF	$1 27/64$
$1 5/8$	$5 1/2$	NS	$1 29/64$

Tap Size	Pitch	Form	75%
$1 3/4$	5	NC	$1 9/16$
$1 7/8$	5	NS	$1 11/16$
2	$4 1/2$	NC	$1 25/32$
$1/16$	27	NPT	R
$1/8$	27	NPT	R
$1/4$	18	NPT	$7/16$
$3/8$	18	NPT	$37/64$
$1/2$	14	NPT	$23/32$
$3/4$	14	NPT	$59/64$
1	$11 1/2$	NPT	$1 5/32$
$1 1/4$	$11 1/2$	NPT	$1 1/2$
$1 1/2$	$11 1/2$	NPT	$1 47/64$
2	$11 1/2$	NPT	$2 7/32$

Self Tapping Screws		
Size	Decimal	Drill
Number 4	0.112	$5/64$
Number 6	0.138	$3/32$
Number 7	0.155	$7/64$
Number 8	0.165	$1/8$
Number 10	0.191	$9/64$
Number 12	0.218	$5/32$
Number 14	0.251	$3/16$

Tap Drill Sizes (ISO Metric Coarse) — Table #44A

Tap Size	Thread Pitch mm	Tap Drill mm	Alt. Tap Drill	Tap Size	Thread Pitch mm	Tap Drill mm	Alt. Tap Drill	Tap Size	Thread Pitch mm	Tap Drill mm	Alt. Tap Drill
I.S.O. Metric Coarse				4	0.70	3.30	30	14	2.00	12.00	$15/32$
1.6	0.35	1.25	$3/64$	4.5	0.75	3.70	27	16	2.00	14.00	$35/64$
1.7	0.35	1.35	55	5	0.80	4.20	19	18	2.50	15.50	$39/64$
1.8	0.35	1.45	54	5.5	0.90	4.60	15	20	2.50	17.50	$11/16$
2	0.40	1.60	$1/16$	6	1.00	5.00	9	22	2.50	19.50	$49/64$
2.2	0.45	1.75	50	7	1.00	6.00	$15/64$	24	3.00	21.00	$53/64$
2.3	0.40	1.90	49	8	1.25	6.80	H	27	3.00	24.00	$61/64$
2.5	0.45	2.05	46	9	1.25	7.80	$5/16$	30	3.50	26.50	$1\ 3/64$
2.6	0.45	2.15	44	10	1.50	8.50	Q	33	3.50	29.50	$1\ 5/32$
3	0.50	2.50	40	11	1.50	9.50	$3/8$	36	4.00	32.00	$1\ 1/4$
3.5	0.60	2.90	33	12	1.75	10.20	Y	36	4.00	35.00	$1\ 3/8$

Tap Drill Sizes (ISO Metric Fine) — Table #44B

Tap Size	Thread Pitch mm	Tap Drill mm	Alt. Tap Drill
9	1.00	8.00	O
10	0.50	9.50	$3/8$
10	0.75	9.25	U
10	1.00	9.00	T
10	1.25	8.75	$11/32$
11	1.00	10.00	X
12	1.00	$1/8$ 1.00	$7/16$
12	1.25	10.75	$27/64$
12	1.50	10.50	Z
13	1.50	11.50	$29/64$
13	1.75	11.25	$7/16$

Tap Size	Thread Pitch mm	Tap Drill mm	Alt. Tap Drill
14	1.25	12.75	$1/2$
14	1.50	12.50	$31/64$
15	1.50	13.50	$17/32$
16	1.00	15.00	$19/32$
16	1.25	14.75	$37/64$
16	1.50	14.50	$9/16$
18	1.00	17.00	$43/64$
18	1.25	16.75	$21/32$
18	1.50	16.50	$41/64$
18	2.00	16.00	$5/8$
20	1.00	19.00	$3/4$

Tap Size	Thread Pitch mm	Tap Drill mm	Alt. Tap Drill
20	1.50	18.50	$47/64$
20	2.00	18.00	$45/64$
22	1.00	21.00	$53/64$
22	1.50	20.50	$13/16$
22	2.00	20.00	$25/32$
24	1.00	23.00	$29/32$
24	1.50	22.50	$7/8$
24	2.00	22.00	$55/64$
24	2.50	21.50	$27/32$

Steel Pipe Dimensions — Table #45													
NPS		Pipe OD		Inside Diameter									
				Schedule 40		Schedule 80		Schedule 160		STD	Extra Strong	Dbl. Extra Strong	
in	mm	in	mm	in	mm	in	mm	in	mm	in[mm]	in[mm]	in	mm
1/16		0.31	7.9										
1/8	6	0.41	10.2	0.27	6.83	0.22	5.46			see Sch. 40	see Sch. 80		
1/4	8	0.54	13.7	0.36	9.25	0.30	7.67						
3/8	10	0.68	17.2	0.49	12.52	0.42	10.40						
1/2	15	0.84	21.3	0.62	15.80	0.55	13.87	0.47	11.78			0.25	6.40
3/4	20	1.05	26.7	0.82	20.93	0.74	18.85	0.61	15.60			0.43	11.02
1	25	1.32	33.4	1.05	26.64	0.96	24.31	0.81	20.70			0.60	15.22
1 1/4	32	1.66	42.2	1.38	35.05	1.28	32.46	1.16	29.46			0.90	22.76
1 1/2	40	1.90	48.3	1.61	40.89	1.50	38.10	1.34	33.99			1.10	27.94
2	50	2.38	60.3	2.07	52.50	1.94	49.25	1.69	42.90			1.50	38.18
2 1/2	65	2.88	73.0	2.47	62.71	2.32	59.00	2.13	53.98			1.77	44.98

Steel Pipe Dimensions — Table #45													
NPS		Pipe OD		Inside Diameter									
				Schedule 40		Schedule 80		Schedule 160		STD	Extra Strong	Dbl. Extra Strong	
in	mm	in	mm	in	mm	in	mm	in	mm	in[mm]	in[mm]	in	mm
3	80	3.50	88.9	3.07	77.93	2.90	73.66	2.62	66.65			2.30	58.42
3 1/2	90	4.00	101.6	3.55	90.12	3.36	85.46						
4	100	4.50	114.3	4.03	102.26	3.83	97.18	3.44	87.33			3.15	79.38
5	125	5.56	141.3	5.05	128.19	4.81	122.25	4.31	109.6	see Sch. 40	see Sch. 80	4.06	103.2
6	150	6.63	168.3	6.07	154.05	5.76	146.33	5.19	131.8			4.90	124.4
8	200	8.63	219.1	7.98	202.74	7.63	193.7	6.81	173.1			6.88	174.6
10	250	10.8	273.1	10.02	254.50	9.56	242.9	8.50	215.8		9.75 [247.7]	8.75	222.3
12	300	12.8	323.8	11.94	303.18	11.37	288.8	10.13	257.2	12.00 [304.7]	11.75 [298.4]	10.75	273.1

NPS	Outside Diameter	Threads per inch	Thread Length		Hand Tight Engagement Length		Wrench Makeup Length	
inches	inches	number	inches	approx. # threads	inches	approx. # threads	inches	approx. # threads
1/16	0.312	27	0.3896	10.5	0.160	4.3	0.111	3
1/8	0.405	27	0.3924	10.6	0.1615	4.4	0.1111	3
1/4	0.540	18	0.5946	10.7	0.2278	4.3	0.1667	3
3/8	0.675	18	0.6006	10.8	0.240	4.5	0.1667	3
1/2	0.840	14	0.7815	10.9	0.320	4.5	0.2143	3
3/4	1.050	14	0.7935	11.1	0.339	4.75	0.2143	3
1	1.315	11 1/2	0.9845	11.3	0.400	4.6	0.2609	3
1 1/4	1.660	11 1/2	1.0085	11.6	0.420	4.8	0.2609	3
1 1/2	1.900	11 1/2	1.0252	11.8	0.420	4.8	0.2609	3

Pipe Thread Dimensions — Table #46

Pipe Thread Dimensions — Table #46								
NPS	Outside Diameter	Threads per inch	Thread Length		Hand Tight Engagement Length		Wrench Makeup Length	
inches	inches	number	inches	approx. # threads	inches	approx. # threads	inches	approx. # threads
2	2.375	11 1/2	1.0582	12.1	0.436	5	0.2609	3
2 1/2	2.875	8	1.5712	12.6	0.682	5.5	0.2500	2
3	3.500	8	1.6337	13.1	0.766	6.1	0.2500	2
3 1/2	4.000	8	1.6337	13.5	0.821	6.6	0.2500	2
4	4.500	8	1.7337	13.9	0.844	6.75	0.2500	2
5	5.563	8	1.8400	14.7	0.937	7.5	0.2500	2
6	6.625	8	1.9462	15.6	0.958	7.7	0.2500	2

Threading Allowance for Pipe — Table#47			
Pipe Size (NPS)		**Allowance**	
inches	**[mm]**	**inches**	**[mm]**
1/16 to 1/8	[3 to 6]	Required	
¼ to 1/2	[8 to 10]	Required	
1/2 to 3/4	[15 to 20]	0.0571	1.45
1 to 2	[25 to 50]	0.0696	1.77
2 1/2 and larger	[65] and larger	0.1000	2.54
Note: Threading allowance is required when using Barlow's Formula to calculate the bursting pressure of a threaded pipe.			

Stress (S-Values) for Steel Pipe — Table #48								
Stress Values Required When Using Barlow's Formula								
		Stress in 1000 PSI [MPa] for various pipe temperatures						
Specification	Grade	-20 to 650°F [-29 to 343°C]		700°F [371°C]		750°F [399°C]		800°F [427°C]	
Seamless								
A53	A	12.0	[82]	11.7	[80]	10.7	[73]	9.0	[62]
	B	15.0	[103]	14.4	[99]	13.0	[89]	10.8	[74]
A106	A	12.0	[82]	11.7	[80]	10.7	[73]	9.0	[62]
	B	15.0	[103]	14.4	[99]	13.0	89]	10.8	[74]
API 5L	A	12.0	[82]	11.7	[80]	10.7	[73]	9.0	[62]
	B	15.0	[103]	14.4	[99]	13.0	89]	10.8	[74]
Continuous Welded								
A53		6.8	[46]	6.5	[44]	—	—	—	—
Electric Resistance Welded								
A53	A	10.2	[70]	9.9	[68]	9.1	[62]	7.7	[52]
	B	12.8	[88]	12.2	[84]	11.0	[75]	9.2	[63]
API 5L	A	10.2	[70]	9.9	[68]	9.1	[62]	7.7	[52]
	B	12.8	[88]	12.2	[84]	11.0	[75]	9.2	[63]

Stress (S-Values) for Steel Pipe — Table #48								
Stress Values Required When Using Barlow's Formula								
		Stress in 1000 PSI [MPa] for various pipe temperatures						
Specification	Grade	-20 to 650°F [-29 to 343°C]		700°F [371°C]		750°F [399°C]		800°F [427°C]	
Electric Fusion - Arc Welded								
API 5L	A	10.8	[74]	10.5	[72]	9.6	[66]	8.1	[56]
	B	13.5	[88]	13.0	[89]	11.7	[80]	9.7	[67]
A139	A	9.6	[66]	7.4	[51]	8.6	[59]	—	—
	B	12.0	[82]	11.5	[79]	10.4	[71]	—	[—
		-20 to 100°F [-29 to 38°C]		200°F [93°C]		300°F [149°C]		400°F [204°C]	
Continuous Welded								
A120	—	6.4	[44]	6.3	[43]	6.1	[42]	5.8	[39]
Electric Resistance Welded								
A120	—	9.1	[63]	9.0	[62]	8.6	[59]	8.3	[57]

Pressure Rating for Steel Pipe — Table #49**

Nominal Size	Schedule #	OD	ID	Threaded Pressure	No thread Pressure
in		in	in	psi	psi
1/8	40	0.405	0.269		5037
1/8	80	0.405	0.215		7037
1/4	40	0.540	0.364		4889
1/4	80	0.540	0.302		6611
3/8	40	0.675	0.493		4044
3/8	80	0.675	0.423		5600
1/2	40	0.840	0.622	1854	3893
1/2	80	0.840	0.546	3211	5250
1/2	160	0.840	0.464	4675	6714
1/2	XXS	0.840	0.252	8461	10500
3/4	40	1.050	0.824	1597	3229
3/4	80	1.050	0.742	2769	4400
3/4	160	1.050	0.612	4626	6257
3/4	XXS	1.050	0.434	7169	8800

| Pressure Rating for Steel Pipe** — Table #49 | | | | | |
Nominal Size	Schedule #	OD	ID	Threaded Pressure	No thread Pressure
in		in	in	psi	psi
1	40	1.315	1.049	1446	3034
1	80	1.315	0.957	2496	4084
1	160	1.315	0.815	4116	5703
1	XXS	1.315	0.599	6579	8167
1 1/4	40	1.660	1.280	2176	3434
1 1/4	80	1.660	1.278	2194	3452
1 1/4	160	1.660	1.160	3260	4518
1 1/4	XXS	1.660	0.896	5646	6904
1 1/2	40	1.900	1.610	1191	2289
1 1/2	80	1.900	1.500	2059	3158
1 1/2	160	1.900	1.338	3338	4437
1 1/2	XXS	1.900	1.100	5217	6316

Pressure Rating for Steel Pipe** — Table #49					
Nominal Size	Schedule #	OD	ID	Threaded Pressure	No thread Pressure
in		in	in	psi	psi
2	40	2.375	2.067	1066	1945
2	80	2.375	1.939	1875	2754
2	160	2.375	1.687	3466	4345
2	XXS	2.375	1.503	4628	5507
2 1/2	40	2.875	2.469	1075	2118
2 1/2	80	2.875	2.323	1837	2880
2 1/2	160	2.875	2.125	2870	3913
2 1/2	XXS	2.875	1.771	4717	5760

** **Note:** Based on ASTM A53 Grade B Seamless Pipe
(Maximum allowable stress 15,000 psi at 120 to 650 °F.)

Allowable pressures calculated using Barlow's formula: $P = 2 \times S \times (T - C)/D$

Where: P = Pipe pressure (psi)   T = wall thickness (inches)
C = Allowance for threading(inches)   D = Outside diameter of pipe (inches)
S = Stress on the pipe material (psi)

If the system is welded (no threading), then: $P = 2ST/D$

Nominal Size (in)	Schedule #	Pipe Flow Rates at Recommended Velocities — Table #50					
		Flow (GPM) Required to Produce					
		2 ft/sec	4 ft/sec	10 ft/sec	15 ft/sec	20 ft/sec	30 ft/sec
1/8	40	0.35	0.71	1.77	2.66	3.54	5.31
1/8	80	0.23	0.45	1.13	1.70	2.26	3.40
1/4	40	0.65	1.30	3.24	4.87	6.49	9.73
1/4	80	0.45	0.89	2.23	3.35	4.47	6.70
3/8	40	1.19	2.38	5.95	8.93	11.90	17.85
3/8	80	0.88	1.75	4.38	6.57	8.76	13.14
1/2	40	1.89	3.79	9.47	14.21	18.94	28.42
1/2	80	1.46	2.92	7.30	10.95	14.60	21.90
1/2	160	1.05	2.11	5.27	7.91	10.54	15.81
1/2	XXS	0.31	0.62	1.55	2.33	3.11	4.66
3/4	40	3.32	6.65	16.62	24.94	33.25	49.87
3/4	80	2.70	5.39	13.48	20.22	26.96	40.44
3/4	160	1.83	3.67	9.17	13.76	18.34	27.51
3/4	XXS	0.92	1.84	4.61	6.92	9.22	13.83

Pipe Flow Rates at Recommended Velocities — Table #50

Nominal Size (in)	Schedule #	Flow (GPM) Required to Produce					
		2 ft/sec	4 ft/sec	10 ft/sec	15 ft/sec	20 ft/sec	30 ft/sec
1	40	5.39	10.78	26.94	40.41	53.88	80.82
1	80	4.48	8.97	22.42	33.63	44.85	67.27
1	160	3.25	6.50	16.26	24.39	32.52	48.79
1	XXS	1.76	3.51	8.78	13.18	17.57	26.35
1 1/4	40	8.02	16.05	40.11	60.17	80.23	120.34
1 1/4	80	8.00	16.00	39.99	59.98	79.98	119.96
1 1/4	160	6.59	13.18	32.94	49.42	65.89	98.83
1 1/4	XXS	3.93	7.86	19.66	29.48	39.31	58.97
1 1/2	40	12.69	25.39	63.46	95.19	126.93	190.39
1 1/2	80	11.02	22.03	55.09	82.63	110.17	165.26
1 1/2	160	8.77	17.53	43.83	65.75	87.66	131.49
1 1/2	XXS	5.92	11.85	29.62	44.44	59.25	88.87

Nominal Size (in)	Schedule #	Pipe Flow Rates at Recommended Velocities — Table #50					
		Flow (GPM) Required to Produce					
		2 ft/sec	4 ft/sec	10 ft/sec	15 ft/sec	20 ft/sec	30 ft/sec
2	40	20.92	41.84	104.60	156.91	209.21	313.81
2	80	18.41	36.82	92.05	138.07	184.10	276.15
2	160	13.94	27.87	69.68	104.52	139.36	209.03
2	XXS	11.06	22.12	55.31	82.96	110.62	165.92
2 1/2	40	29.85	59.70	149.25	223.87	298.50	447.74
2 1/2	80	26.42	52.85	132.12	198.18	264.24	396.36
2 1/2	160	22.11	44.22	110.56	165.83	221.11	331.67
2 1/2	XXS	15.36	30.72	76.79	115.18	153.58	230.37
3	40	46.09	92.18	230.45	345.68	460.90	691.35
3	80	41.18	82.36	205.90	308.85	411.81	617.71
3	160	33.72	67.43	168.58	252.86	337.15	505.73
3	XXS	25.90	51.81	129.52	194.27	259.03	388.55

Pipe Thread Comparisons

Pipe Thread Comparison Chart NPT/NPTF and ISO — Table #51

Nominal Size	Threads per inch	Pipe OD inches	Pitch inches
1/8	NPT/NPTF 27	0.405	0.0370
	ISO 28	0.398	0.0360
1/4	NPT/NPTF 18	0.540	0.0556
	ISO 19	0.535	0.0530
3/8	NPT/NPTF 18	0.675	0.0556
	ISO 19	0.672	0.0530
1/2	NPT/NPTF 14	0.840	0.0714
	ISO 14	0.843	0.0710
3/4	NPT/NPTF 14	1.050	0.0714
	ISO 14	1.060	0.0710

Nominal Size	Threads per inch	Pipe OD inches	Pitch inches
1	NPT/NPTF 11.5	1.315	0.0870
	ISO 11	1.331	0.0910
1 1/4	NPT/NPTF 11.5	1.660	0.0870
	ISO 11	1.669	0.0910
1 1/2	NPT/NPTF 11.5	1.900	0.0870
	ISO 11	1.900	0.0910
2	NPT/NPTF 11.5	2.375	0.0870
	ISO 11	2.375	0.0910

Max. Tube Wall Thickness When Flaring — Table #52

Tube Size (in)	Maximum Wall Thickness (inches)				Tube Size (in)	Maximum Wall Thickness (inches)			
	Single Flare		Double Flare			Single Flare		Double Flare	
	37°	45°	37°	45°		37°	45°	37°	45°
1/8	0.035	0.035	0.025	0.025	3/4	0.109	0.109	0.049	0.049
3/16	0.035	0.035	0.028	0.028	7/8	0.109	0.109	0.065	
1/4	0.065	0.049	0.035	0.035	1	0.120	0120	0.065	
5/16	0.065	0.049	0.035	0.035	1 1/8	0.120		0.065	
3/8	0.065	0.065	0.049	0.049	1 1/4	0.120		0.065	
7/16		0.065		0.049	1 1/2	0.120		0.065	
1/2	0.083	0.065	0.049	0.049	1 3/4	0.120		0.065	
9/16		0.083		0.049	2	0.134		0.065	
5/8	0.095	0.095	0.049	0.049					

Pressure Ratings and Flow Rates for Steel Tubes — Table #53**

Tube Size (in)	Wall Thickness	OD	Max Allowable Pressure	Flow (GPM) Required to Produce					
				2 ft/sec	4 ft/sec	10 ft/sec	15 ft/sec	20 ft/sec	30 ft/sec
1/8	0.028	0.1250	6160	0.02	0.05	0.12	0.17	0.23	0.35
1/8	0.035	0.1250	7700	0.01	0.03	0.07	0.11	0.15	0.22
3/16	0.028	0.1875	4107	0.08	0.17	0.42	0.64	0.85	1.27
3/16	0.035	0.1875	5133	0.07	0.14	0.34	0.51	0.68	1.01
3/16	0.049	0.1875	7187	0.04	0.08	0.20	0.29	0.39	0.59
1/4	0.028	0.2500	3080	0.18	0.37	0.92	1.38	1.84	2.76
1/4	0.035	0.2500	3850	0.16	0.32	0.79	1.19	1.59	2.38
1/4	0.049	0.2500	5390	0.11	0.23	0.57	0.85	1.13	1.70
1/4	0.065	0.2500	7150	0.07	0.14	0.35	0.53	0.71	1.06
5/16	0.035	0.3125	3080	0.29	0.58	1.44	2.16	2.88	4.32
5/16	0.049	0.3125	4312	0.23	0.45	1.13	1.69	2.25	3.38
5/16	0.065	0.3125	5720	0.16	0.33	0.82	1.22	1.63	2.45

Tube Size (in)	Wall Thickness	OD	Max Allowable Pressure	Flow (GPM) Required to Produce					
				2 ft/sec	4 ft/sec	10 ft/sec	15 ft/sec	20 ft/sec	30 ft/sec
3/8	0.035	0.3750	2567	0.46	0.91	2.28	3.42	4.56	6.83
3/8	0.049	0.3750	3593	0.38	0.75	1.88	2.82	3.76	5.64
3/8	0.065	0.3750	4767	0.29	0.59	1.47	2.20	2.94	4.41
1/2	0.035	0.5000	1925	0.91	1.81	4.53	6.79	9.05	13.58
1/2	0.049	0.5000	2695	0.79	1.58	3.96	5.93	7.91	11.87
1/2	0.065	0.5000	3575	0.67	1.34	3.35	5.03	6.70	10.06
1/2	0.083	0.5000	4565	0.55	1.09	2.73	4.10	5.46	8.19
5/8	0.035	0.6250	1540	1.51	3.02	7.54	11.31	15.08	22.62
5/8	0.049	0.6250	2156	1.36	2.72	6.80	10.20	13.60	20.40
5/8	0.065	0.6250	2860	1.20	2.40	6.00	9.00	12.00	18.00
5/8	0.083	0.6250	3652	1.03	2.06	5.16	7.74	10.32	15.47
5/8	0.095	0.6250	4180	0.93	1.85	4.63	6.95	9.27	13.90

Pressure Ratings and Flow Rates for Steel Tubes — Table #53

Pressure Ratings and Flow Rates for Steel Tubes** — Table #53

Tube Size (in)	Wall Thickness	OD	Max Allowable Pressure	Flow (GPM) Required to Produce					
				2 ft/sec	4 ft/sec	10 ft/sec	15 ft/sec	20 ft/sec	30 ft/sec
3/4	0.049	0.7500	1797	2.08	4.16	10.41	15.61	20.82	31.22
3/4	0.065	0.7500	2383	1.88	3.76	9.41	14.12	18.82	28.23
3/4	0.083	0.7500	3043	1.67	3.34	8.35	12.53	16.70	25.05
3/4	0.095	0.7500	3483	1.54	3.07	7.68	11.52	15.36	23.03
3/4	0.109	0.7500	3997	1.39	2.77	6.93	10.39	13.86	20.79
3/4	0.120	0.7500	4400	1.27	2.55	6.37	9.55	12.74	19.10
7/8	0.049	0.8750	1540	2.96	5.91	14.78	22.17	29.56	44.34
7/8	0.065	0.8750	2043	2.72	5.44	13.59	20.38	27.18	40.77
7/8	0.083	0.8750	2609	2.46	4.92	12.31	18.46	24.61	36.92
7/8	0.095	0.8750	2986	2.30	4.60	11.49	17.23	22.98	34.46
7/8	0.109	0.8750	3426	2.11	4.23	10.57	15.85	21.14	31.70
7/8	0.120	0.8750	3771	1.97	3.95	9.87	14.81	19.74	29.62

Pressure Ratings and Flow Rates for Steel Tubes** — Table #53									
Tube Size (in)	Wall Thick-ness	OD	Max Allowable Pressure	Flow (GPM) Required to Produce					
				2 ft/sec	4 ft/sec	10 ft/sec	15 ft/sec	20 ft/sec	30 ft/sec
1	0.049	1.000	1348	3.98	7.97	19.92	29.88	39.84	59.76
1	0.065	1.000	1788	3.71	7.41	18.53	27.80	37.06	55.59
1	0.083	1.000	2283	3.41	6.81	17.03	25.54	34.06	51.09
1	0.095	1.000	2613	3.21	6.43	16.06	24.10	32.13	48.19
1	0.109	1.000	2998	2.99	5.99	14.97	22.46	29.94	44.92
1	0.120	1.000	3300	2.83	5.66	14.14	21.21	28.28	42.42
1 1/4	0.065	1.250	1430	6.14	12.28	30.71	46.07	61.42	92.13
1 1/4	0.083	1.250	1826	5.75	11.51	28.77	43.15	57.54	86.31
1 1/4	0.095	1.250	2090	5.50	11.00	27.51	41.26	55.02	82.53
1 1/4	0.109	1.250	2398	5.22	10.43	26.08	39.11	52.15	78.23
1 1/4	0.120	1.250	2640	5.00	9.99	24.98	37.46	49.95	74.93
1 1/4	0.134	1.250	2948	4.72	9.44	23.61	35.41	47.22	70.83

Pressure Ratings and Flow Rates for Steel Tubes — Table #53**

Tube Size (in)	Wall Thick-ness	OD	Max Allowable Pressure	Flow (GPM) Required to Produce					
				2 ft/sec	4 ft/sec	10 ft/sec	15 ft/sec	20 ft/sec	30 ft/sec
1 1/4	0.148	1.250	3256	4.46	8.91	22.28	33.42	44.56	66.85
1 1/4	0.165	1.250	3630	4.14	8.29	20.72	31.08	41.45	62.17
1 1/4	0.180	1.250	3960	3.88	7.76	19.39	29.09	38.79	58.18
1 1/2	0.083	1.500	1522	8.71	17.43	43.57	65.35	87.14	130.71
1 1/2	0.095	1.500	1742	8.40	16.81	42.02	63.02	84.03	126.05
1 1/2	0.109	1.500	1998	8.05	16.10	40.24	60.36	80.48	120.72
1 1/2	0.120	1.500	2200	7.77	15.55	38.87	58.30	77.74	116.61
1 1/2	0.134	1.500	2457	7.43	14.86	37.16	55.74	74.32	111.48
1 1/2	0.148	1.500	2713	7.10	14.20	35.49	53.24	70.98	106.47
1 1/2	0.165	1.500	3025	6.70	13.41	33.51	50.27	67.03	100.54
1 1/2	0.180	1.500	3300	6.36	12.73	31.82	47.73	63.64	95.45
1 1/2	0.220	1.500	4033	5.50	11.00	27.51	41.26	55.02	82.53

Pressure Ratings and Flow Rates for Steel Tubes** — Table #53									
Tube Size (in)	Wall Thick-ness	OD	Max Allowable Pressure	Flow (GPM) Required to Produce					
				2 ft/sec	4 ft/sec	10 ft/sec	15 ft/sec	20 ft/sec	30 ft/sec
2	0.095	2.000	1306	16.04	32.08	80.21	120.31	160.42	240.63
2	0.109	2.000	1499	15.55	31.10	77.75	116.62	155.49	233.24
2	0.120	2.000	1650	15.17	30.34	75.84	113.76	151.68	227.52
2	0.134	2.000	1843	14.69	29.38	73.45	110.17	146.89	220.34
2	0.148	2.000	2035	14.22	28.44	71.09	106.63	142.18	213.27
2	0.165	2.000	2269	13.66	27.31	68.28	102.42	136.56	204.84
2	0.180	2.000	2475	13.17	26.34	65.85	98.77	131.70	197.55
2	0.220	2.000	3025	11.92	23.83	59.58	89.37	119.16	178.75

**Note: Ratings are for "Hydraulic Grade" annealed steel tubing having a tensile stress of 55,000 psi and using a safety factor of 4.

Allowable pressures are calculated using Barlow's formula: $P = 2 \times S \times T/D$
Where: P = Pipe pressure (psi)   T = wall thickness (inches)
   D = Outside diameter of pipe (inches)   S = Stress on the pipe material (psi)

Recommended Fluid Velocities for Hydraulic Systems — Table #54			
Type of line	**PSI**	**feet/second**	**m/second**
Suction lines		2 - 4	0.6 - 1.2
Return lines		10 - 15	3.1 - 4.6
Working lines	500 - 3000	15 - 20	4.6 - 6.1
	3000 - 5000	15 - 30	4.6 - 9.1

Viscosity — Table #55			
Kinematic cST	Saybolt SUS	Engler Degrees	Redwood Seconds
2	33	1.11	32
4	39	1.31	38
6	46	1.49	44
7	49	1.58	47
10	59	1.84	56
12	66	2.03	63
14	74	2.23	69
16	81	2.44	76
18	89	2.66	83
20	98	2.88	90
25	119	3.47	108
30	142	4.08	127
35	164	4.71	146
40	187	5.35	166

Viscosity — Table #55			
Kinematic cST	Saybolt SUS	Engler Degrees	Redwood Seconds
45	210	5.99	186
50	233	6.63	206
60	279	7.93	247
70	325	9.24	287
80	371	10.5	328
90	417	11.9	369
100	463	13.2	410
120	556	15.8	492
140	649	18.4	574
160	741	21.1	656
180	834	23.7	738
200	927	26.3	820
250	1158	32.9	1025
300	1390	39.5	1230

Viscosity — Table #55			
Kinematic cST	Saybolt SUS	Engler Degrees	Redwood Seconds
350	1621	46	1434
400	1853	53	1639
450	2085	59	1844
500	2316	66	2049
600	2779	79	2459
700	3243	92	2869
800	3706	105	3279

Viscosity — Table #55			
Kinematic cST	Saybolt SUS	Engler Degrees	Redwood Seconds
900	4169	118	3689
1000	4632	132	4098
1200	5559	158	4918
1400	6485	184	5738
1600	7412	211	6557
1800	8338	237	7377
2000	9265	263	8197

Viscosity Conversion — Table #56	
To convert SUS to Centistokes, the formula depends on the SUS value.	
Saybolt Universal Seconds (SUS) to Centistokes (cSt)	
SUS	**cSt**
32 - 100	0.2253 x SUS - (194.4 / SUS)
100 - 240	0.2193 x SUS - (134.6 / SUS)
Over 240	SUS / 4635
To change from Absolute to Relative viscosity:	
Centipoise (cP) = Centistoke (cSt) x density [(kg/m3) x 10^{-3}]	

Metal Properties — Table #57

Metal	Symbol	Specic Gravity	Specific Heat (Btu/lb °F)	Melt °C	Melt °F	Weight lb/ft³	Mass kg/m³	Expansion Coefficient per °F x 10⁻⁶
Aluminum (Cast)	Al	2.56	0.2185	658	1217	159.67	2557.7	12.5
Aluminum (Rolled)	Al	2.71	-	-		169	2707.15	
Antimony	Sb	6.71	0.051	630	1166	418.87	6709.73	6.3
Bismuth	Bi	9.8	0.031	271	520	611.71	9798.77	7.5
Boron	B	2.3	0.3091	2300	4172	143.6	2300.28	1.1
Brass	-	8.51	0.094	-	-	531.36	8511.67	11.0
Cadmium	Cd	8.6	0.057	321	610	536.89	8600.25	16.6
Calcium	Ca	1.57	0.17	810	1490	97.98	1569.51	13.9
Carbon	C	2.22	0.165	-	-	138.59	2220.02	0.67
Chromium	Cr	6.8	0.12	1510	2750	424.57	6801.04	4.5
Cobalt	Co	8.5	0.11	1490	2714	530.67	8500.61	6.7

Metal Properties — Table #57

Metal	Symbol	Specic Gravity	Specific Heat (Btu/lb °F)	Melt °C	Melt °F	Weight lb/ft^2	Mass kg/m^3	Expansion Coefficient per °F x 10^{-6}
Copper	Cu	8.89	0.094	1083	1982	555.03	8890.83	9.1
Columbium	Cb	8.57	-	1950	3542	534.99	8569.82	4.0
Gold	Au	19.32	0.032	1063	1945	1205.97	19,318.01	8.0
Iridium	Ir	22.42	0.033	2300	4170	1399.51	22,418.26	3.5
Iron	Fe	7.86	0.11	1520	2768	455.16	7291.05	6.6
Iron (Cast)	Fe	7.218	0.1298	1375	2507	450.14	7210.63	
Iron (Wrought)	Fe	7.7	0.1138	1500-1600	2732-2912	480.21	7692.31	
Lead	Pb	11.37	0.031	327	621	709.86	11,370.99	16.4
Lithium	Li	0.057	0.941	186	367	36.81	589.65	31.0
Magnesium	Mg	1.74	0.25	651	1204	108.69	1741.07	14.3

Metal Properties — Table #57

Metal	Symbol	Specic Gravity	Specific Heat (Btu/lb °F)	Melt °C	Melt °F	Weight lb/ft³	Mass kg/m³	Expansion Coefficient per °F x 10⁻⁶
Manganese	Mn	8	0.12	1225	2237	499.39	7999.55	12.8
Mercury	Hg	13.59	0.032	38.7	37.7	848.28	13588.30	
Molybdenum	Mo	10.2	0.0647	2620	4748	635.9	10186.25	3.05
Monel Metal	-	8.87	0.127	1360	2480	552.96	8857.67	
Nickel	Ni	8.8	0.13	1452	2646	551.23	8829.96	7.6
Phosphorus	P	1.82	0.177	43	111.4	113.53	1818.60	69.0
Platinum	Pt	21.5	0.033	1755	3191	1342.14	21499.27	4.3
Potassium	K	0.87	0.17	62	144	54.26	869.17	46.0
Selenium	Se	4.81	0.084	220	428	300.67	4816.32	20.6
Silicon	Si	2.4	0.1762	1427	2600	150.34	2408.24	
Silver	Ag	10.53	0.056	961	1761	657.5	10532.26	

Metal Properties — Table #57								
Metal	Symbol	Specic Gravity	Specific Heat (Btu/lb °F)	Melt °C	Melt °F	Weight lb/ft^2	Mass kg/m^3	Expansion Coefficient per °F x 10^{-6}
Sodium	Na	0.97	0.29	97	207	60.48	968.81	39.5
Steel	-	7.858	0.1175	1330-1378	2372-2532	490.58	7858.43	6.5
Strontium	Sr	2.54	0.074	-	-	158.63	2541.04	
Sulphur	S	2.07	0.175	115	235.4	129.6	2076.02	
Tantalum	Ta	10.8	-	2850	5160	674.27	10800.89	3.6
Tin	Sn	7.29	0.056	232	450	455.16	7291.05	12.7
Titanium	Ti	5.3	0.13	1900	3450	330.91	5300.73	3.9
Tungsten	W	19.1	0.033	3000	5432	1192.32	19099.35	2.2
Uranium	U	18.7	-	-	-	1167.26	18697.92	-
Vanadium	V	5.5	-	1730	3146	343.35	5500.00	-
Zinc	Zn	7.19	0.094	419	786	448.93	7191.25	16.5

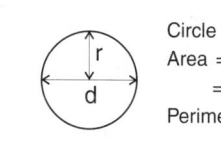

Square
Area = l x w
Perimeter = (l + w) x 2

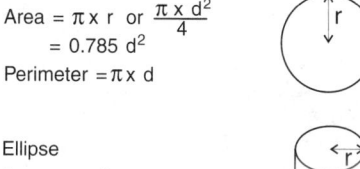

Circle
Area = π x r   or $\frac{\pi \times d^2}{4}$
     = 0.785 d²
Perimeter = π x d

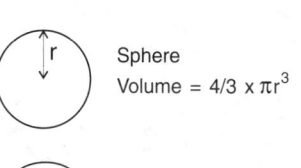

Sphere
Volume = 4/3 x πr³

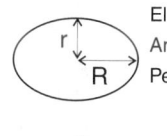

Rectangle
Area = l x w
Perimeter = (l + w) x 2

Ellipse
Area = π x R x r
Perimeter = 6.283 x $\sqrt{\frac{R^2 \times r^2}{2}}$

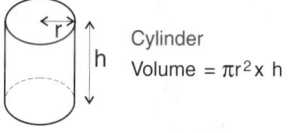

Cylinder
Volume = πr² x h

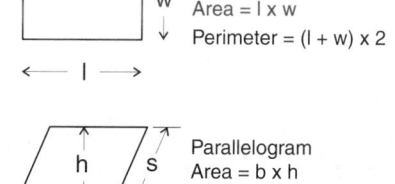

Parallelogram
Area = b x h
Perimeter = (b + s) x 2

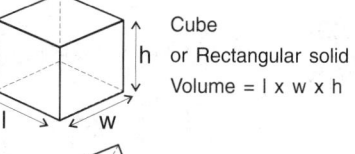

Cube
or Rectangular solid
Volume = l x w x h

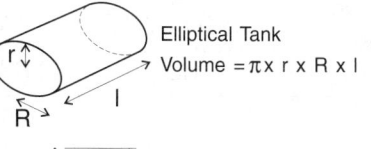

Elliptical Tank
Volume = π x r x R x l

Trapezoid
Area = $\frac{a+b}{2}$ x h
Perimeter = a+b+s₁+s₂

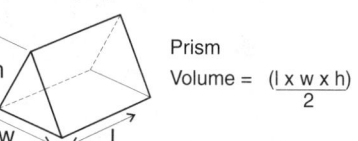

Prism
Volume = $\frac{(l \times w \times h)}{2}$

Cone
Volume = (πr² x h) /3

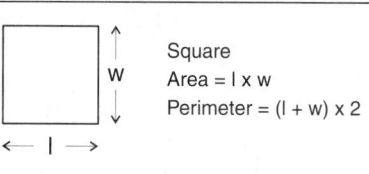

Triangle
Area = $\frac{b \times h}{2}$
Perimeter = a + b + c

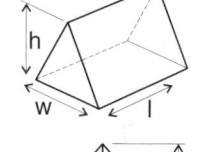

Pyramid
Volume = $\frac{(l \times w \times h)}{3}$

π = 3.1416

Illustration #280 — Useful Formulae

Pressure and Force (Pressure = Force/Area) — Table #58	
P = F/A P = pressure, ft F = force, lb A = area, in^2	**P = F x 10^3/A** P = pressure, Pa or kPa F = force, N A = area, m^2
P = h x 0.433 x sg P = pressure under a column of fluid, psi h = height of the column of fluid, ft sg = specific gravity of the liquid (sg for water = 1)	**P = h (m) x 9.8 x sg** P = pressure under a column of fluid, kPa h = height of the column of fluid, metres sg = specific gravity of the liquid (sg for water = 1)
1 foot column water generates 0.433 psi 1 inch column water = 0.433/12 = 0.0361 psi	1 m column water generates 9.8 kPa 1 mm column water = 9.8/1000 = 0.0098 kPa = 9.8 Pa
Absolute press. = Gage pressure + Atmospheric pressure Absolute pressure (psi) = gage pressure (psi) + 14.7	Absolute press. = Gage pressure + Atmospheric pressure Absolute pressure (kPa) = gage pressure (kPa) + 101.325
Force (lb) = mass (lb) x acceleration (ft/sec^2)	Force (N) = mass (kg) x acceleration (m/s^2)

Fluid Velocity in Pipes and Cylinder Velocity — Table #59	
Velocity = flow rate/area $V = Q \times 231/12 \times A$ $V = Q \times 19.25/A$ $V = Q \times 77/ \times d^2$ V = velocity of pipe or cylinder, ft/sec Q = flow rate, gpm A = area of pipe or cylinder, inches^2 d = diameter of pipe or cylinder, inches	**Velocity = flow rate/area** $V = Q \times 10^{-3}/A \ (m^2)$ $V = Q \times 10^3/A \ (mm^2)$ $V = Q \times 10^3 \times 4/ \ d^2 \ (mm^2)$ V = velocity of fluid or cylinder, m/s Q = flow rate, litres/s A = area of pipe or cylinder, m^2 or mm^2 d = diameter of pipe or cylinder, mm

Hydraulic Motor Speed (rpm = flow rate/displacement) — Table #60	
rpm = (Q x 231)/Disp Q= flow rate to motor, gpm Disp = motor displacement per revolution in^3	**rpm = Q/Disp** Q = flow rate to motor, litres/min. Disp = motor displacement per revolution, litres

General Power Formulae — Table #61

HP = 2π x rpm x T/33,000
T (ft-lb) = 5252 x HP/rpm
T (in-lb) = 63025 x HP/rpm
T = torque, ft-lb or in-lb

1 HP = 33,000 ft-lb/minute = 550 ft-lb/second
1 HP = 42.44 Btu/minute
1 HP = 0.746 kW

Watts = 2π x rpm x T/60
T = 9.55 x Watts/rpm
T = 9550 x kW/rpm
T = torque in newton meters (N·m)

1 kW = 1 kJ/s
1 kW = 1.34 HP

Hydraulic Power Flowing Through Pipes (Power = Flow x Pressure) — Table #62

HP = Q x P/1714 = gpm x psi/1714
Q= flow rate in gallons per minute
P = pressure in lb/inch^2

kW = Q x P x 10^{-3} = litres/s x kPa x 10^{-3}
Q = flow rate in litres/s
P = pressure in kPa

Power Required to Drive a Hydraulic Pump — Table 63

$HP = Q \times P/(1714 \times eff) = gpm \times psi/(1714 \times eff)$

eff = pump mechanical efficiency as a decimal
Q = flow rate in gallons per minute
P = pressure in lb/inch^2
Using a motor efficiency of approximately 83%
$HP = gpm \times psi \times 0.0007$

$kW = Q \times P \times 10^{-3}/eff = litres/s \times kPa \times 10^{-3}/eff$

eff = pump mechanical efficiency as a decimal
Q = flow rate in litres/s
kPa = pressure in kilo Pascals

Power and Torque Produced by a Hydraulic Actuator — Table 64

Theoretical $HP = Q \times P/1714 = gpm \times psi/1714$
Actual $HP = Q \times P \times eff/1714$
$\qquad = gpm \times psi \times eff/1714$
$T = P \times Disp \times eff/2\pi = psi \times in^3/rev \times eff/2\pi$
T = torque, in lbs
eff = actuator mechanical efficiency as a decimal
Q = flow rate in gallons per minute
P = pressure in lbs/inch^2
Disp = actuator displacement, in^3/rev
$\qquad\qquad$ per revolution

Theoretical $kW = Q \times P \times 10^{-3}$
$\qquad\qquad = litres/s \times kPa \times 10^{-3}$
Actual $kW = Q \times P \times 10^{-3} \times eff$
$\qquad\qquad = litres/s \times kPa \times 10^{-3} \times eff$
$T = kPa \times Disp \times eff/2\pi$
T = torque, in N·m
eff = actuator mechanical efficiency as a decimal
Q = flow rate in litres/s
P = pressure in kPa
Disp = actuator displacement, litres per revolution

Thermal expansions — Table #65

$$\Delta L = \alpha \times L \times \Delta T$$

ΔL = Change in length
L = Original length
α = Coefficient of thermal linear expansion
ΔT = Change in temperature (°C) or (°F)
(°C & °F refers to Celsius & Fahrenheit degrees respectively)

Electrical Formulae — Table #66

Volts or EMF **(V) = I x R**
Amperes **(I) = V/R**
Resistance ohms (Ω) **(R) = V/I**
Power **(W) = I^2 x R = V^2/R**

1 Hertz = 60 CPM

Specific Heat Capacity — Table #67

Btu/(lb°F) = 5/(9 x 2.205 x 1.055) kJ/(kg·°C) = 0.238 818 kJ/(kg·°C)	kJ/(kg °C) = 4.187295 Btu/(lb·°F)

SECTION TWELVE

ISO SYMBOLS

BASIC SYMBOLS

Flow Lines:
- Main line conductor
- Pilot line
- Drain line

Mechanical connection (shafts, levers etc.)

Enclosure outline (optional use)
several components assembled as a single unit

Energy conversion unit
(pump, compressor, motor etc.)

Conditioning apparatus
(filter, Lubricator etc.)

Semi-rotary actuator

Control valves
(except non-return valves)

Measuring instrument

Non-return valve,
rotary connection etc.

Mechanical link, roller etc.

Flexible hose, usually
connecting moving parts

Electric line

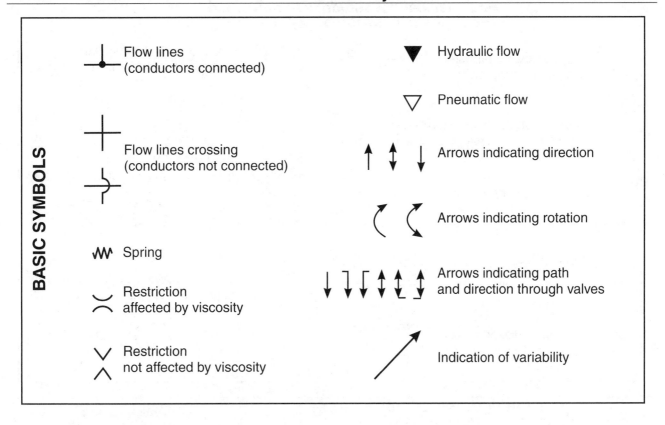

BASIC SYMBOLS

Flow lines
(conductors connected)

Flow lines crossing
(conductors not connected)

Spring

Restriction
affected by viscosity

Restriction
not affected by viscosity

Hydraulic flow

Pneumatic flow

Arrows indicating direction

Arrows indicating rotation

Arrows indicating path
and direction through valves

Indication of variability

PUMPS AND COMPRESSORS

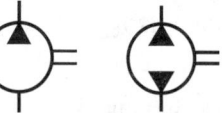

Unidirectional/bidirectional flow
fixed capacity, hydraulic pump

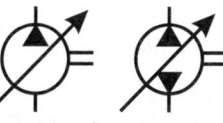

Unidirectional/bidirectional flow
variable capacity, hydraulic pump

Fixed capacity compressor
unidirectional flow

MOTORS

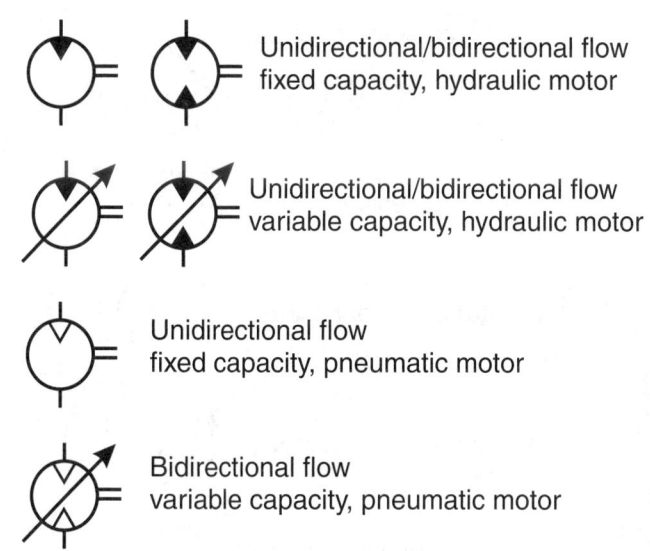

Unidirectional/bidirectional flow
fixed capacity, hydraulic motor

Unidirectional/bidirectional flow
variable capacity, hydraulic motor

Unidirectional flow
fixed capacity, pneumatic motor

Bidirectional flow
variable capacity, pneumatic motor

Hydraulic/pneumatic
oscillating motor

Note: Solid triangles represent hydraulic flow
open triangles represent pneumatic flow

PUMP/MOTOR UNITS

Fixed capacity unit with reversible flow direction functions as a pump or motor according to direction of flow

Same as above except is variable instead of fixed capacity

Fixed capacity unit with single flow direction functions as a pump or motor without change

Same as above except is variable instead of fixed capacity

Fixed capacity unit with reversible flow in two directions functions as a pump or motor with either direction of flow

Same as above except is variable instead of fixed capacity

CYLINDERS

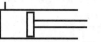 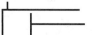

Detailed/Simplified single-acting cylinder, returned by unspecified force

Detailed/Simplified single-acting cylinder, returned by a spring

Detailed/Simplified double-acting cylinder

 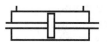 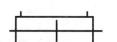

Detailed/Simplified double-acting cylinder, with double-ended piston rod

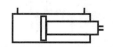 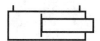

Detailed/Simplified differential cylinder

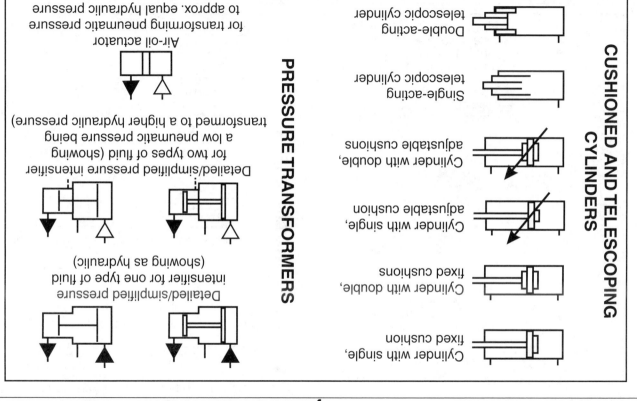

CUSHIONED AND TELESCOPING CYLINDERS

Double-acting telescopic cylinder

Single-acting telescopic cylinder

Cylinder with double, adjustable cushions

Cylinder with single, adjustable cushion

Cylinder with double, fixed cushions

Cylinder with single, fixed cushion

PRESSURE TRANSFORMERS

Air-oil actuator for transforming pneumatic pressure to approx. equal hydraulic pressure

Detailed/simplified pressure intensifier for two types of fluid (showing a low pneumatic pressure being transformed to a higher hydraulic pressure)

Detailed/simplified pressure intensifier for one type of fluid (showing as hydraulic)

DIRECTIONAL CONTROL VALVES (DCVs)

Flow Paths

One flow path
through valve

Two closed ports
no flow path

Two flow paths
through the valve

Two flow paths
with cross connection
(four ports connected)

One flow path
in a bypass position
and two closed ports

Positions

Two position, non-throttling
directional control valve (DCV)

Three position, non-throttling
directional control valve (DCV)

Non-throttling DCV with one
transitory intermediate condition
and two distinct positions

*Note: Throttling DCVs have two extreme
positions and an infinite number of intermediate
conditions with varying degrees of throttling.*

Throttling DCV
with two extreme positions

Throttling DCV with
two extreme and a center
or neutral position

DIRECTIONAL CONTROL VALVES

Non-Throttling DCVs

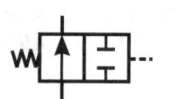

2/2 (2 ports, 2 distinct positions)
Directly controlled by pilot
pressure, spring return

3/2 (3 ports, 2 distinct positions
and a significant transitory position)
Directly controlled by push
solenoid, spring return

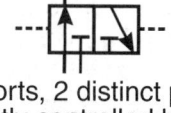

3/2 (3 ports, 2 distinct positions)
Directly controlled by pilot
pressure in both directions

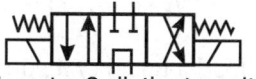

4/3 (4 ports, 3 distinct positions)
Directly controlled by solenoid,
spring centered

Throttling DCVs

2 ports, tracer valve plunger
operated against a return spring

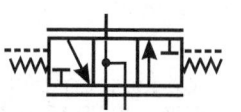

3 ports, controlled by pressure against a return spring

4 ports, single stage electro-hydraulic servo motor

Throttling DCVs

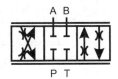

Proportional directional control valve
with a specific ratio of flow rates when
either 2 of the 4 flow paths are active

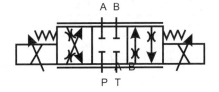

Proportional directional control valve
direct acting, no feedback (force solenoids),
spring centered

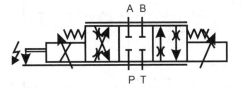

Proportional directional control valve
direct acting, with feedback (force solenoids),
spring centered

DIRECTIONAL CONTROL VALVES

DIRECTIONAL CONTROL VALVES

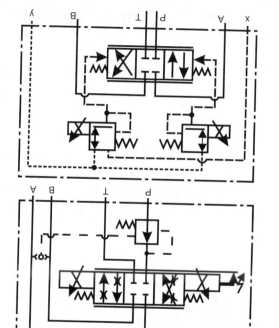

Pilot operated (2 stage) proportional directional control valve (force solenoids) no feedback, spring centered

Throttling DCVs

Proportional directional control valve direct acting, with feedback (force solenoids), and hydrostat spring centered

DIRECTIONAL CONTROL VALVES

Non Return and Shuttle Valves

Free, non-return valve (check valve) uses a light spring pressure that is not critical to operation of the circuit)

Spring-loaded check valve (pressure at which the check valve opens is critical to operation of the circuit)

Check valve, pilot operated to open (pilot pressure used to hold the valve open and allow flow in the normally blocked direction)

Check valve, pilot operated to close (pilot pressure used to hold the valve closed and prevent flow in the normally free flow direction)

Check valve, with restriction, allows free flow in one direction, restricted flow in the other

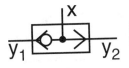

Shuttle valve (the outlet port 'X' is automatically connected to whichever is the higher pressure at 'y_1' or 'y_2'

DIRECTIONAL CONTROL VALVES

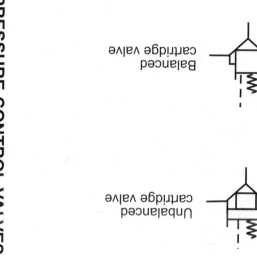

Balanced cartridge valve

Unbalanced cartridge valve

PRESSURE-CONTROL VALVES

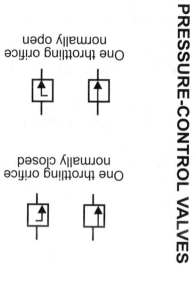

One throttling orifice normally open

One throttling orifice normally closed

DIRECT ACTING PRESSURE-CONTROL VALVES

Sequence or
counterbalance valve
with external drain

Pressure relief valve
inlet pressure is limited
by spring force

Pressure relief valve,
inlet pressure is limited by
the spring or pilot pressure

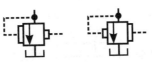

Pressure relief valve,
inlet pressure is limited
to a value proportional
to the pilot pressure

Pressure reducing valve
Outlet pressure is reduced
by a fixed proportion with
respect to inlet pressure

Pressure reducing valve
Outlet pressure is reduced by
a fixed amount (set by the spring)
with respect to the inlet pressure

PRESSURE CONTROL VALVES
(DIRECT ACTION)

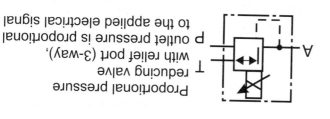

Proportional pressure
reducing valve
with relief port (3-way),
outlet pressure is proportional
to the applied electrical signal

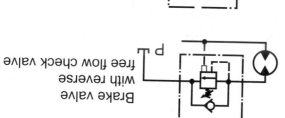

Overcenter valve
with reverse
free flow check valve

Pressure reducing valve
with relief port (3-way).
Outlet pressure is dependent
on the spring setting

Brake valve
with reverse
free flow check valve

Pressure reducing valve
Outlet pressure is dependent
on the spring setting

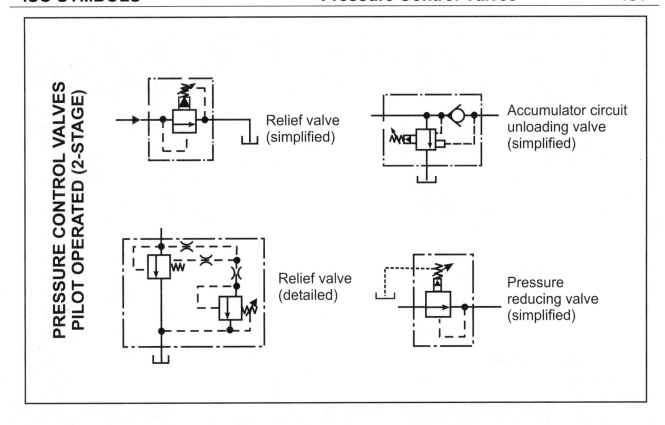

PRESSURE CONTROL VALVES PILOT OPERATED (2-STAGE)

Relief valve (simplified)

Accumulator circuit unloading valve (simplified)

Relief valve (detailed)

Pressure reducing valve (simplified)

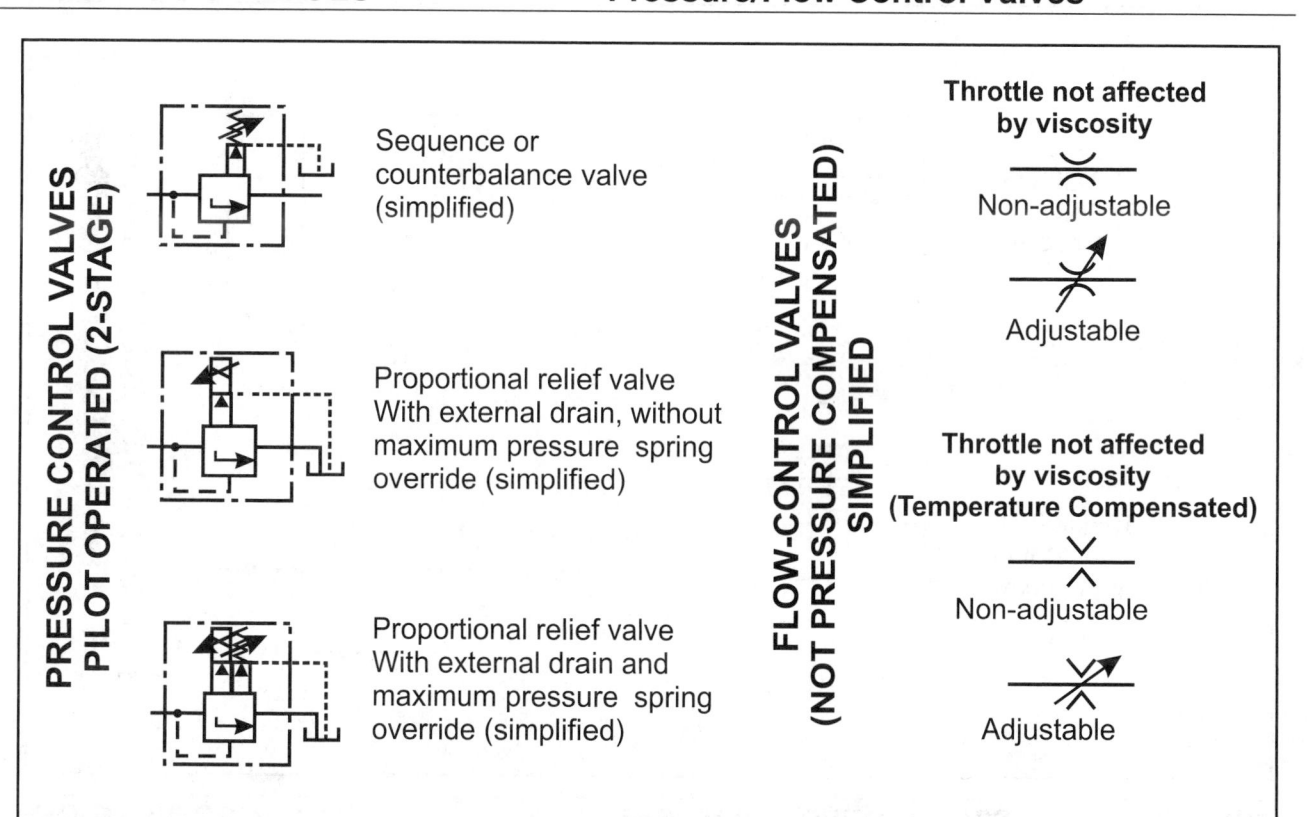

PRESSURE CONTROL VALVES PILOT OPERATED (2-STAGE)

Sequence or counterbalance valve (simplified)

Proportional relief valve With external drain, without maximum pressure spring override (simplified)

Proportional relief valve With external drain and maximum pressure spring override (simplified)

FLOW-CONTROL VALVES (NOT PRESSURE COMPENSATED) SIMPLIFIED

Throttle not affected by viscosity

Non-adjustable

Adjustable

Throttle not affected by viscosity (Temperature Compensated)

Non-adjustable

Adjustable

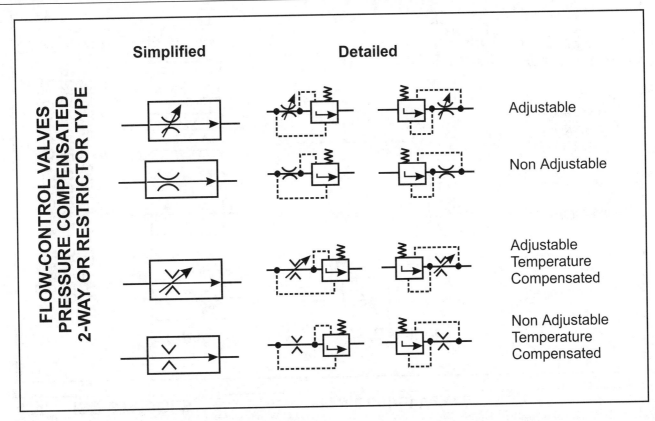

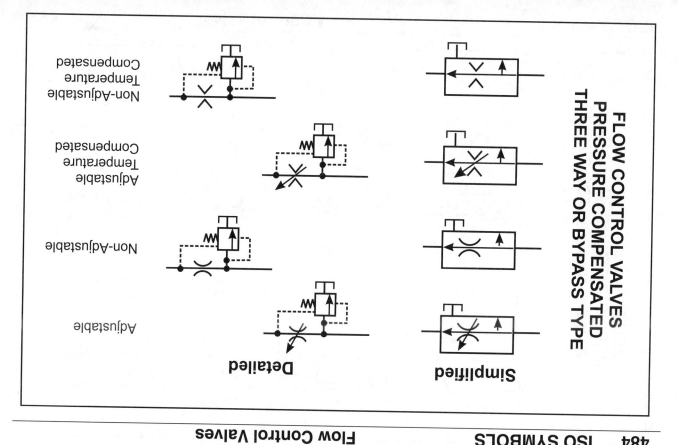

FLOW CONTROL VALVES
PRESSURE COMPENSATED
THREE WAY OR BYPASS TYPE

Simplified

Detailed

Adjustable

Non-Adjustable

Adjustable
Temperature
Compensated

Non-Adjustable
Temperature
Compensated

ENERGY SOURCES AND CONNECTIONS

Hydraulic pressure
source

Power take-off
with a plugged port

Power take-off
with a take-off line

Pneumatic pressure
source

Quick-release
coupling without
non-return valve
(connected)

Quick-release
coupling without
non-return valve
(disconnected)

Electric motor

Quick-release
coupling with
non-return valve
(connected)

Quick-release
coupling with
non-return valve
(disconnected)

Heat engine

One-way
rotary connection

Three-way
rotary connection

RESERVOIRS

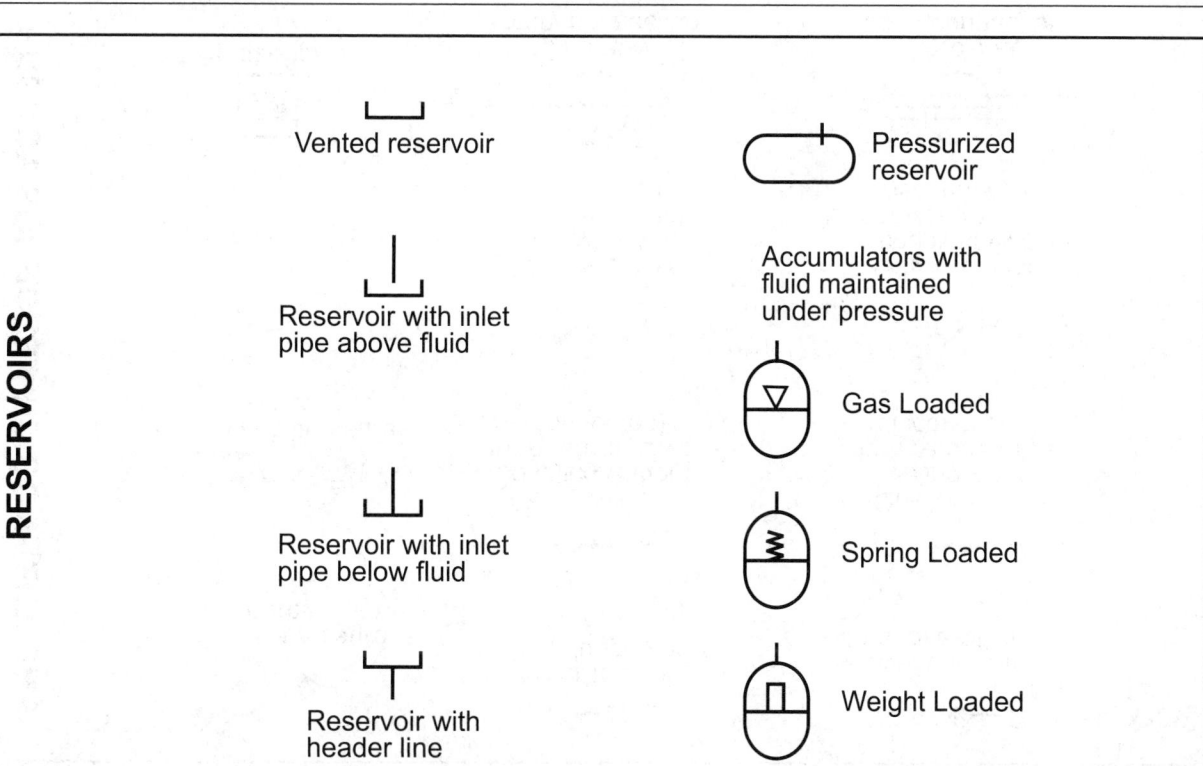

Vented reservoir

Reservoir with inlet pipe above fluid

Reservoir with inlet pipe below fluid

Reservoir with header line

Pressurized reservoir

Accumulators with fluid maintained under pressure

Gas Loaded

Spring Loaded

Weight Loaded

MISCELLANEOUS APPARATUS

Filter or strainer

Cooler

Heater

Liquid to
liquid cooler

Liquid to
liquid heater

Gas to
liquid cooler

Gas to
liquid heater

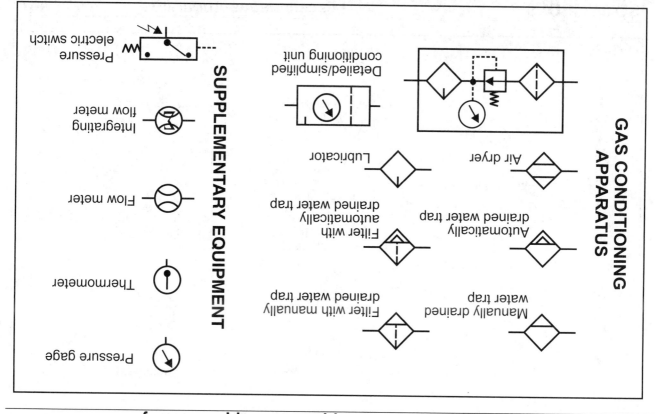

GAS CONDITIONING APPARATUS

Detailed/simplified conditioning unit

Air dryer

Lubricator

Automatically drained water trap

Filter with automatically drained water trap

Manually drained water trap

Filter with manually drained water trap

SUPPLEMENTARY EQUIPMENT

Pressure electric switch

Integrating flow meter

Flow meter

Thermometer

Pressure gage

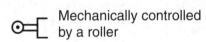 Mechanically controlled
by a roller

 Mechanically controlled
by a roller operating only
in one direction

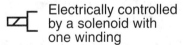 Electrically controlled
by a solenoid with
one winding

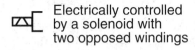 Electrically controlled
by a solenoid with
two opposed windings

 Electrically controlled
by a solenoid with
two opposed windings
and variable progression

 Direct control applied
by hydraulic pressure

 Direct control released
by hydraulic pressure

 Controlled by a
reversing electric motor

 Direct control applied
by pneumatic pressure

Direct control released
by pneumatic pressure

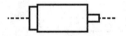 Direct control by
different control areas

CONTROL MECHANISMS

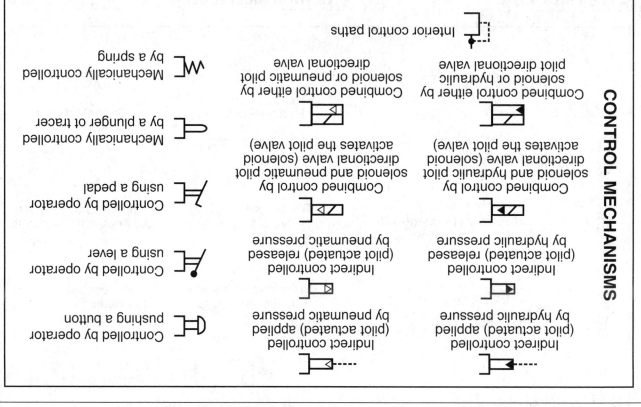

Controlled by operator
pushing a button

Controlled by operator
using a lever

Controlled by operator
using a pedal

Mechanically controlled
by a plunger or tracer

Mechanically controlled
by a spring

Indirect controlled
(pilot actuated) applied
by pneumatic pressure

Indirect controlled
(pilot actuated) released
by pneumatic pressure

Combined control by
solenoid and pneumatic pilot
directional valve (solenoid
activates the pilot valve)

Combined control either by
solenoid or pneumatic pilot
directional valve

Indirect controlled
(pilot actuated) applied
by hydraulic pressure

Indirect controlled
(pilot actuated) released
by hydraulic pressure

Combined control by
solenoid and hydraulic pilot
directional valve (solenoid
activates the pilot valve)

Combined control either by
solenoid or hydraulic
pilot directional valve

Interior control paths